PELICAN BOOKS

A 142

GREEK SCIENCE

BENJAMIN FARRINGTON

D1375267

GREEK SCIENCE

ITS MEANING FOR US

—

BENJAMIN FARRINGTON

PENGUIN BOOKS

MELBOURNE · LONDON · BALTIMORE

Part One first published 1944
New edition 1949
Part Two first published 1949
The two parts first published as
one volume 1953

To my friend

DR MIGNON B. ALEXANDER

—

Made and printed in Great Britain
for Penguin Books Ltd, Harmondsworth, Middlesex
by Northumberland Press Ltd, Gateshead on Tyne

CONTENTS

CONTENTS

INTRODUCTION

TO THE EDITION OF 1953

GREEK SCIENCE, which appeared in two successive volumes in 1944 and 1949, is here reprinted as a single book. This corresponds with the original intention of the writer and should facilitate the comprehension of the book. The new edition provides also an opportunity to bring the book up to date. Knowledge of the subject continues to advance, and this is reflected not only in the bibliographical indications but also, it is hoped, in the text, where I have been allowed to introduce desirable changes. These affect principally the first chapter, which has been largely rewritten.

It may be well here to clear up possible confusion between this book and the volume I have contributed to The Home University Library entitled *Science in Antiquity*. The books differ in substance and purpose. The volume in The Home University Library tells the story of ancient science not only more briefly but in a different way. Following a plan that has been found traditionally useful it outlines the development of ancient science in close relation with the history of philosophy. In my Pelican volume I have sought to explore the connections of Greek science with practical life, with techniques, with the economic basis and productive activity of Greek society.

This second approach being much less usual it has been difficult to suggest to readers a really suitable collection of source material. Traditionally the sources for a knowledge of Greek science have been incorporated in collections intended primarily to illustrate the history of Greek philosophy. It is therefore with special satisfaction that I can now recommend *A Source Book in Greek Science* by Morris R. Cohen and I. E. Drabkin, McGraw-Hill Book Company, 1948. There is no topic of Greek science touched on in my book for which this collection does not afford relevant source material presented in the most authoritative way.

There is one other point on which I take the chance to touch. In my attempt to explain the arrest of the scientific spirit among the Greeks I have not carried all readers with me in seeking the cause of this decline in the growing indifference to applied science, in connecting this indifference with the growth of the institution of slavery, and in detecting in Plato the most influential and thorough-going exponent of the view of science that accompanied this decline. I have sometimes been supposed to be actuated by some obscure hostility to Plato, whereas I conceive myself to be simply doing my duty as an historian of science. I would therefore beg those critics who do not like me, please to like Professor Schuhl. In his highly esteemed work on *The Formation of Greek Thought*, planned as an *Historical Introduction to the Study of the Philosophy of Plato*, he is as insistent on this point as I am myself. He observes that at Tarentum and Athens in the fifth century the stage seemed set for the development of techniques, not excluding even the invention of machines, but this fair prospect was marred by the dominating influence of Plato on the intellectual character of the age. This, indeed, is to go further than I do, for I look upon Plato more as the symptom of a social disease than as the cause. However that may be, Professor Schuhl's point is that the slave-based society of the time reflected itself in the social consciousness and determined a series of choices, springing from the contempt for manual labour, all tending in the same direction and eventuating in what he calls a mental blockage precluding the application of science to techniques.[1] Having written my book in ignorance of Professor Schuhl's work I cannot but be gratified to discover the closeness of our agreement on this point.

B. FARRINGTON

Swansea 1952

1. P.-M. Schuhl, *Formation de la Pensée Grecque*, 2nd ed., 1949, pp. xx and xxi. Readers should also note his more popular book, *Machinisme et Philosophie*, 2nd ed., 1947.

CHIEF PERIODS AND SCHOOLS

1. *Greek Colonies in Asia*

School of Miletus (Thales, Anaximander, Anaximenes) *c.* 600–550 B.C.
Heraclitus of Ephesus, *floruit c.* 500 B.C.
Hippocratic School of Medicine, centred in island of Cos. (Hippocrates is supposed to have lived from 460 to 380 B.C.)

The early period of Greek thought down to Socrates is often loosely referred to as Ionian because it started in the Ionian colony of Miletus and flourished in such Ionian centres as Ephesus and Cos.

2. *Greek Colonies in Italy and Sicily (Magna Graecia)*

Pythagoras of Croton, *fl. c.* 540.
Parmenides of Elea, *fl. c.* 500.
Empedocles of Akragas, *fl. c.* 450.

3. *Mainland of Greece*

Anaxagoras of Clazomenae in Ionia (*c.* 500–428) settled in Athens and taught Pericles.
Democritus of Abdera, *fl. c.* 420.

4. *Athens*

Socrates (469–399), Plato (427–367), Aristotle (384–322).

5. *Alexandrian Age*

Mathematicians: Euclid (*fl. c.* 300), Archimedes (287–212), Apollonius (*fl. c.* 220).
Astronomers: Aristarchus (*c.* 310–230), Eratosthenes (*c.* 273–192), Hipparchus (*fl. c.* 125).
Anatomists: Herophilus and Erasistratus (*fl. c.* 290).
Grammarian: Dionysius Thrax (*fl. c.* 130).

6. *Graeco-Roman Period*

Of the Greek thinkers of this time the two best known were the astronomer and geographer, Ptolemy (*fl. c.* A.D. 150) and the anatomist and physician, Galen (A.D. 129–199).

There is a most intimate connection and almost an identity between the ways of human power and human knowledge. . . . That which is most useful in practice is most correct in theory.

FRANCIS BACON, Novum Organum II, iv

If there be any one on whose ear my frequent and honourable mention of practical activities has a harsh and unpleasing sound because he is wholly given over in love and reverence to contemplation, let him bethink himself that he is the enemy of his own desires. For in nature practical results are not only the means to improve well-being but the guarantee of truth. The true rule of religion, that a man should show his faith by his works, holds good in natural philosophy also. Science too must be known by works. It is by the witness of works, rather than by logic or even observation, that truth is revealed and established. Whence it follows that the improvement of man's mind and the improvement of his lot are one and the same thing.

FRANCIS BACON, Cogitata et Visa

The universe is not to be narrowed down to the limits of the understanding, which has been men's practice up to now, but the understanding must be stretched and enlarged to take in the image of the universe as it is discovered.

FRANCIS BACON, Parasceve, Aphorism 4

PART ONE

FOREWORD

THE subject of this part is the earliest period of Greek science – that is, the science of the sixth and fifth centuries B.C.

In many ways the outlook of this period is closer to our own than that of the later periods, whether the great fourth-century movement in Athens that centres round the names of Socrates, Plato, and Aristotle, or the Alexandrian period which begins with men like Euclid and Archimedes and ends with Ptolemy and Galen.

The science of the earliest Greek period resembles ours, for, naïve and undeveloped as it was, it regarded man as a product of natural evolution, it regarded his powers of speech and thought as a product of his life in society, and it regarded his science as part of his technique of the control of his natural environment. These bold ideas made their first appearance among the Ionian Greeks shortly after 600 B.C., and were developed in the course of a couple of centuries with a comprehensiveness of view and an organic cohesion of design which still astonish us to-day. The emergence of this mode of thought and its supersession by the more sophisticated but less scientific outlook of the age of Socrates, Plato, and Aristotle are the special subject of our enquiry.

B.F.

CHAPTER ONE

The Debt of Greek Science to the Older Civilizations of the Near East – Technology and Science

★

THE DEBT OF GREEK SCIENCE TO THE OLDER CIVILIZATIONS OF THE NEAR EAST

THAT Greek science, like Greek civilization as a whole, was deeply indebted to the older civilizations of the Near East is certain. Equally certain is it that Greek science struck out new paths for itself. What did it borrow and what did it create? This is a question on which knowledge is advancing and opinion changing.

It used to be believed, for instance, and it is an opinion that dies hard, that the Greeks differed from all other peoples of antiquity by their capacity for rational thought. In his standard work (*Greek Mathematics*, Oxford, 1921, Vol. I, pp. 3–6) Sir Thomas Heath asks: 'What special aptitude had the Greeks for mathematics?' and he answers without hesitation thus: 'The answer to this question is that their genius for mathematics was simply one aspect of their genius for philosophy ... The Greeks, beyond any other people of antiquity, possessed the love of knowledge for its own sake ... A still more essential fact is that the Greeks were a race of *thinkers*.'

We now find this view unacceptable. This is partly because we have acquired a distaste for explaining mental characteristics on a racial basis and because, in any case, the Greeks were not a race but a people of mixed descent. But it is also because of decisive advances in the domain of the history of ideas. Perhaps nothing fed the notion of the contrast between the superstitious East and the rational Greeks more than false opinions about the history of astrology. We had a picture of this age-old Chaldean superstition being held in check by Greek rationalism and the sturdy commonsense of Rome until, with the flooding in of eastern peoples, the Orontes emptied itself into the Tiber and the clear perspectives of the classical landscape were submerged by oriental slime. But it is now certain that this account of astrology is not true. It is true that there was a primitive and naïve Babylonian astrology which sought to give warnings about the advent of floods, drought, sickness, and wars – events, that is to say, which had reference to the country or to the king, but not to ordinary individuals. But the astrology that consists in the casting of horoscopes and which links the fate of individuals with the stars, what we really mean by astrology to-day, seems to have been a product of Alexandrian science and to have been unknown in Egypt before the Macedonian Greeks ruled the country. (Martin P. Nilsson, *The Rise of Astrology in the Hellenistic Age*, Lund, 1943.) This example warns us to be cautious in our acceptance of traditional opinions on the relation of Greece to the pre-Hellenic civilizations.

By the pre-Hellenic civilizations are meant first those which flourished in the three great river basins of the Nile, the Tigris-Euphrates, and the Indus. All these cultures by 3000 B.C. were not only technically advanced but possessed written literatures. We can for the present leave the Indus valley out of account; its script has not yet been interpreted. But much has been done to trace the influence of the techniques and the written science of both Egypt and Mesopotamia on the Greeks. Both were important but the influence of the latter was probably greater. This is partly because its scientific record is the more distinguished (O. Neugebauer, *The Exact Sciences in Antiquity*, Copenhagen, Princeton, London, 1951, p. 86), but also because of the different destinies of the two centres of civilization. Egypt had entered upon a period of decline about 1000 B.C.; but Babylonia, under the Assyrians, Persians, and Macedonian Greeks, experienced revivals both of its political power and creative genius during the last millennium of the pagan era. Its culture still maintained its ethnical character and continued its active growth for 1,000 years after the collapse of Egypt, and thus became the contemporary and rival of the culture of the Greeks. The Greek towns which lay along the coastal fringe of Asia Minor were thus in contact with the more active of the two ancient cultures of the Near East (Contenau, *La Médecine en Assyrie et en Babylonie*, Paris, 1938).

But we have also to remember that Egypt and Babylonia influenced Greece through the many derivative cultures of the eastern Mediterranean area. We can here only mention some of the many cultures which mediated between the ancient East and Greece. The graceful Minoan culture of Crete, well known through its material remains, will be still better understood when the interpretation of its scripts, which now seems imminent, has been achieved. To the Hittites was due the discovery of the technique of iron-smelting, a literally epoch-making discovery, modern science being still content to use the terms Bronze Age and Iron Age to mark definite stages of social development. Instead of seeking racial explanations of the mental character of the Greeks it would be more in keeping with modern historical conceptions to reflect that Greek civilization, including their science, is essentially an Iron Age, not a Bronze Age, civilization. Their type of democracy could not have existed without the much wider use of iron tools and weapons which the technique of smelting iron made possible. We should mention also the Phoenicians, the inventors of the phonetic alphabet. The evidence suggests that it was in Miletus about 800 B.C. that this alphabet was adapted to the Greek language. This invention democratized literacy by abolishing the toilsome apprenticeship with which the scribes of the older civilization acquired proficiency in hieroglyphics and cuneiform. Greek democracy could not have existed without it. Lastly we mention the Hebrews whose literature, the most serious rival to that of the Greeks, remains as perpetual proof that not only Greeks could embody in literary forms conceptions of vital moment even to the present day.

Let us return now to the question of the debt of Greek science to the older civilizations in order to give it a more up-to-date formulation if we can. In 1927 this is how it was put by an excellent French historian, Arnold Reymond (*Science in Greco-Roman Antiquity*, Methuen): 'Compared with the empirical and fragmentary knowledge which the peoples of the East had laboriously gathered together during long centuries, Greek science constitutes a veritable miracle. Here the human mind for the first time conceived of the possibility of establishing a limited number of principles, and of deducing from these a number of truths which are their rigorous consequence.' These words represent fairly the state of knowledge a quarter of a century ago and they still contain a large measure of truth, but several corrections seem to be required. In the first place more attention is now paid to the science implicit in techniques, of which more in a moment. In the second place progress in interpretation of the scientific writings of the older civilizations has gone far to abolish the claim of the Greeks to priority or to uniqueness in the creation of abstract theoretical science; and instead now of putting it as a black mark against the older civilizations that they had 'laboriously gathered together' their hardly scientific knowledge 'during long centuries', we are more inclined to remember that in science the first steps are the most difficult. It is with real awe, then, that we view the achievement in mathematics and in mathematical astronomy of the Babylonians. It is clear, even from the lamentably few scientific tablets that have yet been interpreted, that before 1500 B.C. advanced arithmetical procedures had been developed and problems are raised and tackled in a way that irresistibly suggests that in the endeavour to surmount their practical difficulties a strictly scientific intellectual curiosity had been aroused. Our knowledge of the history of Babylonian science is unfortunately gappy in the extreme. But when, about 1,000 years later, the thread can be resumed, it appears that these arithmetical procedures had been applied to the creation of a mathematical astronomy which was not only taken over by the Greeks, and used to supplement their own brilliant creation of geometrical astronomy, but had by 300 B.C. reached the stage at which it remains with Ptolemy in the Almagest in the second century A.D.

In the record of pre-Hellenic science as yet known to us this arithmetical astronomy of the Babylonians has the best title to rank as an exact science. But it would be wrong to overlook such classificatory sciences as the petrology and mineralogy, attested for both Babylon and Egypt, which arose in connection with the practical activities of mining and metallurgy. Nor must we forget the medicine and surgery of the Egyptians as revealed in the Edwin Smith papyrus, nor the Egyptian calendar, which has been called the only intelligent calendar in human history, nor the highly developed systems of weights and measures in use both among the Egyptians and Babylonians. In short, although the methods of transmission require further elucidation, we are in accordance with present knowledge when we say that the Greeks owed to the older civilizations not only techniques but a considerable body of scientific knowledge. We may, to be sure, still talk of the Greeks as deducing from the more empirical and fragmentary knowledge of the peoples of the East a rigorously logical body of science. The encyclopaedia of sciences constituted by Alexandrian times was, with all its limitations, far beyond anything that had previously existed and remained unrivalled until modern times. But in comparing the achievement of the Greeks with that of their predecessors it would be well not to describe as a difference of kind what is, after all, only a difference of degree ; nor should we describe as a miracle what is no more than a brilliant phase in a connected historical development.

TECHNOLOGY AND SCIENCE

So far we have been principally concerned with the theoretical side of science. But it is necessary also to regard science from its more practical side. J. G. Crowther in his *Social Relations of Science* defines science as ' the system of behaviour by which man acquires mastery of his environment'. This too is a helpful approach, and here the tendency has been rather to underrate than exaggerate the originality and proficiency of the Greeks. Many moderns, misled no doubt by some of the ancient Greeks themselves, have combined pride in the theoretical brilliance of Greek science with a wish to ignore or deny its practical triumphs. The result has been a lopsided picture which it is one purpose of this volume to correct.

Science, whatever be its ultimate developments, has its origin in techniques, in arts and crafts, in the various activities by which man keeps soul and body together. Its source is experience, its aims practical, its only test that it works. Science arises in contact with things, it is dependent on the evidence of the senses, and, however far it seems to move from them, must always come back to them. It requires logic and the elaboration of theory, but its strictest logic and choicest theory must be proved in practice. Science in the practical sense is the necessary basis for abstract and speculative science.

As thus conceived, science develops in close correspondence with the stages of man's social progress and becomes progressively more self-conscious as man's whole way of life becomes more purposive. A food-gatherer has one kind of knowledge of his environment, a food-producer another. The latter is more active and purposive in his relation to mother earth. Increased mastery of the environment brings increased productivity, which, in its turn, brings social change. The science of gentile or tribal society cannot be the same as the science of political society. The division of labour has an influence on the development of science. The emergence of a leisured class gives opportunity for reflection and elaboration of theory. It also gives opportunity for theorizing without relation to facts. Furthermore, with the development of classes, the need for a new kind of 'science' arises which might be defined as 'the system of behaviour by which man acquires mastery over man'. When the task of mastering men becomes the preoccupation of the ruling class and the task of mastering nature becomes the forced labour of another class, science takes a new and dangerous turn. Fully to understand the science of any society, we must be acquainted with the degree of its material advancement and with its political structure. There is no such thing as science *in vacuo*. There is only the science of a particular society at a particular place and time. The history of science can only be understood as a function of the total life of society. Hence, in order that we may get an historical understanding of Greek science, we must understand something of the previous evolution of society from the point of view of technical development and political structure, which is the purpose of this chapter.

Man has been on earth, we are told by the best modern authorities, for about five hundred thousand years. He has been civilized for only about one hundredth of that period. To put the point in another way, for about five hundred thousand years there has been on earth a creature who could talk and who had control of fire. It is only about five or six thousand years since there has been on earth a creature who could write and who could call on the police to protect him if someone stole his fuel.

Before writing, before writs, was there anything that could be called science? If we are prepared to accept the definition of science as the system of behaviour by which man acquires mastery of his environment, there certainly was.

The earliest surviving implements used by man to master his environment are stone tools. From these, experts draw proof of the intellectual capacity and slow progress of man even in the Old Stone Age. The growth of manual skill, itself a form of intelligence, is shown in the improved working of the implements. Intellectual advance is shown in the growing ability to discriminate between different kinds of stone. Evidence of increasing purpose and foresight is not lacking. Men mined for flints before they mined for metals. At one stage of his advance man does no more than select suitable stones for his purpose, and trim them. At a later stage he knocks off from a central core flakes of a desired shape and size. It is a revolution in technique. Then his tools are made for increasingly specialized purposes ; he has scrapers, points, and chipping tools. He even has tools for making tools, and tools for making tools for making tools. Nor was stone the only material that he used. Knowledge of materials is a very important part of science. The early tool-maker was aware of the advantages for specific purposes of materials other than stone. Wood, bone, antler, ivory, amber, shells provide him with new tools, and witness to us of his growing knowledge.

Nor is his knowledge only of materials. His growing appreciation of mechanical principles is also evident. He early senses the usefulness of the wedge. He makes a further advance when he combines in one tool the functions of the wedge and the lever. The spear-thrower, the bow and arrow, the bow-drill, are all so many landmarks in his progress in mechanics, although, of course, his appreciation of the principles involved is at first practical, sensuous, merged in the operations, untheoretical. But this practical knowledge is the necessary basis of theory. Of Napoleon's great engineer Conté it was said that he had all the sciences in his head and all the arts in his hands. And even that does not quite strike the nail on the head. 'As a physiologist,' writes J. B. S. Haldane, 'I note that it needs as large an area of brain to control my hands as my vocal organs. And as a scientific worker I note that some of my colleagues appear to do most of their thinking with their hands, and are extremely inexpert at the use of words.' Possibly primitive man talked a great deal of nonsense. There is plenty of evidence that he acted a great deal of sense.

The existence of science before civilization is evident, of course, also in the behaviour of contemporary savages. An excellent observer, Driberg, assures us that savages are reasonable beings capable of inference, logical thought, argument, and speculation. 'There are savage thinkers and philosophers, seers, leaders, and inventors.' Driberg is particularly emphatic on the truly scientific character of some of the activities of the savage. 'Not only does the savage adapt himself to his natural surroundings, he also adapts his natural surroundings to his own needs. It is this unending battle between the forces of nature and human ingenuity which eventually leads to some form of civilization.' To give examples – savages have elaborate devices for securing pure drinking-water ; they practise irrigation ; afforestation is undertaken for a multiplicity of objects – to restore the soil, to provide protection from the wind, for strategic reasons, for material for spear-shafts, to provide bark for cloth ; rivers are stocked ; game is preserved. Out of centuries, out of millennia, of such activities spring the arts and crafts on which civilization is based.

The actual origin of civilization depended on the simultaneous mastery or possession of a number of techniques, some new, some old, which, taken together, sufficed to turn man from being mainly a food-gatherer into being mainly a producer of food. A permanent surplus of food is the necessary basis for the emergence of civil society. Then greater concentrations of population became possible, urban life began, and the neolithic village was overshadowed by the mighty town. The fundamental techniques were the domestication of animals, agriculture, horticulture, pottery, brickmaking, spinning, weaving, and metallurgy. These ways of imitating and co-operating with nature constitute a revolution in man's science and a revolution in his way of life. The first area where civilizations based on the combination of these techniques came into existence was in the Near East in the river valleys of the Nile, the Euphrates, and the Indus. The vital period in which the new techniques were developed is roughly the two millennia from 6000 to 4000 B.C.

When history is really taught as it ought to be taught, so that everybody is made to understand, as the foundation of his intellectual life, the true story of human society, one of the most fundamental lessons will be the concrete and detailed exposition of the nature of this great revolution in man's control over his environment. The film, the museum, the workshop, the lecture, the library will combine to make the significance of these vital two thousand years sink into the historical consciousness of mankind. This technical revolution constitutes the material basis of ancient civilization. No comparable change in human destinies took place between it and the industrial revolution of the eighteenth century. The cultures of the ancient empires of the Near East, of Greece and Rome, and of Medieval Europe, all rest on the technical achievements of the Neolithic Age. Their resemblances to one another result from this fact. Their differences from us to-day can only be understood when we realize that we are separated from them all by the second great technical revolution, the coming of the Machine Age. Nothing short of a comprehensive reform of our system of education would suffice to do justice to the significance of these truths. Meanwhile two books may be brought to the notice of those who wish to understand the rôle of techniques in ancient society. Gordon Childe (*Man Makes Himself*, Watts) has given a brilliant account of the technical revolution of the New Stone Age and the consequent rise of urban life.[1] Partington's *Origins and Development of Applied Chemistry* (Longmans, Green & Co.) gives an exhaustive and up-to-date summary of man's knowledge of materials from the dawn of civilization down to 1500 B.C. – that is to say, to the end of the Bronze Age. There were, he assures us, very few further developments of applied chemistry between the end of the Bronze Age and quite modern times. That amounts to saying that there was stagnation for about 3,000 years in this fundamental branch of knowledge – a period covering half the life-time of the civilization of the Near East, the whole of the Graeco-Roman civilization, and ending only as modern Europe rose out of the Middle Ages. Here surely is a problem for the historian of science. We shall return to it.

'In the study of the development of man,' writes Partington, 'no part is more significant, even if more neglected, than that concerning the use of materials.' We have spoken of some of the materials used by man in the Old Stone Age. In Egypt the various phases of man's progress are registered by his growing use of things. In the Predynastic period – that is, 4000 and earlier – the Egyptians were using stone, bone, ivory, flint, rock-crystal, quartz, carnelian, agate, haematite, amber, and a long list of other semi-precious stones. Then their knowledge of metals begins, and gold,

1. Add now his later book, *What Happened in History* (Pelican).

silver, electrum, copper, bronze, iron in small quantities, lead, tin, antimony, platinum, galena, and malachite are added to the list. A tomb-painting of the Old Kingdom (2980–2475) shows a metal-worker's shop. Some of the men are engaged in blowing the fire in a furnace through what are probably reeds tipped with clay. Others are cutting and hammering metals. Others again are weighing out precious metals and malachite. Weights at this early period were made of hard stone, cut in geometrical figures. Balances were of the beam type.

We shall not attempt to describe the multifarious techniques of the Egyptians. *The Legacy of Egypt* (Oxford University Press, 1942) has excellent chapters on the subject. Enough has been said to raise the questions which are fundamental for our enquiry, and to these we shall address ourselves. What kind of knowledge is implied in these technical operations? In what sort of way did it fall short of the science of the Greeks? Men were weighing for thousands of years before Archimedes worked out the laws of equilibrium; they must have had practical and intuitional knowledge of the principles involved. What Archimedes did was to sort out the theoretical implications of this practical knowledge and present the resulting body of knowledge as a logically coherent system. Book I of his *Treatise on Plane Equilibriums* starts with seven postulates. *Equal weights at equal distances balance. If unequal weights operate at equal distances, the larger weighs down the smaller*. Such are two of the postulates. They make formal and explicit the kind of assumptions which had been tacitly made for centuries. Their number is reduced to the minimum on which the science can be based. Then, arguing from these postulates, Archimedes works up through a series of propositions to the fundamental theorem, proved first for commensurable and then by *reductio ad absurdum* for incommensurable magnitudes, that: *Two magnitudes, whether commensurable or incom-*

mensurable, balance at distances reciprocally proportional to the magnitudes. (*Greek Mathematics*, Heath, Vol. II, p. 75). This is a typical example of what is meant by saying that the empirical knowledge of the East was transformed into theoretical science by the Greeks.

But not all technical practices yield a body of knowledge which can be sorted out so readily into a series of propositions linked together by mathematical logic. Chemical practice, as we have seen, was very far advanced before 1500 B.C. Chemical theory lagged far behind. 'Many of the more historically important ideas were not at first put into words,' writes Haldane. 'They were technical inventions, which were at first handed down by imitation, and only slowly developed a verbal theory. When they did the theory was generally nonsense, but the practice sound. This was obviously the case, for example, until quite recently, with the extraction of metals from their ores.' From the practice of weighing, the Greeks, in the person of Archimedes, succeeded in extracting a science of statics. Aristotle and Theophrastus did not register a similar success in extracting from the crafts of the potter and the smith a sound body of chemical theory, though the treatise of the former, called *Meteorology* IV, and that of the latter *On Fire*, both of which will be discussed later, are most promising and contain genuine scientific elements. The successful constitution of a science of statics and the failure to constitute a science of chemistry give us a clue to the strength and the weakness of the Greek scientific achievement.

But the absence of a correct theory must not blind us to the genuinely scientific elements contained in the techniques in which the Egyptian craftsmen excelled, and which the Greeks borrowed from them. Consider, for instance, the science implied in the manufacture of bronze. Bronze is an alloy of copper and tin, which has certain advantages over pure copper. It has a lower melting point. It is harder. It has a finer colour and keeps it better. The Egyptian smiths were aware of these advantages, and experimented until they got the best results. They knew, for instance, that the hardest bronze contains about 12 per cent of tin, that a lower percentage will not give the required hardness, and that a higher percentage makes the bronze more fragile. Many other processes, such as the making of pottery and the making of glass, equally illustrate their skill in applied chemistry. The Greeks borrowed this applied chemistry. But neither Egyptians nor Greeks produced a body of written chemical theory. Why?

Most techniques require at some stage the use of fire. Fire is a great teacher, man's greatest master in the art of chemistry. Pliny has a finely imaginative description of the rôle it has played in civilization (*Natural History*, xxxvi, 68). 'I have now completed,' he writes, 'my description of the works of human ingenuity by which art imitates nature, and with great wonder I observe that fire is almost everywhere the active agent. Fire takes in sand and gives back, now glass, now silver, now minium, now various kinds of lead, now pigments, now medicines. By fire stones are melted into bronze, by fire iron is made and mastered, by fire gold is produced, by fire that stone is calcined which, in the form of cement, holds our houses over our heads. There are some things which it profits to submit more than once to the action of fire. The same original material becomes one thing at a first firing, another at a second, still another at a third. Coal itself, for example, begins to possess its strength only when extinguished, and when it might be thought to be exhausted its virtue is increased. O fire, thou measureless and implacable portion of nature, shall we rightly call thee destroyer or creator?'

But fire is not only a great teacher, it is also a hard taskmaster. It calls for blood, toil, tears, and sweat. 'I have seen the blacksmith at his work at the mouth of his furnace,' writes the Egyptian satirist, 'his fingers like the skin of a crocodile; he smells worse than the roe of a fish.' 'I have not,' he adds, 'seen a blacksmith on a commission, a founder who goes on an embassy.' Fire, therefore, it appears, has effect not only on things, but on individual men and on the constitution of society. It is the social effect of techniques involving the use of fire, and also of other toilsome techniques, as Gordon Childe has explained, which has determined the development of written science.

The technical revolution of the Neolithic Age provided the material basis for the civilization of the Near East. That revolution also determined the social character of the civilization that was about to arise. It gradually operated to produce a division in society which had not existed before to any comparable extent. At one pole of society it ranged the workers, at the other the administrators – here the peasant, the potter, and the smith ; there the king, the priests, the nobles. Applied chemistry – the practice of transforming things by the agency of fire – was at one pole ; applied politics, or the practice of controlling men by fear, at the other. In ancient Egypt the workshops were owned by the king, by corporations of priests, or by a small class of wealthy merchants. Industry was run in close connection with the great estates; the labourers, agricultural or industrial, were serfs or slaves or, as some now claim, wage-slaves. Such were the main classes in Egyptian society.

Now writing developed step by step with the development of this class-divided civilization, and writing in its origin was an instrument of administration. The scribe belonged, in his humble fashion, to the administrative class. His profession was, in fact, the main avenue by which individuals might climb out of the class of manual workers into the civil service. The literary tradition, accordingly, embraced only such sciences and pseudo-sciences as were useful for administration or served the needs of the administrative class. Before the end of the fourth millennium, books appear. Thereafter mathematics, surgery, medicine, astrology, alchemy, haruspicy, were made the subject of written treatises. But the practical applied sciences, the productive techniques, continued to be handed down exclusively by oral tradition among the members of the depressed class in society. The theory continued to be wholly merged in the operations, and could not, without more leisure for reflection, be disengaged from it. The practitioners of the techniques were not only without share in the art of writing which has played a great rôle in enabling the human mind to advance from the multitude of particulars to abstract generalizations; but the establishment of the division in society between the administrative and the working class had lowered their status and their opportunity.

This is the explanation of the paradox noted long ago by Lord Bacon (*N. O.*, I, lxxxv) that the great technical discoveries 'were more ancient than philosophy and the intellectual arts; so that, to speak truth, when contemplation and doctrinal science began, the discovery of useful works ceased '.

These considerations will be found applicable to the whole development of science in antiquity. They are still to some degree operative even to-day. The history of Greek science, which is our main concern, is unintelligible unless they are constantly borne in mind. To borrow the mechanical arts from Egypt or elsewhere was to borrow also the social consequences, at least to some extent. 'What are called the mechanical arts,' says Xenophon, 'carry a social stigma and are rightly dishonoured in our cities. For these arts damage the bodies of those who work at them or who act as overseers, by compelling them to a sedentary life and to an indoor life, and, in some cases, to spend the whole day by the fire. This physical degeneration results also in deterioration of the soul. Furthermore, the workers at these trades simply have not got the time to perform the offices of friendship or citizenship. Consequently they are looked upon as bad friends and bad patriots, and in some cities, especially the warlike ones, it is not legal for a citizen to ply a mechanical trade.' (*Oeconomicus*, iv, 203.)

This contempt for the mechanical arts came in the end to be a serious obstacle to the development of the physical, chemical, and mechanical sciences in Greece. But this is not yet true of the early phases down to about 500 B.C. It is important to make an effort to understand the technical achievement of the Greeks at this period, though the effort is difficult for those with an exclusively literary education, like the writer of this book and no doubt many of his readers. It is so easy in pronouncing phrases like Bronze Age and Iron Age to forget what long and complicated developments are summed up in the words, and to assume that the invention of the technique of bronze metallurgy or iron metallurgy rests on one simple observation and comprises one simple operation. We read so often of the early men who accidentally heated some new kind of stone at the edge of their camp fire and observed the bright molten metal flowing out, and, hey presto! we think the Iron Age had arrived. But suppose for a change we take down a volume like R. J. Forbes's *Metallurgy in Antiquity* (Brill, Leiden, 1950) and note no more than his careful distinction of five historical stages in copper metallurgy: first, shaping native copper ; then, annealing native copper ; then, smelting oxide and carbonate ores ; then, melting and refining copper ; then, smelting sulphide ores. There begins to dawn upon us a little of what is involved in the elaboration of such a technique. We begin to understand that the busy ingenuity of gifted and determined men, working generation after generation over spans of hundreds of years, were necessary to bring these techniques to full fruition. And even then we have left out of account the toilsome and dangerous exertions of the humbler miners and metallurgists, not to mention also a certain structure of society without which the organization of the extraction, transport, and handling of the necessary materials could not have been achieved. But it is only when our imaginations are informed by such a picture as this that we are in a position to understand the achievement of sixth-century Greek technicians like the Samian artists Rhoecus, Telecles, and Theodorus. These men are credited with the invention of the technique of casting life-size statutes in bronze, and the invention meant that the Greeks had now outstripped the rest of the world in bronze metallurgy. These men also were great builders. It is even recorded that Theodorus, achieving in this a triumph which was not to be repeated till Roman times, introduced a system of central-heating into the temple of Diana at Ephesus. He has many other inventions also to his credit. Readers of my third chapter will see that, in obedience to tradition, and I think a sound tradition, I have given a prominent place in my story of the beginnings of Greek science to another Samian, Pythagoras, the exact contemporary of Theodorus, for both flourished about 530 B.C. Everybody has heard that Pythagoras, as well as being a mathematician, was a vegetarian who yet did not eat beans and who believed in the transmigration of souls. I am loath to disturb such traditional features in the history of thought. I am only anxious to claim also a place for his contemporary and fellow-islander who, as well as bronze-casting and central-heating, is credited with the invention of the level, the square, the rule, the lathe. A better balance is given to the history of science when we approach it also from the technical side.

The mention of bronze metallurgy reminds me, however, that the Greeks were an Iron Age people. From Professor Forbes again we can learn what further demands on human ingenuity were made by the new technique. In bronze metallurgy everything depends on the composition of the alloy, but in iron metallurgy the properties it is desired to impart to the metal depend far more on the handling, on the temperature to which the metal has been heated, on the speed of quenching, on the time and temperature of annealing. In this new and complicated technique also the Greeks came to play a pioneer part. Gordon Childe has shown (*Progress and Archaeology*, p. 40) that before 500 B.C. the Greeks by their invention of new iron tools had made a decisive advance in man's control over nature. These are examples of the technical progress of the age in which Greek science was born.

Though the later Greeks came to be indifferent to technical progress, there is evidence, in their painted vases and elsewhere, of the pride which the Greeks of the end of the sixth century took in these achievements. 'Greek art of the archaic and classical periods,' writes Rostovtzeff (*The Hellenistic World*, p. 1200), 'never neglects representation of the crafts,' as later it came to do in favour of mythology and ornament. And on some vases we may actually see the master smith or the master potter in his shop. On a vase of 515 B.C., for instance, Beazley (*Potter and Painter in Ancient Athens*, p. 6) identifies the figure of the master of a potter's shop in 'an old man with long white hair, dressed in a cloak, and holding no ordinary walking-stick, but a goodly sceptre-like staff', in token, of course, of his dignity. He compares him to a bronze figure from Laconia, of date about 500 B.C., which shows another old man 'with long hair and a clever face', carefully dressed, as befits his importance and again carrying a stick. Him he identifies with the master of a foundry, supposing the bronze portrait to be an offering dedicated by the original himself.

In fifteenth-century Florence, where science as well as art stirred with new life, the goldsmiths' shops were the main centre of the new activity. 'These workshops,' writes Hans Baron (*Journal of the History of Ideas*, Vol. IV, 1943),

' performed in the fifteenth century the function discharged in later centuries by the industrial workshop and the scientific laboratory. Here were found experiment, observation, causal thinking, among men whose handicrafts had risen to high social esteem.' Some such conditions I imagine to have obtained in the first age, the Heroic Age, of Greek science.

CHAPTER TWO

The Chief Periods of Greek Science – The Ionian Dawn – The Milesian School and Heraclitus – The Influence of Techniques

★

THE CHIEF PERIODS OF GREEK SCIENCE

CHRONOLOGICAL divisions of historical movements must always have something arbitrary about them, but they assist the memory at the start. They provide a sort of scaffolding within which the building must be erected. Let us say, then, that the history of Greek science occupies about 900 years and falls into three great divisions of about 300 years each. The first period, the most original and creative period, runs from about 600 B.C. to the death of Aristotle in 322 B.C. The second from the foundation of Alexandria to the completion of the Roman conquest of the East about the beginning of the Christian Era. The third covers the first three centuries of the Roman Empire.

Of these 900 years, the first 300 are the most important and the last 300 the least. Inside these divisions the most vital years are: (1) the period 600–400 B.C., when a scientific outlook on the world and society was constituted for the first time in history, and (2) the period 320–120 B.C., when, under the patronage of the Ptolemies, whole branches of science were constituted on what, roughly speaking, might be called their present basis. The first of these periods has been called by Heidel the Heroic Age. The latter might be called the Age of the Text-book. The intervening period from 400 to 320 B.C., which covers the careers of Plato and Aristotle, is notable for its philosophic development. It created the logical terminology without which the masterly text-books of the later age could not have been written.

The original thing in Greek science at its beginning is that

B

it offers us, for the first time in history, an attempt to supply a purely naturalist interpretation of the universe as a whole. Cosmology takes the place of myth. The ancient empires of the Near East had created or preserved a mass of highly developed agricultural and industrial techniques. They had brought to a certain level of systematization and theoretical development a few officially approved sciences, such as astronomy, mathematics, and medicine. But there is no evidence of an attempt to give a naturalistic explanation of the universe as a whole. There is an official mythology, transmitted in priestly corporations and enshrined in elaborate ceremonial, telling how things came to be as they are. There are no individual thinkers offering a rational substitute for this doctrine over their own names.

This state of science corresponds in general to the stage of social development of the old empires. In the ancient civilizations of the river-valleys life depended on an artificial water-supply. Central governments came into existence, controlling large areas with absolute authority, through their power to give or withhold water. Gigantic works in brick or stone witness to the power of government to direct the co-operative efforts of vast populations. Ziggurats, pyramids, temples, palaces, colossal statues – the dwellings, tombs, and images of kings and gods – apprise us of the organizing ability of the great, the technical skill of the humble, and the superstitions on which society was based. Astronomy was needed to regulate the calendar, geometry to measure the fields, arithmetic and a system of weights and measures to gather the taxes. Medicine had its obvious uses. So, it must be observed, had superstition, and the superstition was such as to preclude the beginnings of a scientific cosmology. A sophisticated Greek of the fourth century B.C. cast a glance at the official religion of Egypt and detected its social utility. The Egyptian law-giver, he remarks, had established so many contemptible superstitions, first, 'because he thought it proper to accustom the masses to obeying any command that was given to them by their superiors ', and, second, ' because he judged that he could rely on those who displayed their piety to be equally law-abiding in every other particular '. (*Isocrates*, Busiris.) This is not the type of society in which men with a rational outlook on the world and human life are encouraged to come to the fore.

THE IONIAN DAWN. THE MILESIAN SCHOOL AND HERACLITUS

In Ionia, on the Aegean fringe of the Anatolian mainland, conditions in the sixth century were very different. Political power was in the hands of a mercantile aristocracy and this mercantile aristocracy was actively engaged in promoting the rapid development of techniques on which their prosperity depended. The institution of slavery had not yet developed to a point at which the ruling class regarded techniques with contempt. Wisdom was still practical and fruitful. Miletus, where Natural Philosophy was born, was the most go-ahead town in the Greek world. It was the mother city of a numerous brood of colonies in the Black Sea ; and its commerce, whereby its own products were exchanged for those of other lands, ranged far and wide over the Mediterranean. It was in contact with the still-thriving civilization of Mesopotamia by land routes and with Egypt by sea. The information we possess makes it clear that the first philosophers were the active type of man, interested in affairs, one would expect to find in such a town. Everything that we know about them confirms the impression that the range of ideas and the modes of thought they applied to speculation on the nature of things in general were those which they derived from their active interest in practical affairs. They were not recluses engaged in pondering upon abstract questions, they were not ' observers of nature ' in an academic sense, but active

practical men the novelty of whose philosophy consisted in
the fact that, when they turned their minds to wondering
how things worked, they did so in the light of everyday
experience without regard to ancient myths. Their freedom
from dependence on mythological explanations was due to
the fact that the comparatively simple political structure of
their rising towns did not impose upon them the necessity
of governing by superstition, as in the older empires.

Thales, the first of the Milesian philosophers, visited Egypt
in the course of business, and brought back from there a
knowledge of geometry. He made a new application of the
technique which the Egyptians had devised for measuring
land. By means of the doctrine of similar triangles, he devised a method of determining the distance of ships at sea.
From the Phoenicians he is said to have borrowed improvements in the art of navigating by the stars. By the aid of
Babylonian astronomical tables he foretold an eclipse of the
sun in 585 B.C. He is said to have made an advance on Egyptian geometry also in the very important sense that he understood better than they the conditions of a general proof. He
not only knew that a circle is bisected by its diameter, but
proved it. His joint reputation as philosopher and business
man is reflected in the story that, being twitted with a lack
of practical sense, he confounded his critics by making a
fortune in olive oil.

The great renown of Thales, however, rests not on his
geometry or his turn for affairs, but on a new commonsense
way of looking at the world of things. The Egyptians and
the Babylonians had old cosmogonies, part of their religious
inheritance, which told how the world had come to be.
Since in both countries, in cold fact, the land on which they
lived had been won in a desperate struggle with nature by
draining the swamps beside their rivers, naturally enough
their cosmogonies embodied the idea that there was too
much water about, and that the beginning of things, in any

sense that mattered to men, was when some divine being did the equivalent of saying, *Let the dry land appear*. The name of the Babylonian creator was Marduk. In one of the Babylonian legends it says: 'All the lands were sea ... Marduk bound a rush mat upon the face of the waters, he made dirt and piled it beside the rush mat.' What Thales did was to leave Marduk out. He, too, said that everything was once water. But he thought that earth and everything else had been formed out of water by a natural process, like the silting up of the delta of the Nile. The later Greeks invented a learned compound to describe the novelty of this outlook. They called the Old Ionians *hylozoists*, or Those-who-think-matter-is-alive. That means that they did not think that life, or soul, came into the world from outside, but that what is called life, or soul, or the cause of motion in things, was inherent in matter, was just the way it behaved. The general picture Thales had of things was that the earth is a flat disc floating on water, that there is water above our heads as well as all round us (where else could the rain come from?), that the sun and moon and stars are vapour in a state of incandescence, and that they sail over our heads on the watery firmament above and then sail round, on the sea on which the earth itself is afloat, to their appointed stations for rising in the East. It is an admirable beginning, the whole point of which is that it gathers together into a coherent picture a number of observed facts *without letting Marduk in*.

This naturalistic kind of speculation, once started, made rapid progress. Anaximander, the second name in European philosophy, and also a native of Miletus, had a much more elaborate account of the universe to give, involving more extensive observation and more profound reflection. As in the case of Thales, the observation and the reflection were turned primarily on techniques, and the phenomena of nature were interpreted in the light of the ideas derived from them. His general idea of how things came to be as they are is this.

Once upon a time the four elements of which the world is made lay in a more stratified form: earth, which is the heaviest, at the centre, water covering it, mist above the water, fire embracing all. The fire, heating the water, caused it to evaporate, making the dry land appear, but increasing the volume of mist. The pressure grew to breaking point. The fiery integument of the universe burst and took the form of wheels of fire enclosed in tubes of mist circling round earth and sea. That is the working model of the universe. The heavenly bodies we see circling above our heads are holes in the tubes through which the enclosed fire glows. An eclipse is a closing, or partial closing, of a hole. This very arresting cosmology, while it has obvious reminiscences of the potter's yard, the smithy, or the kitchen, leaves no room for Marduk at all. Even men are accounted for without his help. Anaximander thought that fish, as a form of life, preceded land animals, and that man, accordingly, had once been a fish. But as the dry land appeared, some fish adapted themselves to life on land.

Certain striking advances in logic were also made by this great thinker. He objected to the notion of Thales that everything is water. Why not Earth, or Mist, or Fire, since all change into one another? Better to say that all four are forms of a common *indeterminate substance*. He saw also the naivety of supporting the earth on water. On what does the water rest? Rather should we say that the world is poised in space yet stays where it is 'because of the equal distance from everything'.

The third thinker, Anaximenes, the last of the Milesians, plumped for Mist as the fundamental form of things. This looks like a step back. But he had, in fact, a most valuable contribution to make. His idea was that everything is Mist, but that it gets harder and heavier according as more of it is packed into a given space. The idea, to judge by his terminology, was suggested to him by the industrial process of felting woven materials by pressure, and was confirmed by his observation of the processes of evaporation and condensation of liquids. *Rarefaction* and *condensation* were his key words. Rarefied Mist is Fire. Condensed Mist becomes first Water and then Earth. He thought also that rarefaction was accompanied by heat and condensation by cold. He 'proved' this by an experiment. You were not just to take his word for it. Open your mouth wide and blow on your hand. The 'rarefied' vapour comes out warm. Now purse your lips together and emit a thin stream of 'condensed' vapour and feel how cold it is. He did not know the true explanation of this phenomenon. Do you?

Observe, in following this succession of thinkers, how their logic, their stock of ideas, their powers of abstraction, increase as they grapple with their problem. It was a great advance in human thinking when Thales reduced the manifold appearances of things to one First Principle. Another great step was taken when Anaximander chose, as his First Principle, not a visible form of things like water, but a concept like the Indeterminate. But Anaximenes was still not content. When Anaximander sought to explain how the different things emerged from the Indeterminate, he gave a reply that was a mere metaphor. He said it was a process of 'separating out'. Anaximenes felt that something more was needed, and came forward with the complementary ideas of Rarefaction and Condensation, which offered an explanation of how quantitative changes could produce qualitative ones. This again marked an advance. It gave a possible explanation of the way in which one fundamental substance might exist in four different states. But something was still lacking – namely, some explanation as to why things should not stay as they are instead of being subject to perpetual change. The Milesians attempted no answer to this question. It occupied the attention of a solitary thinker of another Ionian town, Heraclitus of Ephesus.

THE INFLUENCE OF TECHNIQUES

As Anaximenes had chosen Mist as his First Principle, Heraclitus chose Fire. He was the philosopher of change. His doctrine has been summed up in the phrase *Everything flows* ; but his choice of Fire as his First Principle was probably not due, as is often said, to its being the most impermanent of things, but to its being the active agent which produces change in so many technical and natural processes. Still more important was his idea of Tension, brought in to explain the relative permanence and fundamental impermanence of things. It is one of the richest and most helpful ideas of the old philosophers, not a whit reduced in significance when we remember that it, too, had its origin in the techniques of the time. The doctrine of *Opposite Tension* which Heraclitus applied to the interpretation of nature was derived, as his own words inform us, from his observation of the state of the string in the bow and the lyre. According to Heraclitus there is in things a force that moves them on the Upward Path to Fire, and an opposite force that moves them on the Downward Path to Earth. The existence of matter in any particular state is the result of a balance of opposing forces, of Tension. Even the most stable things in appearance are the battleground of opposing forces, and their stability is only relative. One force is gradually gaining on the other all the time. Nature as a whole is either on the Upward Path to Fire or on the Downward Path to Earth. Its mode of existence is an eternal oscillation between these two extremes.

There is great danger, in discussing these old thinkers, that one may read into them the meaning of a later age. It must always be remembered that they were ignorant of all the accumulated knowledge of modern science and all the refinement of ideas that centuries of philosophical discussion have produced. In the world of thought, as in the world of nature, everything flows. The very words with which we translate the sayings of Heraclitus are charged with meanings unknown to him. It takes an effort of historical research and of historical imagination to put oneself back into the frame of mind of this great old thinker when he supposed himself to have solved the riddle of the universe by saying that there was a tension in things, 'like the bow and the lyre'. But, if there is danger of exaggerating the import of these ancient philosophies, there is also danger of denuding them of significance. The judgement of Brunet and Mieli (*Histoire des Sciences. Antiquité*, p. 114), whose book is one of the latest and one of the best on the subject, is worth quoting. 'These philosophers are,' they write, 'according to the accurate title given to them in antiquity, *physiologoi*, that is to say, observers of nature ... They observe the phenomena which present themselves to their eyes, and putting aside all supernatural or mystical intervention, they endeavour to give strictly natural explanations of them. It is in this sense, and by their rejection of all magical intervention, that they make the decisive step towards science and mark the beginning, at least the conscious and systematic beginning, of a positive method applied to the interpretation of the facts of nature.' This judgement is worth quoting, but it needs supplementing. The Milesians were not simply observers of nature. They were observers of nature whose eyes had been quickened, whose attention directed, and whose selection of phenomena to be observed had been conditioned, by familiarity with a certain range of techniques. The novelty of their modes of thought is only negatively explained by their rejection of mystical or supernatural intervention. It is its positive content that is decisive. Its positive content is drawn from the techniques of the age.

CHAPTER THREE

Pythagoras – The Religious Tradition in Greek Philosophy – The Mathematical Universe

★

PYTHAGORAS

LATER Greeks recognized in the history of their thought about the nature of things a double tradition – the purely naturalistic, or materialistic, or, as they sometimes called it, atheistic tradition of Ionia, and the religious tradition which originated with Pythagoras in Magna Graecia in the West.

Plato, in the tenth book of his *Laws*, gives a brief characterization of both systems of thought. The opinions he ascribes to the Ionian naturalists are as follows: The four elements, Earth, Air, Fire, and Water, all exist by nature and chance, none of them by design or providence. The bodies which come next in order – the earth, the sun, the moon, the stars – have been created by those absolutely inanimate elements, which are moved by some inherent force according to certain affinities among them. In this way the whole heaven has been created and all that is in the heaven, as well as all plants and animals. The seasons also result from the action of these elements, not from the action of mind, or God, or providence, but by nature and chance only. Design sprang up afterwards and out of these. It is mortal and of mortal birth. The various arts, embodiments of design, have sprung up to co-operate with nature – arts such as medicine, husbandry, and even legislation. The gods likewise are products, not of nature, but of design, being constituted by the laws of the different states in which they are worshipped. Morality also, like religion, is a product of human design. The principles of justice have no existence in nature; they are a mere convention. To sum up, the natural philosophers say that Fire, Water, Earth, and Air are the first elements of all things, that these constitute Nature, and that the soul is formed out of these afterwards.

Plato next sets forth the main ideas of the religious tradition of thought, which is also his own. According to this view, the soul is the first of things. She is before all bodies, and is the chief author of their changes and transpositions. The things of the soul come before the things of the body. That is to say, Thought, Attention, Mind, Design, Law are prior to the qualities of matter. Design, or Mind, or Providence comes first, and after it come nature and the works of nature. What is called nature is under the government of Design and Mind. This is the tradition which is said to have originated with Pythagoras. Henceforth we shall need to keep in mind the double tradition. Both traditions are often embodied in a single philosopher.

Pythagoras, for example, is not only the founder of the religious tradition ; he is also one of the greatest of Greek scientists. An Ionian Greek by origin, who probably (as is also said of Thales) had Phoenician blood in his veins, he emigrated to the West when the advance of the Persian power to the Aegean threatened the liberties of the Asiatic Greeks, and settled in Croton in southern Italy. He is the founder of European culture in the western Mediterranean sphere.

Pythagoras was a native of the island of Samos, which at this time, like the city of Miletus, which saw the birth of Greek science, was a commercial power in a vigorous, even violent, stage of growth. Its dictator, Polycrates, had broken the power of the landed aristocracy and was running the island with the backing of the merchant class. In their interest he enlarged and improved the harbour, and, as his capital city grew, he caused to be executed one of the most astonishing feats of ancient engineering. Fetching an engineer from Megara, one Eupalinus by name, he had him run a tunnel through the hill of Kastro to serve as an aqueduct to supply the town. The tunnel, which is over 900 yards in length, was begun from both ends. Modern excavations show that when the two digging parties met in the centre their borings fell short of exact coincidence only by a couple of feet.

The fact is full of warning and instruction for the historian of science. If we were dependent on the literary record alone, we should have to wait for a late writer, Hero of Alexandria, who probably lived in the second century A.D., for a geometrical construction explaining how to perform this feat. But the job was done, and well done, 600 years earlier, and we may be certain that the necessary mathematical knowledge also existed then, though we have no record of it.

Pythagoras was about forty years of age when, about the year 530 B.C., the Persian conquest of Ionia disturbed his prospects in Samos and he fled for refuge to Croton. Here, as no doubt he knew before he made the venture, he found a commercial city not unlike his own. He was an active politician, and the probability is that he attached himself to the merchant class in his new home, which, here as elsewhere, occupied a middle position between the land-owning aristocracy and the peasants and workers. He became enormously influential in his new home. Its political and religious life were reshaped by him. Professor George Thomson, in his *Aeschylus and Athens*, compares his position to that of Calvin at Geneva.

THE RELIGIOUS TRADITION IN GREEK PHILOSOPHY

Pythagoras, however, as we have said, was not only a religious reformer and politician, but a scientist. We shall understand his science better if we do not forget his religion and his politics, for they were intimately blended. The

Pythagorean community was a religious brotherhood for the practice of asceticism and the study of mathematics. The brethren were required every day to conduct, in private meditation, an examination of conscience. They believed in the immortality of the soul and its transmigration; the perishable body was but a tomb or prison which the soul inhabited for a time. These beliefs they held in common with other adherents of the mystery religions then widespread in Greece. Pythagoreanism was, in effect, a sophisticated form of mystery religion. The peculiarity of the system was that it found in mathematics a key to the riddle of the universe and an instrument for the purification of the soul. 'The function of geometry,' says Plutarch, speaking like a good Pythagorean, 'is to draw us away from the sensible and the perishable to the intelligible and the eternal. *For the contemplation of the eternal is the end of philosophy, as the contemplation of the mysteries is the end of religion.*' The parallel is significant. The Pythagoreans were the originators of the religious attitude towards mathematics. They did not indeed, at least in the earlier generations of the school, despise the practical applications of mathematics. Systematic town-planning, which began in Greece at this period, is due to Pythagorean influence. But the growth of religious mysticism based on mathematics must be ascribed to this school.

THE MATHEMATICAL UNIVERSE

The school quickly registered remarkable advances in geometry and the theory of numbers. It is generally agreed that by the middle of the fifth century they had arrived at most of the results which are systematized by Euclid in Books I, II, VII, and IX of his *Elements*. This is a scientific achievement of the first order. But if you study their mathematics in the sober pages of Euclid's famous textbook, you will not recover its other aspect, the religious fervour with which their views were held. A quotation from a fifth-century Pythagorean will help us to do that.

'Consider,' exclaims Philolaus, 'the effects and the nature of number according to the power that resides in the decad. It is great, all-powerful, all-sufficing, the first principle and the guide in life of Gods, of Heaven, of Men. Without it all is without limit, obscure, indiscernible. The nature of number is to be a standard of reference, of guidance, and of instruction in every doubt and difficulty. Were it not for number and its nature, nothing that exists would be clear to anybody either in itself or in its relation to other things ... You can observe the power of number exercising itself not only in the affairs of demons and of gods, but in all the acts and the thoughts of men, in all handicrafts and in music. Nor does harmony and the nature of number admit of any falsity. Falsity is in no way akin to it. Only to the unlimited, the unintelligible, the irrational, do falseness and envy belong.'

This passage, however, does something more than emphasize the religious aspect of Pythagorean mathematics. It also stresses the importance of mathematics for the practical arts. This is characteristic of the early period of Greek philosophy, and remains to some extent characteristic of it to the end. Plato, as may be seen from the quotation with which we began this chapter, associated the Ionian philosophy with a definite theory as to the nature and social function of the practical arts. For the early Ionians there was no essential difference between natural and technical processes. The claim of the early Ionians that nature was intelligible was based on their view that the practical arts were intelligent efforts of men to co-operate with nature for their own good. The Pythagoreans, the prime movers in the next great philosophical movement, still have the same outlook. Number, for them, is not only the first principle of the heavens, but exhibits its power also 'in all the handicrafts'.

The harmony produced by number will still be our theme, no matter what part of the Pythagorean universe we examine. Here we shall confine our attention to the two branches of knowledge most powerfully influenced by Pythagorean mathematical theory – cosmology and music.

The cosmology of the Pythagoreans is very curious and very important. They did not, like the Ionians, try to describe the universe in terms of the behaviour of certain material elements and physical processes. They described it exclusively in terms of number. Aristotle said long afterwards that they took number to be the matter as well as the form of the universe. Numbers constituted the actual stuff of which their world was made. They called a point One, a line Two, a surface Three, a solid Four, according to the minimum number of points necessary to define each of these dimensions. But their points had bulk, their lines breadth, their surfaces depth. Points added up to lines, lines to surfaces, surfaces to solids. Out of their One, Two, Three, and Four they could really build a world. No wonder that Ten, the sum of these numbers, was a sacred and omnipotent power. It follows also that the theory of numbers which they brought to such perfection was for them something more than mathematics. It was physics.

The identification of numbers with things is apt to appear puzzling to the student. It will be found less puzzling if we follow the clue provided by the mathematical procedure which led the Pythagoreans to this view. We have spoken of their study of the theory of numbers. In this study their method was to employ what are called figurate numbers. They represent the triangular numbers thus:

.

. .

. . .

. . . .

. . . . and so on.

The square numbers thus:

```
                              .   .   .   .   .
                          .   .   .   .   .   .
                      .   .   .   .   .   .
                  .   .   .   .   .   .
          .   .   .   .   .   .   .   .   .   .   .   .   . and so on.
```

And the pentagonal numbers thus:

```
                      .
                  .   .   .
              .   .   .   .
          .   .   .   .   . and so on.
```

It was this new technique of analysing the properties of numbers which made possible their identification of numbers with things and determined, as we shall see, the peculiarity of their cosmological system.

This mathematical philosophy appeared as a rival to the natural philosophy of the Ionians. And here it becomes immediately apparent that, as a theory of the universe, it contained less of sensuous intuition and more of abstract thought than the Ionian view. Mathematical relations now take the place of physical processes or states, like rarefaction and condensation, and tension. The universe, so it appeared to the Pythagoreans, could be better, and more quickly, understood by drawing diagrams on sand than by thinking about phenomena like raised beaches, silting up of river mouths, evaporation, felting, and so forth. Herein lay a danger. This mathematical approach was adjusted both to the religious and social preconceptions of the school. Mathematics not only seemed to provide a better explanation of things than the Ionian view. It kept the souls of the brethren pure from contact with the earthly, the material, and suited the changing temper of a world in which contempt for manual labour kept pace with the growth of slavery. In a society in which contact with the technical processes of production became ever more shameful, as being fit only for slaves, it was found extraordinarily fortunate that the secret constitution of things should be revealed, not to those who manipulated them, not to those who worked with fire, but to those who drew patterns on the sand. For Heraclitus, who came at the end of a school of thought in which industrial technique had played a prominent rôle in providing the stock of ideas by which nature was explained, nothing seemed more natural than to regard fire, the chief agent in the technical manipulation of things, as the fundamental element. The substitution of number for fire as the First Principle marks a stage in the separation of philosophy from the technique of production. This separation is of fundamental importance in the interpretation of the history of Greek thought. Henceforth the banausic associations of the oven, the soldering-iron, the bellows, and the potter's wheel reduce their influence on Greek thought in comparison with the more gentlemanly pursuit of theory of numbers and geometry.

The Pythagoreans, having constructed matter out of numbers, next proceeded to arrange the main members of the universe according to a plan in which there was a little observation of nature and a lot of *a priori* mathematical reasoning. Since they attached moral and aesthetic values to mathematical relations, and since they held the heavenly bodies to be divine, they had little difficulty in deciding that the heavenly bodies are perfect spheres and move in perfect circles, the word 'perfect' here having a moral as well as a mathematical significance. It has not, in fact, proved true that the heavenly bodies are perfect spheres, nor that they move in perfect circles. Nevertheless the fact that the Pythagoreans made great advances in mathematics and that they applied their new technique to astronomy made them pioneers in this domain. Their plan of the universe is, historically, of great importance. In the centre they put a mass of fire; round it revolved the earth, the moon, the sun, the five planets, and the heaven of the fixed stars. The distances of the heavenly bodies from the central fire they supposed to correspond to the intervals of the notes in the musical scale. This provided a sort of ground plan for subsequent workers. Gone are the tubes of fire of Anaximander, which seem primitive in one aspect, but which attempted to supply a mechanical model of the universe. Their place is taken by a purely geometrical astronomy which aims at mapping out the positions of heavenly bodies conceived of as divine. Vast improvements in the understanding of the relative sizes, distances, and positions of the heavenly bodies, the result of the application of a new mathematical technique to a few observed facts, were to transform in the course of centuries the simple Pythagorean plan into the complicated system of Ptolemy which was not seriously attacked until the sixteenth century of our own era. But from now on the heavenly bodies, being divine and therefore immortal, cease to have a history. They are removed, though not without a sharp struggle, from the sphere of natural philosophy and incorporated in theology.

The Pythagorean contribution to music, or, to be more accurate, to acoustics, is of even greater interest than their cosmology. How did they make the discovery of the fixed intervals in the musical scale? It seems reasonable to claim it as an early triumph of the method of observation and experiment. A story is told about it in a late writer, Boethius, who belongs to the sixth century A.D. Since it is the kind of story that antiquity was more inclined to forget than to invent, I agree with Brunet and Mieli that it is likely to be true. Here is the narration of Boethius, slightly condensed.

Pythagoras, haunted by the problem of giving a mathematical explanation of the fixed intervals in the scale, happened, by the grace of God, to pass a blacksmith's shop, and found his attention gripped by the more or less musical chime rung out by the hammers on the anvil. It was an opportunity to investigate this problem under new conditions which he could not resist. In he went and observed long. Then he had an idea that the different notes might be proportioned to the strength of the men. 'Would they change their hammers round?' It was plain that his first idea was wrong, for the chime was unaltered. The explanation must lie in the hammers themselves, not in the men.

There were five hammers in action. 'Might he weigh them?' Ah, miracle of miracles, the weights of four of them were in a proportion of 12, 9, 8, 6. The fifth, the weight of which bore no significant numerical relation to the rest, was the one that was spoiling the perfection of the chime. It was rejected, and Pythagoras listened again. Yes, the heaviest hammer, which was double the weight of the lightest, gave him the octave lower. The doctrine of the arithmetic and harmonic mean (12 – 9 – 6 and 12 – 8 – 6) revealed to him the ratios which give the intervals of the fourth and fifth sounded by the other two hammers. Surely it was the will of God that he had passed that blacksmith's shop. He hurried home to continue his experiments – this time, one might say, under laboratory conditions.

Did the whole reason for the harmony of these notes consist in the mathematical relations which had been observed? Pythagoras tried it out in a new medium, vibrating strings. He found that the note given was proportioned to the length. But what about the thickness and the tension of the strings? Into these two questions also he probed. Finally, returning to the relations of length he tried the matter out again on reed pipes of appropriate dimensions. Then at last he was sure. Such is the tradition Boethius records.

There is some confusion in the tradition. The experiment on the hammers could not give the results it is said to have given. If he did experiment on tension, his findings must have puzzled him. The number of vibrations in a stretched cord depends not on the weight which stretches it, but on the square root of the weight. We lack evidence that Pythagoras, or any ancient, knew this. Nevertheless these experiments are of crucial significance in the history of science. It is admitted that the Greeks never brought experiment to anything like the system and thoroughness which have characterized it in modern times. But that is not to admit that they never practised it. Brunet and Mieli are right to conclude from these experiments that 'they constitute a formal disproof of the belief affected by many that the Greeks did not know experimental science. It is further to be remarked,' they add, 'that it is to Pythagoras himself that tradition ascribes this discovery, and in this case one may, with all probability, admit the attribution. The development of experimental method in acoustics and in other parts of physics is one of the fairest titles to glory of the Pythagorean school.' (*Op. cit.*, p. 121.)

It remains to add one word about the crisis that overtook the Pythagorean geometrical view of the world about the middle of the fifth century. The Pythagoreans, as I have explained, built up their world out of points with magnitude. It might not be possible to tell how many points there were in any particular line; but, theoretically, they were finite in number. Then, with the progress of their own mathematical science, the foundation of their universe was suddenly swept away. It was discovered that the diagonal and the side of a square are incommensurable. $\sqrt{2}$ is an 'irrational' number. The term originated with them and indicates their shock when they, who held that number and reason were the same thing, found that they could not express $\sqrt{2}$ by any number. Their confusion was great. If the diagonal and the side of a square are incommensurable, it follows that lines are infinitely divisible. If lines are infinitely divisible, the little points of which the Pythagoreans built their universe do not exist. Or, if they do exist, they have got to be described in other than purely mathematical terms. In the fifth century B.C. they also had their crisis in physics.

CHAPTER FOUR

Parmenides and the Attack on Observational Science — Empedocles and Anaxagoras to the Rescue — The Atoms of Democritus

★

PARMENIDES AND THE ATTACK ON
OBSERVATIONAL SCIENCE

THE natural philosophy of the Ionians, simple as it is, comprises two elements. There is an element of observation and an element of thought. In order to explain the phenomena of the senses they had had to invent a system of abstract ideas. Earth and water, it is true, might seem names for things seen and felt, but even these terms pass over into the more general ideas of solid and liquid ; that is to say, they tend to become abstract terms. Still more clearly abstract are such ideas as The Indeterminate, or Condensation and Rarefaction, or Tension. The terms may, indeed, be taken from everyday life, but, as used by the philosophers, they become names of concepts invented to explain percepts. The distinction between the mind and the senses begins to appear. The first to express an awareness of this distinction was the deep thinker Heraclitus. 'The eyes and ears,' he said, 'are bad witnesses for men, if the mind cannot interpret what they say.' And again, as if aware of the newness and difficulty of this distinction between thought and sense, he observes: 'Of all those whose discourse I have heard there is not one who attains to the understanding that wisdom is apart from other things.'

Once the distinction had become clear there was bound to arise controversy as to which of the two, reason or sense, was the true method of approach to the understanding of nature. In the attempt to solve this problem the Pythagoreans played a prominent part. A younger contemporary of Pythagoras, and an adherent of his school, Alcmaeon of Croton, in the endeavour to expose the physical basis of sense-experience, laid the foundations of experimental physiology and empirical psychology. He dissected and vivisected animals. He discovered, among other things, the optic nerve, and he came to the correct conclusion that the brain is the central organ of sensation. His description of the tongue as the organ of taste is worth quoting. 'It is with the tongue that we discern tastes. For this being warm and soft dissolves the sapid particles by its heat, while by the porousness and delicacy of its structure it admits them into its substance and transmits them to the sensorium.' These striking words, which formed part of a general account of the physiology of sensation, are proof both of his powers of observation and of the systematic researches carried on in the Pythagorean school.

The achievements of the Pythagorean experimenters soon came under the criticism of philosophers who believed in seeking truth by pure reason alone unaided by the evidence of the senses. Their criticism, such as it is, has its place in the history of science. The attack on the senses was opened by the founder of another Italian school, Parmenides of Elea, the second of the religious philosophers of the Greeks. He composed a poem in two books, called respectively *The Way of Truth* and *The Way of Opinion*. In the first he propounded a view of the nature of reality based on the exclusive use of reason; in the second it is probable that he set forth, and rejected, the Pythagorean system which contained too much observation for his liking. Considerable fragments of his poem survive. One passage contains his attack on the experimentalists, which is sweeping and direct. 'Turn your mind away from this path of enquiry,' he cries. 'Let not the habit engrained by manifold experience force you along this path, to make an instrument of the blind eye, the echoing ear, and the tongue, but test by reason my contribution to the great debate.'

What had Parmenides in mind when he attacked the use of the eye, the ear, and the tongue? Most commentators seem to believe that he was addressing a general caution to mankind to beware of the treachery of the senses. But his words preclude this interpretation: he specifically attacks a method of research. Nor is it difficult to suggest the contemporary activities which he denounced. The astronomical activities of the Ionian school were carried on at this time in an observatory on the island of Tenedos. This affords an outstanding example of the use of the 'blind eye' in the interpretation of the universe. The 'echoing ear' irresistibly suggests the acoustic experiments of the Pythagoreans. The tongue, no doubt, is to be understood, not as the organ of speech, as so many commentators strangely suppose, but as the organ of taste so accurately described by Alcmaeon. The Hippocratic doctors, whose contribution to science we shall discuss in our next chapter, were already testing by taste the waters of every locality in which they settled, not to mention the humours and *excreta* of the human body. It was against an established practice of observational science applied in a variety of different fields that Parmenides' attack was directed.

If Parmenides thus fiercely attacked the scientists, of what positive opinion was he the champion? Like his contemporary, Heraclitus of Ephesus, at the other end of the Greek-speaking world, he was preoccupied with the problem of reason and the senses, and he thought that one should follow reason exclusively. His reason, however, led him to a diametrically opposite conclusion from that of Heraclitus. Heraclitus said: Everything changes. Parmenides said: Nothing changes. Heraclitus said: Wisdom is nothing but the understanding of the way in which the world works. Parmenides said that the universe did not really work at all, but remained absolutely still. For him change, motion, variety, were all illusions of sense.

He had an argument, but no evidence, for this. He started

off with two general and contradictory ideas, Being and Not-Being, What-is and What-is-not, which between them exhaust the universe of discourse. He then advanced two simple propositions: What-is is; What-is-not is not. If you take these propositions seriously it is impossible to introduce change, motion, or variety into the universe. Being can suffer change of any kind only by admixture of something else – that is, of Not-Being. But Not-Being does not exist. Therefore there is nothing in existence but absolute fulness of Being. The idea of Anaximenes, that you could change the primary substance from Earth into Water, from Water into Mist, by having less of it in a given place, can only mean that you dilute it, so to speak, with empty space, with nothing, with What-is-not, which does not exist. Satisfied with this reasoning, Parmenides asserted that the reality was a solid uncreated eternal motionless changeless uniform sphere. There is nothing wrong with this argument except that it flouts all experience. It is a way of thinking about things which is perpetually refuted by actual contact with things. Hence the warning against reliance on ear, eye, or tongue. With Parmenides thought finds itself at variance with action, with life.

What is the meaning of this strange philosophy of Parmenides? What is the significance of the fact that man, proud in the possession of a newly defined activity, reason, ventures by its aid to deny the reality of the manifold world of sense? We must understand the position of Parmenides in its double aspect, as a protest and an assertion. On the one hand he is protesting against the atheistic consequences of the Ionian philosophy which was banishing the divine from nature. On the other hand he is asserting the primacy of a new technique now coming into notice for the first time, the technique of logical argument. Parmenides has seized hold of the logical principle of contradiction. He cannot admit that a thing can both be and not be at the same time; yet this admission is necessary if we are to account for change. For him, a man principally occupied with religious conceptions (historically he should be regarded as a reformer of Pythagorean theology), it meant nothing to throw change overboard. He was, indeed, glad to do so. But, from the point of view of the old Ionian school, whose modes of philosophical explanation had arisen in close association with the active processes of altering nature which are the business of techniques, it was impossible to dispense with change. They could not admit that philosophy should condemn and reject life. The controversy went deeper than words. Eleaticism marks a further stage in the separation of philosophy from its roots in practical life.

EMPEDOCLES AND ANAXAGORAS TO THE RESCUE

The next great thinker among the western Greeks, Empedocles of Agrigentum in Sicily, did not find the stagnant philosophy of Parmenides to his taste. He, too, cast the exposition of his views into the form of verse, and in some extant lines we find his reply to the Parmenidean attack on the senses. He, of course, recognizes the fallibility of the senses, but defends the critical employment of the evidence they supply. ' Go to, now,' he writes, ' consider with all thy senses each thing in the way in which it is clear. Hold nothing that thou seest in greater credence than what thou hearest, nor value thy resounding ear above the clear instruction of thy tongue ; and do not withhold thy confidence from any other bodily part by which there is an opening for understanding, but consider everything in the way in which it is clear.'

Empedocles took up the championship of the senses because, like the old Ionians, he drew upon techniques for the ideas by which he sought to explain the processes of nature. The mixing of colours for painting, bread-making, and the sling, he mentions as sources of his ideas. Also he was him-self an experimentalist like Pythagoras and Alcmaeon. His great contribution to knowledge was his experimental demonstration of the corporeality of the viewless air. Before him air had not been distinguished from empty space. The four recognized forms of matter had not been Earth, *Air*, Fire, and Water, but Earth, *Mist*, Fire, and Water. Em-pedocles undertook an experimental investigation of the air we breathe. The Greeks had a water-clock, *clepsydra*,[1] which consisted essentially of a hollow cylinder, open at one end and terminating at the other in a cone with a small aperture at the tip. The clepsydra was used to measure time by filling it with water and letting the water escape through the small hole at the tip of the cone. Like the sand in an hour-glass, the water ran through in a measured interval of time. Em-pedocles now showed that, if the open end of the clepsydra was thrust under water while a finger was held over the hole in the tip of the cone, the contained air prevented the water from entering the clepsydra. Conversely, the full clock, though turned upside-down, could not empty itself so long as a finger was kept over the hole. The pressure of the air kept the water in. By these experiments he demonstrated the fact that the invisible air was something that could occupy space and exert power. The experiment is all the more inter-esting in that it was but part of a more comprehensive effort to establish a relation between the external atmosphere and the movement of the blood. He thought the blood moved up and down in the body. As it rose it drove the air out ; as it sank it let it in again.

Both the method and the conclusion are memorable. The

1. I have allowed the traditional rendering of *clepsydra* as ' water-clock ' to stand in my text. But Hugh Last (*Classical Quarterly*, xviii) has proved to my satisfaction that the device referred to by Empedo-cles was not the water-clock, which might hold gallons, but the ' toddy-lifter ' — a household vessel of small dimensions.

former affords further illustration of the fact that the Greeks, though they had nothing like the modern technique of interrogating nature by an elaborate system of experiments with instruments designed for the purpose, yet were not without the practice of experimental research. As for the result established, the proof of the corporeality of the air, it seems to have been too little noted that it was crucial for the whole future of Greek theory on the nature of matter and the degree of validity of sense-evidence. It had now been experimentally shown that matter could exist in a form too fine to be apprehended by sight, and yet, in that form, exert considerable power. The bearing of this went far beyond the single point established. Empedocles had not merely shown the corporeal nature of air ; he had shown how we can overcome the limitations of our sensuous apprehension and discover, by a process of inference based on observation, truths we cannot directly perceive. He had, by his cautious and critical use of the senses, conquered in the name of science a world that lay beyond the normal range of man's perceptions. He had revealed the existence of an imperceptible physical universe by examining its effects on the perceptible world.

The importance of this as a step towards the atomic theory was decisive. For the Atomists, if we may anticipate our account of their system, it was essential to show that 'Nature works by unseen bodies'. Of the truth of this proposition the power that could be exerted by the invisible air was the most convincing proof. In his first book of the *De Rerum Natura* Lucretius gathers together the traditional proofs that nature works by unseen bodies. He makes a list of 'bodies that are in the number of things but which yet cannot be seen '. Of these the most important is air. 'First of all,' he writes, 'the force of the wind when aroused beats on the harbours and whelms huge ships and scatters clouds ; sometimes in swift whirling eddy it scours the plains and strews them with huge trees and scourges the mountain summits with forest-rending blasts ; so fiercely does the wind rave with a shrill howling and rage with threatening roar. *Winds therefore sure enough are unseen bodies* ... since in their works and ways they are found to rival great rivers which are of visible body.'

Nothing else in Empedocles was equally important with his defence of the method of observation and his famous experiment. In cosmology he was an eclectic. He adopted as his first principles all the four states of matter recognized by his predecessors, except of course that Air now took the place of Mist. Earth, Air, Fire, and Water he called the Roots of all things. As an equivalent for the Tension of Heraclitus he taught that two forces, Love and Hate, set the elements in motion, Love tending to draw the four elements into a mixture and Hate to separate them again. Under the sway of these forces nature went through a cycle like that imagined by Heraclitus.

With these cosmological ideas he coupled a theory of sense-perception which shows that the true nature of the problem had not been grasped. He thought that, as men are composed of the same elements as the rest of nature, sense-perception might be explained on the basis of a physical intermingling of like elements. By Fire we recognize Fire, by Water Water, and so on. But perception is something different from a physical mixing of material substances. When salt dissolves in water the process is not accompanied by consciousness, at least so far as we know. It is consciousness that needs to be explained. His biological speculations have more interest. He thought that the earth, when she was younger, had produced a much greater variety of living things, but that 'many races of living things must have been unable to beget and continue their breed. For in the case of every species that now exists, either craft or courage or speed has from the beginning of its existence protected and preserved it.' Here is a clear hint of the doctrine of the survival of the fittest. Noteworthy also is the suggestion that the earth once had powers she does not now possess.

Empedocles, by choosing four first principles, no doubt hoped to circumvent the logic of Parmenides. By introducing plurality into the first principles, he sought to preserve the possibility of change and motion. In this, he did not squarely meet the logic of the great Monist, but he at least revealed his determination to evade its consequences. A similar determination was shown by Anaxagoras of Clazomenae, a philosopher of the Ionian school resident at Athens from about 480 till his expulsion in 450 B.C. He went as far as it is possible to go in the direction of pluralism. According to him, the first principles, which he called 'seeds', are infinite in number and variety, and every one of them contains a little of all the qualities of which our senses give us knowledge. He was led to this view by his meditations on physiology. How does bread, for instance, when we eat it, turn into bones, flesh, blood, sinews, skin, hair, and the rest, unless the particles of wheat contain, in some hidden form, all the variety of qualities which are later manifested in the several constituents of the body? Digestion must be a sorting out of elements already there.

These considerations of Anaxagoras, deduced from physiological observations, show an increasing awareness of the complexity of the problem of the structure of matter. He approached the same problem also from the physical side. Aristotle (*Physics*, IV, 6, 213a) speaks of him as repeating the experiment of Empedocles with the clepsydra and further demonstrating the resistant power of air by puffing up bladders and endeavouring to compress them. He also contributed to the debate on the validity of sense-evidence. There can be no question but that he regarded sense-evidence as indispensable for the investigation of nature, but, like Empedocles, he was concerned to show that there were physical processes too subtle for our senses to perceive directly. He devised a choice experimental demonstration of this fact. He took two vessels, one containing a white liquid, the other a black. He transferred one liquid into the other drop by drop. Physically there must be a change of colour with every drop, but the eye is not able to discern it till several drops have been let fall. It is hardly possible to imagine a neater demonstration of the limits of sense perception. We shall have occasion later to speak of the reaction of the Athenian public to the presence of an Ionian philosopher in their midst. Anaxagoras was not one of those who was prepared to yield astronomy to the theologians. In astronomy he followed the old Ionians, and his hardihood brought him into trouble.

THE ATOMS OF DEMOCRITUS

It only remains, among fifth-century speculations on the nature of matter and the structure and workings of the universe, to speak of the atomic theory of Democritus. The theory has been revived in modern times, and the degree of similarity between the theory of Democritus and that of Dalton entitles the ancient speculation to be described as a wonderful anticipation of the conclusions of later experimental science. This is true, though it is easy to misunderstand the relation between ancient and modern atomism. 'Atomism was a brilliant hypothesis,' writes Cornford (*Before and After Socrates,* p. 25). 'Revived by modern science, it has led to the most important discoveries in chemistry and physics.' Surely this is to put the cart before the horse. It ought to read: 'Atomism was a brilliant hypothesis; important discoveries in modern chemistry led to its revival.' In the long series of researches that led to the enunciation by Dalton of his atomic theory in the first decade of the nineteenth century the speculations of Democritus played no part. The true glory of the atomism of Democritus is that it answered better than any other current theory the problems of his own day. It is the culmination in antiquity of the movement of rational speculation on the nature of the universe begun by Thales. Its factual basis consists in observations of technical and natural processes by the unaided senses, together with a few experimental demonstrations of the kind we have described. Its theoretical merit is to have reduced these results to a greater logical coherence than any other ancient system. The need for a renovation of the whole ancient system of speculation did not arise until the advance of techniques had put into man's hands instruments of investigation which enormously extended the range and accuracy of his sense perceptions. Ancient science had clearly established the fact that Nature works by unseen bodies. Modern science has devised progressively better methods of seeing the unseen.

The atomism of the ancients asserted that the universe was made up of two things, the atoms and the void. The void, or empty space, was infinite in extent, the atoms infinite in number. The atoms were all alike in substance, but might differ from one another in size, shape, arrangement, and position. The atoms, like the One of Parmenides, were uncreated and eternal, solid and uniform in substance, in themselves incapable of change ; but, being in perpetual motion in the void, they wove, by their various combinations and dissolutions, all the pageant of our changing world. Thus was provided an element of eternal rest to satisfy Parmenides and an element of eternal change to satisfy Heraclitus. A world of Being underlay the world of Becoming. But the achievement of this reconciliation required a bold revision of the logic of Parmenides in the light of experience. The existence of void had to be admitted equally with the existence of matter. The experience of the fact of change compelled the assertion that What-is-not exists just as certainly as What-is.

Matter, or the atom, was defined as an absolute plenum, void as an absolute vacuum. The atom was completely impenetrable, void completely penetrable.

One originality of atomism was the assertion of the existence of the void. Another was the concept of the atom itself. The Pythagoreans, it will be remembered, had attempted to build the universe out of points with bulk, and, when they discovered that space was infinitely divisible, they could no longer provide any clear definition of a point with bulk. For the mathematician a point simply marked position but did not occupy space. Out of such points nothing could be built. Democritus defined the unit of which the universe is built not in mathematical but in physical terms. His atoms, having bulk, were spatially divisible, but physically indivisible. The concept of impenetrability, which derives from the Parmenidean One, was the essential quality of the atom. Democritus thus presented the Pythagoreans with a solid little brick with which to build their mathematical world. The atomic theory also solved the problem of Anaxagoras, so far as it is permissible to speak of a solution in ancient times when theories of the constitution of matter could only be more or less logical and could not be put to the proof. On the atomic hypothesis the problem of digestion and assimilation of food was easily solved. There was no difficulty in supposing that a fresh arrangement of the atoms might transform bread into flesh and blood, just as a fresh arrangement of the letters of the alphabet could transform a Tragedy into a Comedy. The illustration is an ancient one. By such analogies did the old Atomists eke out the inevitable paucity of their observed facts.

Democritus made also a contribution of capital importance to the problem of sense-perception. Every perceptible thing, according to him, is an arrangement of atoms which differ only in size and shape. The *qualities* which we ascribe to this arrangement of atoms – the colours, the tastes, the noises, the smells, the tactile qualities – are not qualities of the bodies in themselves, but effects of the bodies on our organs of sense. Galileo in his day could do no better than to repeat this brilliant suggestion.

To the other merits of his system must be added his superb powers of generalization. His cosmology followed the general Ionian plan, and need not detain us here. But the great principles on which his argument rested were enunciated with a new clarity. 'Nothing is created out of nothing.' 'By necessity were fore-ordained all things that were and are and are to be.' In such terms did he announce for the first time the doctrines of the conservation of matter and the reign of universal law. The disappearance of his book is probably the greatest loss we have suffered by the almost total destruction of the works of the pre-Socratic philosopher-scientists.

CHAPTER FIVE

Hippocratic Medicine – The Cook and the Doctor – The Emergence of the Idea of Positive Science – Science in the Service of Mankind – Limitations of Hippocratic Medicine

*

HIPPOCRATIC MEDICINE

WE have spoken in the last chapter of the almost total destruction of the record of Greek science before Socrates. Only for one department of early science has exception to be made. We are fortunate enough to possess a collection of medical writings the oldest of which belong to the beginning of the fifth century. Several different schools are represented in the collection. Nevertheless the collection has come down to us under the name of one, the Hippocratic. It is possible that it formed originally the library of the Hippocratic school in the island of Cos. It owes its preservation to the famous library of Alexandria, founded in the third century, where manuscripts were copied, corrected, and kept. There the collection was put together in its present state, and its fortunate preservation enables us to form a good idea of the progress of medical science in the Greek world during the two preceding centuries. Not all the treatises in the collection are of equal value, but the best of them show a fine blend of science and humanity, while two or three are among the highest products of Greek culture.

THE COOK AND THE DOCTOR

The origins of Greek medicine are generally sought by historians in three sources – the old temple practice of Asclepius, the God of Healing ; the physiological opinions of the philosophers; and the practice of the superintendents of gymnasia. It is probable that the first of these sources is to be rejected. 'Arts are not learned,' says Withington, 'in temples by observing real or supposed supernatural intervention, but, as the Hippocratic writers tell us, by experience and the application of reason to the nature of men and things.'[1] With this opinion of Withington's the author of this book is in complete agreement. He would, however, add that, if we need to supply, as a source of medicine, a substitute for the priest, whom we have rejected, we might find him in the cook.

This, at any rate, was the opinion of one of the greatest of Greek scientists, the unknown author of the Hippocratic tract, *On Ancient Medicine*, which belongs to the middle of the fifth century. The treatise is, perhaps, the most important of the whole collection. The author, whoever he was, deserves to be quoted at length. 'The fact is,' he writes, 'that sheer necessity has caused men to seek and to find medicine, because sick men did not, and do not, profit by the same regimen as men do in health. To trace the matter yet further back, I hold that not even the mode of living and nourishment enjoyed at the present time by men in health would have been discovered, had a man been satisfied with the same food and drink as satisfy an ox, a horse, and every animal save man, I mean the raw products of the earth — fruits, leaves, and grass. For on these cattle feed, grow, and live without distress, not needing any other diet. And indeed I believe that to begin with men used the same food. Our present ways of living have, I think, been discovered and elaborated during a long period of time. For many and terrible were the sufferings of men from strong and brutish living when they partook of crude foods, uncompounded and possessing strong qualities — the same in fact as men would

1. See his brilliant article, *The Asclepiadae and the Priests of Asclepius*, in Singer's *Studies in the History and Method of Science*, vol. II, pp. 192–205.

suffer at the present day, falling into violent pains and diseases quickly followed by death. Formerly indeed they probably suffered less, because they were used to it, but they suffered severely even then. The majority naturally perished, having too weak a constitution, while the stronger resisted longer, just as at the present time some men easily deal with strong foods, while others do so only with many severe pains. For this reason the ancients seem to me to have sought for nourishment that harmonized with their constitution, and to have discovered that which we use now. So from wheat, by winnowing, grinding, sifting, steeping, kneading, and baking it, they produced bread, and from barley they produced cake. Experimenting with food they boiled or baked, they mixed and mingled, putting strong pure foods with weaker, until they adapted them to the power and constitution of man. For they thought that from foods which are too strong for the human constitution to assimilate will come pain, disease, and death, while from such as can be assimilated will come nourishment, growth, and health. To this discovery and research what juster or more appropriate name could be given than medicine, seeing that it has been discovered with a view to the health, well-being and nourishment of man, in place of that mode of living from which came the pain, disease, and death? '

I have given this quotation at length so that readers might have the chance to appreciate its remarkable historical insight, its combination of richness of ideas with close attention to fact, and its clear realization of the unbroken development of medical science from the oldest and humblest of the techniques. It is noteworthy that the author of this brilliant scientific work loves to call himself by the name of worker, craftsman, technician. It is because he sees his origin in the cook that he describes his Art as ancient.

By the dialect which he employs the author betrays that he was an Ionian Greek. Medicine, no doubt, like other practices, first became scientific in Ionia. But now, in the fifth century, there were rival medical schools in the West which did not possess the same understanding of medicine as originating in a technique, but sought to deduce the rules of medical practice from *a priori* cosmological opinions. It was to combat this new ' philosophical ' medicine that the treatise we are discussing was written.

One of the western schools was at Croton, and its founder was possibly the Pythagorean Alcmaeon whose researches on the sense-organs we have already mentioned. After him, if he was the founder of the school, the standard of Pythagorean medicine declined. Observation dwindled, speculation increased. Philolaus of Tarentum, who lived towards the end of the fifth century, and whose panegyric on the decad we have already quoted, shows the new trend. His opinions are not without interest, but they concern philosophy rather than the healing art. The Pythagoreans attached special importance to the number four. Philolaus decided that there were four principal organs in the human body. His choice of the organs, as well as their number, was determined by considerations of a philosophical order. As all living things have the power of reproduction, he included the organs of sex. Then, following a classification of living things into plants, which have only the power of growth, animals, which add sensation, and men, who alone have reason, Philolaus chose, as the other principal organs, the navel, the seat of the vegetable life, to link man with the plants ; the heart, the seat of sensation, to link man with the animals ; and the brain, the seat of the reason, which set men above the rest. This somewhat arbitrary scheme is intended to assign man his place in nature's plan; and the choice of the principal organs is determined by this philosophical purpose. From the point of view of the practical healer it might have been more helpful to assign a less important place to the umbilicus and say something more about the liver and the lungs. Or, if that is to ask too much of an ancient doctor, at least it must be observed that, if the philosopher had not forgotten the connection between the doctor and the cook, he could not have overlooked the stomach!

But it was in the school of Empedocles at Agrigentum that cosmology produced its worst effects on the healing art. There man, like everything else, was supposed to consist of the four elements. The doctrine of the elements included a theory as to their characteristic qualities. Earth was said to be Cold and Dry; Air, Hot and Wet; Water, Cold and Wet; Fire, Hot and Dry. The distemperature of man's body, like the distemperature of nature, was ascribed to the excess or defect of one or other of these qualities. Fever was to be interpreted as an excess of the Hot, a chill as an excess of Cold. This being so, what remedies would a physician who was also a philosopher suggest? Would he not recommend a dose of the Hot to cure a chill and of the Cold to cure a fever?

THE EMERGENCE OF THE IDEA OF POSITIVE SCIENCE

When the new-fangled doctrines of the western philosophical schools began to be spoken of in his beloved Ionia, anger seized the heart of the author of *Ancient Medicine*. In his opening sentence he leaps to the attack. 'All who attempt to discuss the art of healing on the basis of a postulate – heat, cold, moisture, dryness, or anything else they fancy – thus narrowing down the causes of disease and death among men to one or two postulates, are not only obviously wrong, but are especially to be blamed because they are wrong in what is an art or technique (*technè*), and one moreover which all men use at the crises of life, highly honouring the practitioners and craftsmen in this art, if they are good.'

Into this first sentence our author has managed to pack four separate objections to the new trend in medicine. As they are all of great significance in the history of science, it will be well for us to pick them out and discuss them one by one.

First he objects to the basing of medicine on postulates. The effect of this objection is to separate medicine as a positive science, depending on observation and experiment, from cosmology where experimental control was not possible in antiquity. We proceed to quote his own words: 'Postulates are admissible in dealing with insoluble mysteries ; for example, things in the sky or below the earth. If a man were to pronounce on them neither he himself nor any of his audience could tell whether he was speaking the truth. *For there is no test the application of which would give certainty.* But medicine has long had all its means to hand, and has discovered both a principle and a method, through which the discoveries made over a long period are many and excellent, and through which full discovery will be made, if the enquirer be competent, conduct his researches with knowledge of the discoveries already made, and make them his starting-point.'

Secondly, he protests that the new-fangled doctors are 'narrowing down the causes of death and disease'. This is most remarkable. It is a protest by a practising technician, conscious of the richness of his positive science, against the barrenness of metaphysics. The historical significance of this is very great. The technician is appalled at the ignorance of the philosophers. Art had not yet been made tongue-tied by authority. For the Hippocratic doctor the qualities of things which affect a man's health were not three or four. They were infinitely various. 'I know,' he protests, 'that it makes a difference to a man's body whether bread be of bolted or unbolted flour, whether it be of winnowed or unwinnowed wheat, whether it be kneaded with much or little water, whether it be thoroughly kneaded or unkneaded, whether it be thoroughly baked or underbaked, and there are countless other differences. The same applies to barley. The properties of every variety of grain are powerful and no one is like another. But how could he who has not considered these truths, or who considers them without learning, know anything about human ailments? For each of these differences produces in a human being an effect and a change of one sort or another and upon these differences is based all the dieting of a man, whether he be in health, convalescent or ill.' Then he proceeds to supplement the handful of Empedoclean concepts with a list of others more relevant to medical science – in foods, such qualities as sweetness, bitterness, acidity, saltness, insipidity, astringency ; in human anatomy, the shapes of the organs ; in human physiology, the capacity of the organism to react to an external stimulus. Thus does the cook rebuke the cosmologist.

The third reason for his anger is, not that the philosopher should be wrong, but that he should be wrong in a technique or art (*technè*). The reason why ignorance in respect of a *technè* is inexcusable is that no knowledge was worthy to be called a *technè* unless it gave results. Here the justifiable pride of the craftsman is noticeable; and it admonishes us that the test of early science was, not the laboratory, but practice. We must not overlook this fact when we debate the point, whether Greek science knew experiment or not. A technique was a mode of imitating nature. If it worked, that was proof that the technician understood nature.

The fourth reason for his anger with the doctor who possesses only philosophical postulates but is ignorant of the art is that it is the patient who suffers. This concern for the patient is specially characteristic of the Hippocratic doctors. They were severely scientific at their best, but at their best they also maintained that the first duty of the doctor is to heal the sick rather than to study disease. In this there was a certain measure of disagreement between them and the neighbouring school at Cnidus. We might express the difference by saying that the ideal of the men of Cnidus was science, that of the men of Cos science in the service of humanity.

SCIENCE IN THE SERVICE OF MANKIND

We have now listed the four chief objections of our practising physician to the medical innovations of the philosophers. At this early date, before much positive knowledge had accumulated, and before specialization had in consequence become necessary, it was natural that a philosopher should embrace every branch of knowledge. There is nothing therefore surprising in Empedocles turning his attention to medicine. But his doing so brought sharply into view the fact that there was a kind of speculation that was admissible in cosmology but inadmissible in medicine. Cosmologists tended to start from some observation, or some few observations (change of water into ice or steam ; the mathematical relation between the lengths of vibrating strings ; the transmutation of food into flesh), and then elaborate on this slender foundation a theory of the universe, satisfied if the system they evolved hung together with reasonable logic. But this could not satisfy the doctor, whose theories were continually tested in practice, proved right or wrong by their effect on the patient. A stricter conception of the scientific method was formed. It can truly be said that the Hippocratic doctors at their best advanced fully to the idea of a positive science. What differentiated their science from ours was less the failure to realize the importance of experiment than the absence of instruments of exact measurement and of any technique of chemical analysis. They were as scientific as the material conditions of their time permitted. This statement we proceed to justify by a few quotations.

Our first quotation is again from the author of *Ancient Medicine*. In it he claims that the method of observation and experiment practised by the doctors, and not the *a priori* method of the cosmologists, is the only way to find out about the nature of man. 'Certain physicians and philosophers assert that nobody can know medicine who is ignorant what man is: he who would treat his patients properly must, they say, learn this. But the question they raise is one for philosophy; it is the province of those who, like Empedocles, have written on natural science, what man is from the beginning, how he came into being at first, and from what elements he was originally constructed. But my view is, first, that all that philosophers or physicians have said or written on natural science pertains less to medicine than to literature. I also hold that clear knowledge about the nature of man can be acquired from medicine and from no other source, and that one can attain this knowledge when medicine itself has been properly comprehended, but till then it is impossible – I mean to possess this information, what man is, by what causes he is made, and similar points accurately' (*Ancient Medicine*, chap. xx).

Our next quotation concerns the correct use of inference where facts are involved which are not directly accessible to sense. The writer is discussing the difficulty of treating internal complaints. 'Without doubt no man who sees only with his eyes can know anything of what has been here described. It is for this reason that I have called these points obscure, even as they have been judged to be by the art. Their obscurity, however, does not mean that they are our masters, but as far as is possible they have been mastered, a possibility limited only by the capacity of the sick to be examined and of researchers to conduct research. More pains, in fact, and quite as much time, are required to know them as if they were seen by the eyes; *for what escapes the eyesight is mastered by the eye of the mind*, and the sufferings of patients due to their not being quickly observed are the fault, not of the medical attendant, but of the nature of the patient and of the disease. *The attendant in fact, as he could neither*

*see the trouble with his eyes nor learn it with his ears, tried to
track it by reasoning'* (*The Art*, chap. xi). The reader will
not fail to observe that what the Hippocratic doctor meant by
'the eye of the mind' was something very different from
what Plato meant when he used the same phrase. Plato
meant deduction from *a priori* premises. The Hippocratic
writer meant the inferring of invisible facts from visible
symptoms.

Our third quotation enumerates some of the devices
employed to get at the hidden secrets of the body. 'Now
medicine, being prevented, in cases of empyemas, and of
diseased liver, kidneys, and the cavities generally, from seeing with the sight with which all men see everything most
perfectly, has nevertheless discovered other means to help it.
There is clearness or roughness of the voice, rapidity or slowness of respiration, and the character of the customary
discharges: sometimes smell, sometimes colour, sometimes
thinness or thickness furnishing medicine with the means of
inferring what condition these symptoms indicate. Some
symptoms indicate that a part is already affected, others that
a part may be thereafter affected. When this information is
not afforded, and nature herself will yield nothing of her own
accord, medicine has found means of compulsion, whereby
nature is constrained, without being harmed, to give up her
secrets; when these are given up she makes clear to those
who understand the art what course ought to be pursued.
The art, for example, forces nature to disperse phlegm by
acrid foods and drinks, so that it may form a conclusion by
vision concerning those things which were before invisible.
Again, when respiration is symptomatic, by making patients
run uphill it compels nature to reveal symptoms' (*The Art*,
chap. xiii).

Our last quotation shows the physician attempting to
sketch a theory of cognition. 'One must attend in medical
practice not primarily to plausible theories, but to experience

combined with reason. A true theory is a composite memory of things apprehended with sense-perception. For the sense-perception, coming first in experience and conveying to the intellect the things subjected to it, is clearly imaged, and the intellect, receiving these things many times, noting the occasion, the time and the manner, stores them up in itself and remembers. *Now I approve of theorizing if it lays its foundation in incident, and deduces its conclusions in accordance with phenomena.* For if theorizing lays its foundation in clear fact, it is found to exist in the domain of intellect, which itself receives all its impressions from other sources. So we must conceive of our nature as being stirred and instructed under compulsion by the great variety of things ; and the intellect, as I have said, taking over from nature the impressions, leads us afterwards to the truth. *But if it begins, not from a clear impression, but from a plausible fiction, it often induces a grievous and troublesome condition. All who act so are lost in a blind alley* ' (*Precepts,* chap. i).

These quotations should serve to make clear the extent to which the ancient doctors had advanced to the modern conception of a positive science. They also throw some light on the question of the debt of Greek medicine to the philosophers, the second source usually mentioned by historians. When we have in mind the tendency of the philosophers to foist on to medicine the *a priori* methods of cosmology, then we are inclined to feel that Hippocratic medicine owed as little to the philosophers as to the priests. On the other hand, when we consider the contribution of an Empedocles or an Anaxagoras to the problem of the correct use of sense-evidence, we see that their opinion on this point was identical with that of the doctors. Furthermore, it was not altogether bad for medicine that it should become a subject of discussion among the philosophers. A science can suffer if it becomes divorced from the general intellectual life of the age, and the philosophers acted as something of a clearinghouse of ideas, and contributed to the formation of a systematic body of medical theory which, even if premature, fed a natural impatience with the belief that the slow progress of scientific investigation had reached its goal. In very truth, life is short and art is long, and premature generalization is sometimes better than none at all.

The third tributary to the stream of Greek medicine usually mentioned in the books is that which flowed from the directors of the gymnasia. They possessed a wonderfully accurate knowledge of surface anatomy, developed a sound technique of handling dislocations, and in their general concern for the preservation as well as the restoration of the health of their patrons, paid attention to massage, diet, and graduated systems of exercise. This was a genuine contribution, so far as it went, and the most important of the three sources discussed by the historians. It is not out of contempt for it that we pass it by to deal with the major failure of Greek medicine which this topic inevitably suggests. For the gymnasia were the haunts of the citizen, and of the wealthier citizen at that. They provided the opportunity for members of the leisured class to submit themselves, under expert direction, to regimens of health. But the question we now wish to enquire into is the health of the workers.

We have already quoted a passage from Xenophon which says: 'What are called the mechanical arts carry a social stigma and are rightly dishonoured in our cities. For these arts damage the bodies of those who work at them or supervise them, by compelling the workers to a sedentary life and to an indoor life, by compelling them, indeed, in some cases to spend the whole day by the fire.' Now it is certain that these workers, with their damaged bodies, did not form the clientèle of the directors of the gymnasia, and, conversely, that the contribution the directors made to medicine was not intended, nor adapted, to the needs of the workers. Indeed, it is clear that, as society developed more and more in the direction of making a sharp cleavage between the categories of citizen and worker, medicine tended more and more to become a service directed to the needs of a leisured class. This produced a very paradoxical result.

One of the glories of Hippocratic medicine is that it endeavoured always to see man in relation to his environment. The treatise *Airs Waters Places* is a pioneer work in its clearcut conception of the effect upon the human constitution not only of man's natural, but of his political environment. The Hippocratic doctor took into consideration the food a man ate, the kind of water he drank, the climate he lived in, and the effect on him of Greek freedom or Oriental despotism. But there is no aspect of a man's environment that affects him more intimately or more constantly than his daily occupation, and on this subject the Hippocratic treatises are dumb. The study of occupational diseases did not begin till quite recent times – with Paracelsus (c. 1490–1541) and, still more important, Ramazzini (1633–1714).

CHAPTER SIX

Before and After Socrates — The First Science of Society — The Sophists — The Socratic Revolution in Thought

★

BEFORE AND AFTER SOCRATES

WE HAVE now completed our survey of the chief figures in the first age of Greek science, the Heroic Age, which runs from Thales to Democritus. Philosophers call this the pre-Socratic Age, and it has been common with historians to regard this age as having been mainly concerned with bold, but unfounded, speculation on 'things in the heavens'. A story, meant to be symbolical, was current in antiquity that Thales, walking absent-mindedly through the town of Miletus, had fallen into a well. His preoccupation with the 'things above' had made him neglect what was at his feet. Such was the inevitable consequence of the impious attempt to establish a philosophy of nature. From this false start mankind was rescued, according to this view of the history of thought, by the great Athenian moralist, Socrates. He 'brought philosophy down from heaven to earth'. He insisted that the proper study of mankind is man. He diverted attention from physics to ethics. Under his influence philosophy abandoned its presumptuous attempt to understand the heavens and turned to the humbler task of teaching men how to behave as men.

This account of the relationship of Socrates to his predecessors is, in our view, false. The older natural philosophers did not concentrate on speculation about the things in the heavens to the neglect of human affairs. On the contrary, the original and characteristic thing about the Ionian way of thought was that it recognized no ultimate distinction between heaven and earth, that it sought to explain the mysteries of the universe in terms of familiar things. To be precise, the source from which Ionian philosophy sprang was the new outlook on the world resulting from the control over nature exercised by the technician who was also an honoured member of a free society. A technique was a way of helping oneself by imitating nature. It was the success with which he applied the techniques that gave the Ionian natural philosopher his confidence that he understood the workings of nature. The belief in the identity of natural and technical processes is the clue to the mentality of the period.

The sixth and fifth centuries, the period known as that of pre-Socratic philosophy or as the Heroic Age of Science, are characterized not only by a development of abstract thought. They were also a time of great technical progress, and what is new and characteristic in their mode of thought is derived from the techniques. Technical development was the magic wand which was changing the old form of society based mainly on the land into a new form of society based largely on manufacture. Technical progress was calling into existence a new class of manufacturers and merchants which quickly assumed political control in the cities. In the first decade of the sixth century, Solon, who represented the new class, attempted to modernize Athens, the old Athens torn with the strife between landlord and peasant. In order to achieve this, Solon, we are told by Plutarch, 'invested the crafts with honour'. He 'turned the attention of the citizens to arts and crafts, and made a law that a son need not support his father in old age unless the father had taught him a trade'. 'At that time,' says Plutarch, 'work was no disgrace, nor did the possession of a trade imply social inferiority.' The men then honoured were men like Anacharsis the Scythian, whose titles to glory were that he had improved the anchor and invented the bellows and the potter's wheel. Or men like Glaucus of Chios, the inventor of the soldering-iron; or

Theodorus of Samos, who was credited with a long list of technical inventions – the level, the square, the lathe, the rule, the key, and the method of casting bronze. These navigational and industrial achievements were appreciated by the merchants of Miletus, among others. Their growing prosperity depended on manufacture for export. It was among them that Thales applied his skill in mathematics and geometry to the improvement of the art of navigation. It was for them that Anaximander made the first map of the world. It was there that the world began to be thought of as a machine. The temper of the age was such that honour was still given to the technician. The Greek word for wisdom, *sophia*, still meant at this time technical skill, not abstract speculation. Or rather the distinction between the two was not forced, for the best speculation was based on technical skill. The author of *Ancient Medicine* knows no higher title than technician. It is in this context that the natural philosophy of the Ionians was born. To represent it as wholly absorbed in speculation on the heavens to the neglect of human interests is false.

But the ripest product of this new outlook is still to be mentioned. In the free cities of old Ionia the conquest of nature through techniques gave birth to the ambition of extending the domain of reason over the whole of nature, including life and man. There was a definite and conscious movement of rational thought over the whole sphere of existence. There was a propaganda of enlightenment, as many pages in the Hippocratic writings show. 'It seems to me,' says one writer, dealing with the mysterious affliction epilepsy, 'that the disease is no more divine than any other. It has a natural cause, just as other diseases have. Men think it divine merely because they do not understand it. But if they called everything divine which they do not understand, why, there would be no end of divine things.' These are truly classical words. They mark the advent of a new epoch

in human culture. In their gentle irony they pronounce final
judgement on a past age, on the period of mythological
explanation. True, their point of view has not yet prevailed
everywhere on earth. The battle is still joined and the issue
doubtful. Miracles are still the basis of the world-view of
large sections even of civilized mankind. Christendom has
not yet made up its mind to accept a strictly naturalistic
history of Christianity, or even, for that matter, of Joan of
Arc. But the old Ionian formulation remains to do its silent
work in the mind of civilized man. 'Men think it divine
merely because they do not understand it. But if they called
everything divine which they do not understand, why, there
would be no end of divine things.' The identification of the
divine with the not-yet-explained was the shrewdest of blows
for reason and nature.

THE FIRST SCIENCE OF SOCIETY

The movement of enlightenment which has left its mark
on the Hippocratic writings produced also a sketch of the
rise of human culture, which is a contribution of the Ionian
school to science of absolutely first-class importance.[1]

'At the time of the original constitution of the universe,'
runs the text, 'heaven and earth had but one form, their
elements being mixed together. Then their substances separated, and the cosmos completely assumed the order we now
observe in it, but the Air continued in a state of agitation.
As a result of this movement, the fiery portion of the Air
collected in the upper spaces, its nature tending to rise on

---

1. This sketch survives in the history of Diodorus Siculus, Bk. I,
chaps. vii and viii. Its attribution to Democritus was plausibly
suggested by K. Reinhardt (*Hermes*, Band 47, pp. 492 ff.), but this
attribution is contested by others on the ground that the sketch contains no clear reference to atomism. It may well be pre-atomic. The
point is immaterial to our argument.

account of its lightness, and for this reason the sun and all the rest of the heavenly bodies were caught up in the general rotatory movement. The more dense and turbid portion of the Air joined the moist element and settled into the same region with it by reason of its weight. When this heavier matter had long crowded and revolved upon itself, it formed the sea out of its moist elements and the earth out of its more solid elements.

'The earth at first was muddy and quite soft. It was only owing to the action of the sun's heat that the earth began to harden. Then, on account of the heat, some of the moist elements swelled and the earth began to bubble up at many places. At these places there formed fermentations enclosed in delicate membranes, a phenomenon still to be observed in marshes and bogs when a rapid rise in the temperature of the air supervenes suddenly on a chilling of the earth. In this manner, through the action of the heat, the moist elements began to produce life. The embryos thus formed got their nourishment at night from the mist which fell from the surrounding air, while by day the action of the sun's heat imparted firmness. At the end of this stage, when the embryos had got their full development and the membranes had been dried up by the heat and had burst, all sorts of living things came forth. Of these, those which had the largest share of heat went off to the upper regions and became birds; those which had a greater admixture of earth formed the class of creeping things and other land animals; while those which had more of the moist element went off to the region akin to them and became what we call fish. But the continuing action of the sun and wind hardened the earth still more, until it was no longer able to bring to life any of the larger creatures, but each of the larger living things was reproduced through intercourse of like with like.

'The first men lived a random life like wild animals, going out to pasture independently of one another, moving towards whatever vegetation attracted them and to the uncultivated fruits of the trees. It was expediency that taught them to co-operate because individuals became the prey of wild beasts. It was only when fear brought them together that they slowly arrived at mutual recognition of their common form. Their utterance was at first confused and without significance. It was only gradually that they became articulate, agreed on conventional sounds for each object, and made their discourse on every topic mutually intelligible.

'Groups like this formed over the whole habitable earth; but they did not all use the same forms of speech, for each group had determined their locutions as chance decided. Accordingly all sorts of languages came into existence. The first groups of men to be constituted became parents of all the races of mankind. Since none of the conveniences of life had been discovered, the first men lived a burdensome life. They were without any clothing, unacquainted with houses or fire, and had no idea at all of cultivated foods. Even the idea of making a store of wild foods had not occurred to them and they made no provision against want. The result was that they died in great numbers during the winters through cold and lack of nourishment. Gradually, however, learning from experience, they began to take refuge in caves during the winter, and to store such fruits as admitted of being kept. Then fire and other conveniences were discovered, and the arts and all the things that promote social life were invented. The general law of the process is that it is necessity that teaches man everything. Necessity is the intimate guide who conducts man through every lesson, and necessity has in man a naturally apt pupil, equipped as he is with hands, speech, and mother-wit for every purpose.'

Diodorus, who has preserved for us this summary sketch of the history of man and society, was, as we know from a careful study of his book, not the most intelligent of men. It is unlikely that he has done full justice to the thought of his original. But enough remains to be extraordinarily impressive. The writer, it appears, had a dialectical concept of the evolutionary process. Under certain historical conditions he imagines that new forms of existence can arise. At a certain stage of its development the earth is able to produce living organisms. When this stage passes, spontaneous generation is succeeded, at least for the larger creatures, by sexual generation. The process of evolution combines quantitative development with qualitative leaps. Further, this dialectical process is applied not only to the origin and development of life, but to the origin and development of society. Man is not by nature a political animal. He *becomes* a political animal by a gradual process of experience, since only those men who learn to co-operate escape destruction by wild beasts. Man is not divinely endowed with the gift of speech. He becomes a talking animal by a process of historical development. The meanings of words are conventional. Instead, therefore, of endeavouring to understand nature by examining the meanings of words – a procedure which later became the characteristic vice of Greek thought – the writer was for understanding the meanings of words by the study of social history. Man is not by definition, and in his essential nature, a rational animal. He becomes a rational animal through a rigorous schooling by necessity, and largely because he is possessed of a capable pair of hands. The writer recognized the importance of the techniques in the history of human culture. He makes clear that man out-distanced the other animals in the race for survival by his superior teachability. From other sources we learn that Democritus, who may be the author, thought that man had got the hint for weaving from the spider, and for architecture from the swallow, and that it was by imitating the birds that he had learned to sing.

THE SOPHISTS

The influence throughout Greek lands of the new modes of thought which had been fashioned and published by such men as Anaximander, Empedocles, Anaxagoras, and Democritus is not easy to assess accurately. There is no doubt that it was great. Anaxagoras, a native of Clazomenae, who lived at Athens from 480 to 450 and taught Pericles as a youth, did much to spread the new knowledge. Another distinguished foreigner who spent much of his life at Athens was Protagoras of Abdera. He is the first example we have had occasion to mention of a new class of man, the Sophist, characteristic of this time. The Sophists were itinerant lecturers who went from town to town spreading the new ideas. They specialized in history and politics, and professed to be able to teach the art of government. There is little room to doubt that the general background of their ideas on society was that of the sketch by the unknown writer we have just quoted. Plato, who was diametrically opposed to this theory of the origin and nature of civilization, singled out the opinions of the Sophists, and their manner of life, for attack.

The three most distinguished of the Sophists were the Protagoras already mentioned (who came from the same town as Democritus – Abdera seems to have been a most enlightened place), Gorgias, of Leontini in Sicily, and Hippias, of Elis in the Peloponnese. Plato has given them a bad name, and much that has survived about them is designed to illustrate the irresponsibility of their teachings and the vulgarity of their self-advertisement. It is doubtful if these criticisms are well founded. Protagoras said: *Man is the measure of all things.* For this he figures in the history of philosophy as the representative of the principle of subjectivity in its most extreme form. Gorgias said: *There is no truth; if there were, it could not be known; if known, it could not be communicated.* He has become the type of sceptic. Hippias, who has the reputation of a braggart, distinguished himself by attending the games at Olympia in festive attire, every particle of which had been made by his own hands, and professing himself ready to lecture on any subject from astronomy to ancient history. Subjectivity, scepticism, and boastfulness, not to mention love of gain, such were the vices of the Sophists from which Socrates, according to Plato, rescued Greek thought by the example of his life and conversation.

It can be no part of a short history of Greek science to enter upon the discussion of the philosophical issues raised by the Platonic attack upon the Sophists. But from the point of view of the historian of science a few words must be said about each of the three. With regard to the first, Protagoras, it is extremely doubtful whether the saying attributed to him is correctly interpreted as an uncompromising assertion of the principle of subjectivity. Protagoras was a legislator. At the request of Pericles he made a constitution for the famous colony of Thurii in south Italy, a progressive community which believed in planning and employed the Pythagorean architect, Hippodamus of Miletus, to build them a model town. The enlightened legislator for this community regarded laws as a human creation. He had much the same view of the evolution of human society as his fellow-townsman, Democritus. He believed, like the Ionian philosophers generally, in the contractual view of justice. When he said that man was the measure of all things, he almost certainly meant that human institutions should be adapted to suit changing human requirements. But this idea was anathema to Plato, who, through the mouth of Socrates in his *Republic,* taught that the Idea of Justice was eternal and was to be understood not through the study of history but by pure reason. This, and not the principle of subjectivity, would appear to be the real ground of difference between Protagoras and the Platonic Socrates.

How the saying of Gorgias is to be interpreted is unsure. Let us take it at its face value as an expression of extreme scepticism. As such it can in no sense be regarded as the product of Ionian materialism. The natural philosophy of the Ionians provides a much better answer to such scepticism than the Ideal theory of the Platonic Socrates. The authors of the Hippocratic treatises were convinced that truth exists, that truth can be known, and that truth can be communicated. So were Empedocles, Anaxagoras, and Democritus. The tradition of science they built up is the only way to establish the objectivity of truth. It was the Platonic schools which later drifted into a scepticism which might very aptly be summed up in the formula of Gorgias. To this day it is the Platonic philosophy, not the scientific tradition, which is the breeding-ground of scepticism.

As for Hippias, arrayed entirely in articles of his own making down to the ring on his finger, he is a perfect illustration of the fact that the older tradition of wisdom included the techniques. A spinner, weaver, tanner, tailor, cobbler, and smith, all in his own person, he is typical of the older generation of wise men whose title to wisdom was not compromised by the ability and readiness to use their hands. He was prepared, we are told, to lecture on ancient history. Nothing is more certain that his conception of history gave recognition to the crafts as a factor in human development.

THE SOCRATIC REVOLUTION IN THOUGHT

If we sum up the evidence given in this chapter, we see that it is quite inadequate to describe the older philosophers as dreamers about the things in heaven to the detriment of their understanding of human affairs. It follows that it cannot be correct to describe the Socratic revolution in thought as consisting essentially in his having brought philosophy down from heaven to earth. It would be more in accordance

with the evidence to state the matter thus. The Ionian school
of natural philosophers had offered a materialistic explanation of the evolution of the cosmos, they inculcated the ideal
of positive science and the reign of universal law, they gave
an account of the development of civilization in which man,
through his conquest of techniques, figured as the author of
his own progress, they supported the contractual theory of
justice. Socrates, on the other hand, discouraged research
into nature, substituted for the ideal of positive science a
theory of Ideas closely linked with a belief in the Soul as an
immortal being temporarily inhabiting a house of clay,
sought to explain nature teleologically and human history
providentially, and regarded Justice as an eternal idea
independent of time, place, and circumstance. In a word,
Socrates abandoned the scientific view of nature and man
which had been developed by the thinkers of the Ionian
school from Thales to Democritus, and substituted for it a
development of the religious view which had come down
from Pythagoras and Parmenides. He did not so much bring
philosophy down from heaven to earth as devote himself to
persuading men that they must so live on earth that when
they died their souls would return at once to heaven. It is
likely that he made important contributions to logic. Aristotle
credits him with introducing Induction and Definition. But
his mastery of these arts was displayed solely in the sphere
of ethics and politics, and, at that, was metaphysical rather
than historical in character. He made no contribution to
science.

CHAPTER SEVEN

Plato – The Platonic Attitude to Natural Philosophy – Theological Astronomy – The Eye of the Soul and the Eye of the Body – Philosophy and Techniques

★

PLATO

APART from the Hippocratic corpus we have no complete works of Greek philosophy or science extant before Plato, and none of the Hippocratic writings can be assigned with absolute certainty to any particular author. Of Plato we not only have complete works extant, we have all his published work. He is thus the first philosopher about whose opinions we are adequately informed. True, the record of his oral instruction in the Academy has not survived, but none of his dialogues has perished. About thirty of the dialogues ascribed to him are accepted as genuine. They constitute a great bulk of writing, roughly equal to the Bible in size. The largest of them, the *Republic* and the *Laws*, are in ten and twelve books respectively.

The *Republic*, written in his forties, and the *Laws*, lacking only its final polish when he died in his eighty-first year, dominate the whole collection. The first attempts to sketch an ideal society ; the second resumes the same theme in a more practical spirit and in the light of greater experience ; together they inform us of what was the major effort of his life, the regeneration of the political life of Greece. The Academy was founded for the same purpose, to train a new type of citizen of the ruling class, who was not to remain in the Academy, but go back to public life. This attempt to reform public life by the training of a new type of individual was, like the general trend of his philosophy, Pythagorean.

The only important prose which had been written in

Athens before Plato was history. The implicit purpose of Herodotus, the explicitly avowed purpose of Thucydides, was so to present the record of the past that it might serve to guide men's actions in the future. Historians, respectively, of the rise and fall of Athenian democracy, they sought to make their public conscious of the drama of Greek civilization in which Athens had played the leading part. History with them was the school of politics. Their temper was objective, like that of the Ionian Natural Philosophers to whose movement they essentially belong. They sought the law of the development of human society, as the philosophers had sought the law of the development of nature. There is the closest resemblance in world outlook between Thucydides, Democritus, and the best writers in the Hippocratic corpus. An idea common to all is that, as men are products of nature, so their characters are products of their society. Thucydides paints a terrifying picture of the moral degeneration of Greece during the Peloponnesian War. The degeneration of the individual is the *consequence*, not the *cause*, of the war.

THE PLATONIC ATTITUDE TO NATURAL PHILOSOPHY

With Plato the emphasis shifts to the individual soul. Wars, external and internecine, are the product of the individual man's unruly desires (*Phaedo* 66c). 'The *Republic*,' says Professor A. E. Taylor, 'which opens with an old man's remarks about approaching death and apprehension of what may come after death, and ends with a myth of judgement, has all through for its central theme a question more intimate than that of the best form of government or the most eugenic form of propagation ; its question is, How does a man attain or forfeit eternal salvation ? ' The heart of Plato's thought is a doctrine of the immortality of the soul which he shares with the Pythagoreans. Man's soul becomes the field on which the battle between good and evil is fought out, and the battle, at the same time, takes on a transcendental significance, for man's soul is not a part of nature, but a visitor from a celestial realm. This individual salvation will not be effected by public policies nourished on a study of history, but by arriving at an understanding of the eternal values: Truth, Beauty, and Goodness. The path to this understanding lies through mathematics and dialectics. Over the door of his Academy Plato had written up: *You cannot enter here unless you know geometry*. When the great moment of his life came and he was invited to assist in the government of Syracuse, the most powerful city at that time in the Greek world, Plato's appreciation of this opportunity was shown by the use he made of it. He began to teach the young prince who had invited him geometry. Thus early did the word *academic* merit its present significance.

The mere bulk of his writings, surviving in the midst of the general wreck, would suffice to give Plato, in the eyes of modern students of antiquity, a unique importance. To this must be added their superb artistry. Being endowed with dramatic gifts that matched his discursive powers, Plato cast his thoughts into the form of dialogues. Here, grouped generally round the central figure of Socrates, he brought upon the scene his sophists, generals, statesmen, artists, and others, and made them talk. If the disquisitions are sometimes tedious and arbitrary as well as profound, they are set off with a golden eloquence to which wit, irony, imagination, passion alike contribute. Furthermore, these writings are preserved to us with a textual purity due mainly, no doubt, to the fact that the Academy enjoyed as an institution an uninterrupted life of some nine hundred years, which is unique in the record of ancient literature. The student who masters his idiom can enter, with a fullness of knowledge rarely paralleled until modern times, into the life of the Athens that was the school of Hellas then and has since become the school of mankind.

For these reasons, and many more, the Platonic writings have long attracted, and still attract, a degree of attention which the earlier philosophers and sophists cannot claim. But the great prestige of his writings constitutes a difficulty for the historian of science. Plato wrote much about those problems of epistemology which lie on the border between philosophy and science. There is no doubt about his eminence as a philosopher. His contribution to science is, however, open to question. Does he deserve the same place in the history of science which by universal accord he holds in philosophy?

Science before Plato had achieved remarkable advances which we may roughly classify under three heads. The first and decisive step, which we associate especially with the Milesians, was the new attitude of attempting to explain the phenomena of nature, including human nature, without supernatural intervention. Secondly, we find that a rudimentary technique of interrogating nature by means of experiments had begun. There was a growing practice of observation and experiments, in Ionia, in Italy, in Sicily, in Athens itself, accompanied, as its philosophical implications became more clearly understood, by a lively debate on the validity of sense-evidence. Thirdly, although the importance of this has been little recognized and the fact has been denied by some, there was the vital connection between natural philosophy and techniques, which determined the character of the early philosophy of nature. In developing his attack on the Ionian philosophers, Plato accords their recognition of this connection an important place in their general world-outlook. The following are the words in which he describes their point of view: 'The arts which make the most serious contribution to human life are those which blend their own power with that of nature, like medicine, agriculture, and gymnastics' (*Laws*, X, 889d). This plainly implies a philosophy of the techniques, an attempt to define their essential character and to assign them their very important place in the development of civilized society. We shall discuss Plato's attitude to the science of his predecessors under these three heads. First we shall consider his attitude to the naturalism, or atheism, of the Ionians.

THEOLOGICAL ASTRONOMY

When the Ionians began to explain the phenomena of the heavens in naturalistic terms, there can be no doubt either of the novelty of their outlook or of the scandal it caused. The new teaching conflicted not only with vague popular beliefs in the divinity of the heavenly bodies, but with formal theological doctrines inculcating similar views. An effort was made by the Pythagoreans, and later by Plato, to put the supernatural back into astronomy ; and, in fact, astronomy did not really make its way with the Greek public until it had been rescued from atheism. This is a typical occurrence in the history of thought. A scientific hypothesis has often failed to gain currency until it has received the stamp of religion. A modern, and more familiar, example, will illustrate the phenomenon in question. It is not without its importance for the understanding of the history of science.

' It seems probable to me,' wrote Newton, echoing Gassendi, ' that God in the beginning formed matter in solid, massy, hard, impenetrable particles, of such sizes and figures, and with such other properties, in such proportions to space, as most conduced to the end for which He formed them ; and that these primitive particles, being solids, are incomparably harder than any porous bodies compounded of them ; even so very hard as never to wear or break in pieces : no ordinary power being able to divide what God Himself made one in the first creation.' Here it is obvious that two traditions are mingled. The atoms, with their various properties, belong to the scientific tradition ; they are nothing more or less than the atoms of Democritus. But the atoms, as they left the mind of Democritus, belonged to an atheistic universe which was to be explained entirely by natural law. This had at all times proved an obstacle to their acceptance. Newton, however, wove another tradition in with his account of the atoms. God, the Creation, the end God has in view, and the impossibility of putting asunder that which God has once joined, belong to the religious tradition. The passage then, as it left the pen of Newton, is a strange amalgam of religion and science ; and it is to the intimate blend of the two that the success of Newton's views is partly due. The scientific hypothesis would have had little chance of making its way in seventeenth-century Europe if it had clashed violently with the theological fashion of the age. It was therefore altogether fortunate for the success of the Newtonian physics that the author should have been convinced that the atoms of Democritus had been made by God, which was no part of the original conception. Descartes, it may be relevant to recall, had had to hold up his *Principia Philosophiae* for eleven years while he sought a formula by which his unorthodox position might be made to appear acceptable to authority. In the end he did not find one. Newton was more fortunate. In good faith he re-wrote the first verse of the first chapter of *Genesis* in the light of the science of the Greek atomists: *In the beginning God created the atoms and the void*. The English genius for compromise has never been better illustrated.

The atoms had to await the seventeenth century of our era to be baptized into Christianity. Astronomy was Pythagoreanized and Platonized within a few generations of the Ionian dawn. In one of the best text-books of ancient science which has come down to us, an Alexandrian hand-book on astronomy by one Geminus, we have this account of the Pythagorean influence on astronomy:

'There underlies the whole science of astronomy,' he

writes, 'the assumption that the sun and the moon and the five planets move at even speeds in perfect circles in an opposite direction to the cosmos. It was the Pythagoreans, the first to approach these questions, who laid down the hypothesis of a circular and uniform motion for the sun, moon, and planets. Their view was that, in regard of divine and eternal beings, a supposition of such disorder as that these bodies should move now more quickly and now more slowly, or should even stop, as in what are called the stations of the planets, is inadmissible. Even in the human sphere such irregularity is incompatible with the orderly procedure of a gentleman. And even if the crude necessities of life often impose upon men occasions of haste or loitering, it is not to be supposed that such occasions inhere in the incorruptible nature of the stars. *For this reason they defined their problem as the explanation of the phenomena on the hypothesis of circular and uniform motion.*'

We have already spoken of the blend of science, religion, and politics in Pythagorean thought. It is here illustrated in a topic of major importance for the history of European culture. The application of mathematics to astronomy was a scientific step ; the belief that the heavenly bodies are divine belongs to religion ; the notion that a gentleman partakes in an especial degree of the characteristics of divinity belongs to class politics, which have throughout the history of civilization been granted a cosmic significance they do not deserve.

When beggars die there are no comets seen;
The heavens themselves blaze forth the death of princes.

Not till the time of Kepler did astronomy rid itself of the necessity of interpreting the behaviour of the planets in terms of the social prejudices of the Pythagoreans.

These politico-religious prejudices remained to trouble the astronomical science of Plato, who felt the scandal of the planets in an especial degree. Plato was the author, or propagator, of an astral theology in which the stars were cast for the rôle of patterns of divine regularity. He found it incompatible with this requirement that, conspicuous among the hosts of heaven, where

> Round the ancient track marched rank on rank
> The army of unalterable law,

should be a parcel of five disorderly vagabonds (the word planet means vagabond in Greek). The inconvenience was especially great inasmuch as the problem of human vaga-bondage had reached a crisis at this time in Greece.

Plato's contemporary, Isocrates, had made a special study of the problem of these sturdy beggars. The remedy he proposed was not increased production and better distribu-tion of this world's goods. Faced with an ever-increasing throng of roving outcasts, his idea was to enlist them, drill them, and hurl them against the Persian Empire. If they could not conquer it outright, they could at least tear enough off its territory to provide living-space for themselves. The alternative was revolution at home. 'If we cannot check the growing strength of these vagabonds,' wrote Isocrates, 'by providing them with a satisfactory life, before we know where we are they will be so numerous that they will con-stitute as great a danger to the Greeks as to the barbarians' (*Philip*, 121). Under these circumstances it is not surprising that, as a contribution to the liquidation of vagabondage on earth, Plato should have determined to liquidate it in heaven. He 'set it as a problem to all earnest students to find "what are the uniform and ordered movements by the assumption of which the apparent movements of the planets can be accounted for"'. Until this problem could be solved, his astral theology, by which he set much store in his pro-posed reconstruction of society, risked total failure. Why worship the stars if these divine beings could do no better than set a conspicuous example of irregularity and disorder?

D

It is altogether false to regard Plato's challenge to the mathematicians to reduce the planets to order as proof of a disinterested love of science. It was not an attempt to find out the facts, but to conjure away socially inconvenient appearances on the basis of any plausible hypothesis.

Plato's disciples were not slow in providing him with the desired solution of his problem. The apparent paths of the planets were analysed, by Eudoxus and Callippus, into the resultants of over thirty circular rotatory movements. On this basis, astronomy, which had before been tainted with atheism, was given citizen rights in Greece. Plutarch, in his *Life of Nicias*, is our informant on this point, the military disaster at Syracuse, brought about by that distinguished general's superstitious dread of eclipses, prompting his biographer to give some account of the progress of astronomical knowledge among the public at large.

'The eclipse frightened Nicias very much, as well as all the others who were ignorant or superstitious enough to mind such things. For though by this time even the masses had accepted the idea that an eclipse of the *sun* towards the end of the month had something to do with the moon, they could by no effort conceive what could get in the way of the *moon* to produce the effect of a full moon suddenly becoming obscured and altered in colour. This they thought uncanny, a sign sent from God to announce some great calamity. Anaxagoras, the first man who had the understanding and the courage to commit to writing an explanation of the phases of the moon, was but a recent authority and his book little esteemed. In fact, it circulated in secret, was read by few, and was cautiously received. For in those days there was no tolerance for the natural philosophers or "babblers about things in heaven" as they were called. They were charged with explaining away the divine and substituting for it irrational causes, blind forces, and the sway of necessity. So Protagoras was banished, Anaxagoras was gaoled and it was all that Pericles could do to get him out, and Socrates, though he had nothing to do at all in the matter, was put to death for being a philosopher. *It was only much later, through the brilliant repute of Plato, that the reproach was removed from astronomical studies and access to them opened up for all. This was on account of the respect in which his life was held and because he made natural laws subordinate to the authority of divine principles.'*

Such is Plutarch's account of the matter. Nor are we dependent only on such a late authority. In a curious passage in the *Laws* (820–822) Plato himself gives us the same information. There he makes his mouthpiece say that a new astronomical discovery has made it unnecessary to submit to the generally accepted view that astronomy is a dangerous and impious study. And what is this new discovery? Simply that the sun, moon, and with them those vagabonds, the planets, do not really move irregularly, as they appear to do. Accordingly, says Plato, our attitude to the teaching of astronomy needs to be revised. It has now become a safe, even a desirable subject, up to a point. Students must by no means be allowed to hear, as the old natural philosophers taught, that the sun and moon are lumps of inanimate matter. But they will pray and sacrifice to the heavenly bodies in a more acceptable spirit when they have been made to understand that they are divine beings whose motions are patterns of regularity.

This kind of astronomy, in which natural laws were subordinated to divine principles, and in which more regard was paid to the heavenly bodies as objects of worship than subjects of scientific study, was further developed by Aristotle. Systematizing the doctrines of Plato and the Pythagoreans, he taught, not only that the circular motions of the heavenly bodies are proof of their being under the control of divine intelligence, but that the very substance of which they are made – what he called 'the fifth element', to distinguish it from Earth, Air, Fire, and Water – is different from any that exists below the circle of the moon. The astronomy which he taught in his theological mood (it must be stressed that it is not characteristic of his scientific outlook) is that inherited by the Middle Ages.

Aristotle's account was that the universe consists of fifty-nine concentric spheres, with the earth at the centre. To the earth were allowed four spheres, one for each of the four elements. Outside the four terrestrial spheres were fifty-five celestial spheres, that of the moon being the lowest and that of the fixed stars the highest. The spheres were supposed to revolve round a stationary earth and carry with them, in their revolutions, the heavenly bodies. Only below the moon, in Aristotle's scheme of the universe, was change possible. There the four elements, whose 'natural' movements were up and down, might mingle and be transformed into one another. But above the moon, in the etherial spheres, whose 'natural' movement was in circles, no change occurred. In this scheme, as the substance of heaven is different from that of earth, so are the laws of motion different. There is a celestial mechanics and a terrestrial mechanics, and the rules of one are not valid for the other. Not till Newton did terrestrial mechanics regain control of heaven.

It would be wrong, however, to leave the impression that the Platonic compromise, which sought to 'make natural laws subordinate to divine principles', met with no opposition or was universally accepted. Aristotle himself affords proof of the uneasiness with which it was regarded. In the account of his astronomical opinions which we have given so far we have been following his treatise *On the Heavens*, which seems to be an early work written when he was strongly under the influence of Plato and the Academy. In his *Metaphysics* (XI. 8, 1073b 8 ff.), discussing the apparent motion of the heavenly bodies, he puts forward a more cautious view which is worth quoting. ' That the movements are more numerous than the bodies that are moved is evident to those who have given even moderate attention to the matter ; for each of the planets has more than one movement. But as to the actual number of the movements, we now – to give some notion of the subject – quote what some of the mathematicians say, that our thought may have some definite number to grasp ; *but, for the rest, we must partly investigate for ourselves, partly learn from other investigators, and if those who study this subject form an opinion contrary to what we have now stated, we must esteem both parties, indeed, but follow the more accurate.'*

This is spoken like the great scientist that Aristotle was ; and it is relevant here to observe that sometimes, even when Aristotle reverses a *correct* opinion of his predecessors, he does so because he is in possession of more abundant evidence than they. Some justification may be found, from this point of view, even for his disastrous separation between terrestrial and celestial mechanics. The old Ionians, ignorant of the true or even approximate sizes of the heavenly bodies, their distances from one another, and their distances from earth, had been incapable of a true distinction between astronomy and meteorology. For them the heavenly bodies were small in comparison with the earth. A couple of centuries of the application of mathematics to astronomy had changed all this. Aristotle can casually remark (*Meteorologica*, 340a), 'The bulk of the earth is infinitesimal in comparison with the whole universe which surrounds it'. Accordingly, while the Ionians could argue, without misgiving, from processes going on on earth to processes in the sky, Aristotle felt he could no longer do so. 'It is absurd,' he writes, ' to make the universe to be in process of change because of small and trifling changes on earth, when the bulk and size of the earth are surely as nothing in comparison with the whole universe' (*ib.*, 352a). Aristotle could thus support his incorrect celestial philosophy by the latest findings of astronomy.

Science does not advance evenly along its whole course, but, like the planets, now hurries, now halts, and sometimes even seems to be in reverse.

THE EYE OF THE SOUL AND THE EYE OF THE BODY

The second gain we put to the credit of thinkers before Plato was the progress made towards the conception of positive science and the beginnings of a correct theory of the rôle of observation and experiment in the building up of the positive sciences. What was Plato's attitude to the new habit of interrogating nature in order to wrest her secrets from her? On the whole, it must be admitted that he was opposed to it. It is in regard to astronomy and acoustics that he expresses his attitude most clearly. We shall take up these two subjects in turn.

In his dialogue the *Phaedo*, in which he expounds the doctrine of the immortality of the soul, Plato makes Socrates say: 'If we are ever to know anything absolutely, we must be free from the body and behold the actual realities with the eye of the soul alone. ... While we live we shall be nearest to knowledge when we avoid, so far as possible, intercourse and communion with the body, except what is absolutely necessary, and are not infected by its nature, but keep ourselves free from it until God himself sets us free.' There is no room for doubt that Plato allowed this desire, to be free from the body and behold the actual realities with the eye of the soul alone, to affect his attitude to research. It checked the impulse to physical research and shifted the whole emphasis to abstract mathematics. Plato was one of those who was prepared to listen to Parmenides. Like him, he distrusted the blind eye and the echoing ear.

In *Republic* vii, 529, 530, he gives the following advice with regard to astronomy: 'The starry heaven which we behold is wrought upon a visible ground, and therefore, although the fairest and most perfect of visible things, must necessarily be deemed inferior far to the true motions of absolute swiftness and absolute slowness. ... These are to be apprehended by reason and intelligence, but not by sight. ... The spangled heavens should be used as a pattern and with a view to that higher knowledge. ... But a true astronomer will never imagine that the proportions of night and day, or of both to the month, or of the month to the year, or of the stars to these and to one another, and any other things that are material and visible can also be eternal and subject to no deviation – that would be absurd ; and it is equally absurd to take so much pains in establishing their exact truth. ... In astronomy, as in geometry, we should employ problems, and let the heavens alone if we would approach the subject in the right way.'

His attitude to experiment in acoustics is as hostile as his attitude to observation in astronomy. In a continuation of the passage on astronomy just quoted, he makes Socrates complain : 'The teachers of harmony compare the sounds and consonances which are *heard* only, and their labour, like that of the astronomers, is in vain.' To which Glaucon rejoins : 'Yes, by heaven! And it is as good as a play to hear them talking about their condensed notes, as they call them ; they put their ears close alongside of the strings like persons catching a sound from their neighbour's wall – one set of them declaring that they distinguish an intermediate note and have found the least interval which should be the unit of measurement ; the others insisting that the two sounds have passed into the same – either party *setting their ears before their understanding.*' Socrates fully approves of this : 'You mean those gentlemen who tease and torture the strings and rack them on the pegs of the instrument ... they too are in error, like the astronomers ; they investigate the numbers of the harmonies which are *heard*, but they never attain to problems.' From all of which two things are apparent; first, that a certain amount of systematic experiment was going forward, and second, that Plato strongly discouraged it.

Here again, as in the matter of reviving the belief in the divinity of the stars, Plato marks a reaction. But again, as before, there is something to be said on the other side. Plato added nothing to science in the observational and experimental sense. It is extremely doubtful whether he added anything to mathematics. Heath's judgement on his mathematical attainment is that ' he does not appear to have been more than up to date ' (*op. cit.*, p. 294). But he did contribute to the philosophy of mathematics. What fascinated him was the meaning of those mathematical truths which seem to be independent of experience. In *Republic* vi, 510, he says of the geometers: ' You know that they make use of visible figures and argue about them, but in doing so they are not thinking of these figures but of the things which they represent ; thus it is the absolute square and the absolute diameter which is the object of their argument, not the diameter which they draw.' In distinguishing this type of knowledge from the knowledge which appears to be wholly dependent on sensuous impressions, Plato made a fundamental contribution to epistemology. It is his concern for this that must excuse, if anything can excuse, a hostility to practical geometry so great that he regarded the mere construction of figures as essentially antagonistic to a true study of the subject.

PHILOSOPHY AND TECHNIQUES

When we come to the third point, the connection between philosophy and the techniques, which had proved so fruitful in an earlier period, we find that Plato has nothing to contribute. Preoccupied with theological, metaphysical, or political problems, and disbelieving in the possibility of a science of nature, Plato has little appreciation of the connections between Greek thought and Greek practice which were clear to an earlier age. These connections are many. Astronomy was, of course, not studied out of mere curiosity. It was studied in order to solve those very problems concern with which Plato deprecates – the exact relations of the lengths of day and night, of both to the month, and of the month to the year. On the solution of these problems depended the improvement of the calendar. On the improvement of the calendar depended improvements in agriculture, navigation, and the general conduct of public affairs. Neither was geometry studied, outside the Academy, purely for the good of the soul. It was studied in connection with land-surveying, navigation, architecture, and engineering. Mechanical science was applied in the theatre, the field of battle, the docks and dockyards, the quarries, and wherever building was afoot. Medicine was a conspicuous example of applied science. It was a scientific study of man in his environment with a view to promoting his well-being. But the political programme put forward by Plato in the *Republic* and the *Laws* is all but barren of understanding of the rôle of applied science in the improvement of the lot of humanity. In his *Republic* and *Laws* Plato is wholly occupied with the problem of managing men, not at all with the problem of the control of the material environment. Accordingly the works, if full of political ingenuity, are devoid of natural science.

Plato carries this hostility, or indifference, to the science implicit in the techniques to very great lengths. A characteristic of the Ionian scientists had been the honour paid to great inventors, such as Anacharsis, who invented the bellows and made an improvement in the design of the anchor, or Glaucus of Chios, who invented the soldering-iron. These were examples of human ingenuity to an older age. Plato, however (*Republic* x, 597), did not think a human craftsman could originate anything ; he had to wait for God to invent the Idea or Form of it. A carpenter, says Plato, could only make a bed by fixing his mind's eye on the Idea of the bed made by God. Theodorus of Samos, who invented the level, the lathe, the set-square, and the key, was thus shorn of his originality and of his title to honour; and Zopyrus, who invented the *gastrophetes*, or cross-bow held against the belly, had stolen the patent from God. The propounders of the modern theory of evolution found themselves embarrassed by the teaching of the Old Testament, that the various species of plants and animals, as they now exist, had been created by God. The technicians of the ancient world must have found it still more embarrassing to be told to wait upon the divine initiative before originating, or even improving, any technical device, since the present stage of technical development represented the divine plan.

But Plato went further than this in depressing the intellectual status of the technician. Not only is the technician robbed of the credit of inventiveness, he is also denied the possession of any true science in the art of manufacture. By an ingenious piece of sophistry Plato proves, in the same passage of the *Republic*, that it is not the man who *makes* a thing, but the man who *uses* it, who has true scientific knowledge about it. The user, who alone has true science, must impart his science to the maker, who then has 'correct opinion'. This doctrine effectually exalts the position of the consumer in society and reduces the status of the producer. Its political importance, in a slave-owning society, is obvious. A slave who made things could not be allowed to be the possessor of a science superior to that of the master who used them. But it constitutes an effective bar to technical advance or a true history of science. Plato has here, in fact, prepared the way for the grotesquely unhistorical opinion later current in antiquity, that it was philosophers who invented the techniques and handed them over to slaves.

Why did Plato think in this way? Plato had one of the best brains of which human history holds record. Why do his arguments lead sometimes to such wrong-headed conclusions? The answer is not difficult to give. It will be argued more closely in our last chapter. Suffice it here to suggest that Plato's thought was corrupted by his approval of the slave society in which he lived. Plato and Aristotle regretted the fact that any free labour still survived. In his *Politics* (Bk. I ; chap. xiii) Aristotle remarks : 'The slave and his master have a common existence ; whereas the artisan stands to his master in a relation far less close and participates in virtue only in so far as he participates in slavery.' In his *Laws* (806d) Plato organizes society on the basis of slavery, and, having done so, puts a momentous question : 'We have now made arrangements to secure ourselves a modest provision of the necessities of life ; the business of the arts and crafts has been passed on to others ; agriculture has been handed over to slaves on condition of their granting us a sufficient return to live in a fit and seemly fashion ; how now shall we organize our lives?' A still more pertinent question would have been : 'How will our new way of life reorganize our thoughts?' For the new way of life did bring a new way of thinking, and one that proved inimical to science. It was henceforth difficult to hold to the view that true knowledge could be arrived at by interrogating nature, for all the implements and processes by which nature is made to obey man's will had become, if not in fact yet in the political philosophy of Plato and Aristotle, the province of the slave.

We have now examined the respects in which Platonism constitutes a reaction from Ionian science. Plato, however, had an all-important contribution to offer in another sphere. The debate as to whether the reason or the senses is the true path to knowledge was now an old one. Plato had come down strongly on the side of reason. The consensus of opinion among scientists was that reason could not contribute anything without the evidence of the senses. Plato could not avoid the discussion, and in two dialogues, the *Theaetetus* and the *Sophist*, his treatment of it yields results of classic importance.

In the former dialogue, abandoning the intransigent attitude of the *Phaedo*, Plato is prepared to admit that the data of sensation are the material of knowledge, but insists (as, indeed, others had done before him) that sensation is not in itself knowledge. Here he makes a more thorough analysis of the problem than his predecessors, the Hippo-cratic doctors, whose opinions we have quoted, had done. He clearly distinguishes between sense-perception and thought, and teaches that knowledge is the result of the action of the latter on the former. We may quote his own words. 'The simple sensations which reach the soul through the body are given at birth to men and animals by nature, but their reflections on these and on their relations to being and use are slowly and hardly gained, if they are ever gained, by edu-cation and long experience.'

Here there is a very valuable thought very clearly expressed. But even here it might be urged that, if Plato had been able to follow out the train of his thought to its logical conclusion, the result would have disrupted his whole philosophy as dramatically as the discovery of the irrationality of $\sqrt{2}$ did the number physics of the Pythagoreans. For it is obvious that, if the source and growth of knowledge are such as Plato now describes – namely, reflection on simple sensations matured by education and experience – then human con-sciousness is externally conditioned by nature and by society, and does not consist in the perception by the soul of eternal verities. If Plato had pursued this line of thought, he would have had to admit, with the Ionians, what in the back of his mind he clearly knew, the connection between human practice and human knowledge. In short, he would have been dangerously near to adopting the views of Democritus. But it is time to stop speculating on what Plato might have said and report what he actually did say.

As we have seen, Plato had now arrived at the position that the sensory faculties are organs by which *mind* apprehends external nature. We proceed to give, in condensed form, the further steps of his argument – 'We do not see with the eyes but through them. We do not hear with the ears but through them. Nor could any one sense itself distinguish between its own activity and that of another sense.' A new point this, and a fine one, of which there was no hint in the Hippocratic writers. 'There must be something connected with both senses,' Plato continues, 'call it soul or anything else you like – *with* which we truly perceive all that is conveyed to us *through* the sensory faculties. It is the soul, or *psyche*, that makes us aware that we perceive and that distinguishes the data of one sense-organ from those of another.'

The contribution here made is already of first importance, and Plato has still more to give. He points out that we have other psychic activities less directly dependent on sense-stimulation than those already mentioned. Such activities are recollection, expectation, imagination, and those higher operations of the mind by which we apprehend mathematical or logical arguments, or lay hold of such absolute Ideas as the Good, the Beautiful, and the True. It is not necessary to accept Plato's view that these activities prove the immortality of the soul and its independence of the body in order to admit that he has here raised the whole problem of consciousness to a higher level.

In the *Sophist* the immateriality of the soul is strongly emphasized. The materialists are impaled on the horns of a dilemma. Do they, or do they not, admit the existence of soul, and that some souls are wise and good, others foolish and bad? If they say Yes, as they must, they are to be asked whether this does not imply that wisdom and the other virtues are something, and whether they are things that can be seen and handled. They may try to save themselves by saying that the soul is a kind of body. They will find it hard to say that wisdom is a kind of body. If they can be got to admit that anything can *be* without being a body, the point has been gained.

We cannot pursue further this early stage of the now ancient controversy on the nature of the soul. But it is fair to add that we know what answer the materialists made. The Epicureans have preserved it for us. They said: Yes, we admit, of course, the existence of soul, of mind, of characters good and bad; we merely deny their existence apart from the appropriate physical and physiological structure, 'far away from the sinews and the blood' (Lucretius III, 788, 9).

We conclude that Plato not only made no direct contribution to positive science, but did much to discourage it. That is not to say, however, that he made no contribution to thought. He fostered the study of mathematics, an essential element in the modern conception of science. He advanced the study of logic more than all the thinkers who preceded him. His criticism of the rôle of sense-perception and mind in the process of the cognition of the external was epoch-making. The foundation of the Academy was no mean contribution to the conception of science as an organized and co-operative effort. The composition of his great series of dialogues, touching so many aspects of human life and thought with language of subtlety and power, was an imperishable gift to mankind. As for what was corrupt in his thought, we shall best understand it and most fairly judge it when we see in it the corruption of the age. For the most vital, the most valuable, thing in Plato is that he endeavoured to think like a citizen, even if a reactionary citizen of a decaying society. It is his sense of the social and political implications of men's thought on every subject under heaven that both warps his own thinking and lends it life, complexity, passion, weight. When we observe him, who had such a luminous intellect, putting the lamps of knowledge out, we see through his personal crisis into the crisis of ancient society. He lacked the serenity of a former age when to think meant to foresee progress for mankind. When he looked into the future he was afraid. But he was not above the battle. He was the least in the world like the pure philosopher lost to all considerations of place and time that his present defenders represent him to be. It is owing, indeed, to his absorption in political problems that he made an important contribution to our knowledge of the conditions of labour in the Greek world of his time. In several passages we have cited from him it is possible to note his concern with the organization of the labour process. So prominent is this interest that Glotz (*Ancient Greece at Work*, London, 1926, p. 220) is able with some colour to claim that the genius of Plato gave to the economic sciences for the first time a theory of the division of labour.

CHAPTER EIGHT

Aristotle

*

WE HAVE spoken of Plato as being the first philosopher whose writings have survived in bulk. Aristotle was both a great philosopher and a great scientist, and his writings have also survived in bulk. Apart from the Hippocratic writings, which are with difficulty ascribed to definite authors and represent a school rather than a man, the Aristotelian corpus is the first body of scientific writings to survive. He is the earliest Greek scientist whose words can be adequately studied in their original form. From Thales to Democritus we are dependent on fragments, on later quotations and comments. We have voluminous treatises from the pen of Aristotle.

But though the works of both Plato and Aristotle have survived, the fortune of the two men has been very different. We have all the works of Plato which he prepared for publication ; we merely guess at the substance of his lectures in the Academy. Aristotle, when he was still a member of the Academy, wrote and published dialogues. We have lost them all. What we do possess is the substance of the lectures he gave as head of his own institution, the Lyceum. The works of Aristotle which we possess are technical treatises. With the exception, therefore, of isolated passages of general import and exceptionally finished form, Aristotle is not readable as Plato is.

Neglecting certain smaller works we may classify the Aristotelian writings under four heads – (1) physical, (2) logical and metaphysical, (3) ethical and political, (4) biological. *The physical treatises*, from the point of view of modern science, are the least satisfactory. They are under the domination of the teleological philosophy of the Academy. *The logical and metaphysical treatises* represent a great effort of criticism of the work of his predecessors, especially of Plato. The net result of Aristotle's criticism is to transform the Ideal Theory into an instrument for the study of nature. With Aristotle the Ideas or Forms do not exist apart from nature, but are embodied in nature and have no other existence. Science consists in finding the permanent Forms which underlie the shifting phenomena of nature. With *the ethical and political treatises* we cannot be directly concerned here ; but they are of great importance, nevertheless, in so far as they reveal to us the connections, which are numerous and intimate, between Aristotle's views on nature and his views on society. In *biology* Aristotle made his great contribution to science. It has been called the greatest contribution to science ever made by an individual.

Obviously the mental history of such a man as Aristotle, if we could come by it, would be of extraordinary interest. We may feel confident that we do, in its main outlines, possess that history, though it has been understood only quite recently. It *is* of extraordinary interest. But how can we be sure that we possess it? And how did it lie concealed so long?

It must be understood that the interest in the mental history of the individual is quite a modern thing. Plato has given us a voluminous account of the life and conversation of Socrates. In vain do we look in it for an intelligible account of the mental development of his hero. Socrates was the wisest man Plato knew ; Plato makes him the vehicle for his own wisdom. He did not play Boswell to Socrates' Johnson. Plutarch, again, has left us a gallery of portraits of the great men of Greece and Rome. He accepted no sitter unless he was a general or a statesman. No artist, scientist, or philosopher figures in the list. It is not biography in the modern sense that Plutarch writes, but rather military and political history from a new angle, that of the individual participants. The same is true of his Roman imitator, Cornelius Nepos. The great crisis of the ancient world, the breakdown of paganism and the evolution of Christianity, inaugurated a change. In the *Meditations* of Marcus Aurelius and the *Confessions* of St Augustine, we have the records of mental histories, but they bore no great fruit. When the Christian world had taken shape we begin to get again an abundant biographical literature. But the Lives of the Saints are not, except in the most superficial sense, the mental histories of men. They are schematized accounts of the operations of Divine Grace. It was the movement of Humanism that foreshadowed the birth of biography in the modern sense.

But long before this, Aristotle, an Aristotle without mental development, had become part of European culture. The medieval schoolmen constructed Christian theology on the basis of Aristotle's works. Scientists at the Renaissance accepted or rejected Aristotle's views. In either case 'Aristotle' meant anything that had survived with Aristotle's name attached to it. All his writings had equal authority. No one knew in what order his works had been written, or bothered to enquire. That is the reason why the mental history of Aristotle was concealed from us.

The detailed reconstruction of the order of composition of Aristotle's works is not easy. Probably it is impossible. To his pupils at the Lyceum, Aristotle lectured on a vast range of subjects over a period of many years. His courses on all these subjects grew under his hands. They have in them earlier and later strata, and have numerous cross-references to one another. Nevertheless their general development is clear. The acceptance by W. D. Ross (*Aristotle*, p. 19) of the order of composition suggested by Werner Jaeger in his *Aristoteles* represents the final judgement of informed opinion. With this order the mental development of Aristotle corresponds to the external events of his life.

Aristotle was the son of a physician at the court of the Macedonian king Philip II, and doubtless was expected to follow his father's profession. It is almost certain that, in accordance with the practice of the time, he had been apprenticed to his father's art. If so, he had, as a boy, had opportunity to understand the double aspect of Hippocratic medicine, which was, as we have seen, both a science and a technique. He would have conceived of the healing art as a growing body of positive knowledge ; and, as a future practitioner in that art, he would have been taught to let blood, to bind wounds, to apply poultices, and perform many other simple medical operations. Then, as a youth of about seventeen, we find that he had transferred himself to the Academy at Athens, there to be introduced to a different mental and spiritual world. He would now receive an initiation in Pythagorean mathematics which would be succeeded by a rigorous training in dialectics. He would be taught to understand things, as Parmenides had advised, not through the senses but through reasoning. He would accept the Parmenidean maxim that the logical and the real are identical. The goal of his ambition would no longer be to know nature but the absolute. He would meditate long on the words of Socrates in the *Phaedo* : 'If we are ever to know anything absolutely, we must be free from the body and must behold the actual realities with the eye of the soul alone.'

Together with this introduction to the ideal philosophy, Aristotle would learn in the Academy to despise techniques. If as a boy he had learned to employ the hand in healing, he would now be taught that to employ the hand in learning, even to the limited extent of making physical models of mathematical objects, was a vulgar thing of which he ought to be ashamed. But probably Aristotle did not need this lesson. His early training in surgery would not imply exemption from the growing prejudice against manual labour in general. The important thing for his future career as a biologist was that in this one department at least he was not ashamed to use his hands.

Aristotle remained nearly twenty years in the Academy. Jaeger has remarked that so protracted a pupilage in a man afterwards distinguished for originality is without parallel in the intellectual history of mankind. It must, however, be remembered that Aristotle was already an author of repute while still a member of the Academy. 'The ancient schools of philosophy,' Ross reminds us, 'were bodies of men united by a common spirit and sharing the same fundamental views, but following out their own enquiries in comparative independence.' That Aristotle was, while still a member of the Academy, critical of some features of Platonism is clear, and in 348, when Plato died and was succeeded in the headship of the Academy by his nephew Speusippus, the divergence of view became still more marked. Aristotle complained of the tendency of the Academy to 'turn philosophy into mathematics' and abandoned it. He would be then about thirty-five years old.

The next thirteen years of his life were spent away from Athens, mainly in Assos and Mitylene. To this period belong many of his researches in biology. Fleeing from Athens and mathematics, Aristotle took refuge in Ionia and natural history. Would that we knew more of his associates at this time and of the strength of the old Ionian tradition! Then, in 334, being now near fifty years of age, Aristotle returned to Athens and set up school for himself at the Lyceum. To the next twelve years, when he was head of the Lyceum, the completion of his own wonderful extant corpus of writings belongs. He withdrew again from Athens in 323, and died the next year. The inner tension in his writings, producing glimpses of a spiritual drama underneath their dry technical exterior, resides in his combination of respect for Platonic idealism with devotion to positive research. 'If we ask in what order it is psychologically most likely that Aristotle's works were written,' says Ross, 'the answer must be that presumably his writings would reflect a progressive withdrawal from Plato's influence. ... The general movement was from otherworldliness towards an intense interest in the concrete facts both of nature and of history, and a conviction that the "form" and meaning of the world is to be found not apart from but embedded in its "matter".'

A hundred and forty years ago the famous Platonist, Thomas Taylor, summed up the general difference between the two philosophers by remarking that Aristotle, even when he considered theology, did so physically, while Plato considered even physics theologically. The theological physics of Plato are set forth in his famous, or notorious, dialogue, the *Timaeus*, and the best introduction to the physical treatises of Aristotle, which are the earliest and most Platonic part of his extant writings, is the *Timaeus*. In this dialogue Plato gives an account of the creation of the world. The work constitutes the high point of the Pythagorean tradition of theological philosophy. Its teaching is that the phenomenal world is an image of the eternal world, and that the cause of the creation of this phenomenal world on the model of the eternal world is the goodness of God. In other words, its major themes are providence and teleology. *A priori* arguments are adduced for the opinion that the world is one, that it is in the form of a perfect sphere, that it is necessarily made up of the four elements, Earth, Air, Fire, and Water, and that it has a soul. Human bodies, we next learn, are likewise made up of the four elements and likewise contain souls. These souls have been divinely instructed in the moral law of the universe. The purpose of God in endowing men with sight and hearing was that they might learn the lesson of law and order from astronomy and music and apply it to their own lives.

The following passage, which seeks to explain why the world had to be made of the four elements, will make clear what Thomas Taylor meant when he said that Plato treated physics theologically. ' Being bodily, that which has come to be must be visible and tangible. Without fire nothing visible can come to be, nothing tangible without solidity, nothing solid without earth. Hence God, in the beginning of his fashioning, made the body of the universe out of fire and earth. Now two terms cannot be brought together without a third. There must be a bond between them to bring them together. ... If the body of the universe could have been a plane without depth, one middle term would have sufficed to bind together the extremes and itself. But in fact the world was to be solid, and solids must always be conjoined not by one middle term, but by two. So God inserted water and air between fire and earth, and made them all, so far as was possible, proportional to one another, air being to water as fire to air, and water to earth as air to water.' The magic wand of Pythagorean mathematics has transformed the natural philosophy of the Ionians into theology.

The constitution of human bodies is treated in the same *a priori* way by verbal logic. The pathology of both body and mind is deduced from the general account of the structure of the universe, in the manner long before denounced by the author of *Ancient Medicine*. By way of finale, the existence of women and the other lower animals is accounted for by a doctrine of the progressive deterioration of men! 'Those of the men first created who led a life of cowardice and injustice were suitably reborn as women in the second generation, and this is why it was at this particular juncture that the gods contrived the lust of copulation.' ' Beasts who go on all fours came from men who were wholly unconversant with philosophy and had never gazed on the heavens.' When he goes as far as this Plato is probably intending to be consciously funny, but it is to be noted that his shafts of wit are directed against the old Ionian thinkers. Anaximander, anticipating modern views and basing himself on evidence, had taught

that man was descended from a fish. Accordingly Plato
maintains that fish are descended from men. 'The fourth
kind of animal, whose habitat is water, came from the most
utterly mindless men.' And if, says Plato, fools like Anaximander have been turned into fish, other philosophic fools
have been turned into birds. 'Birds sprang by a change of
form from harmless but light-witted men who paid attention
to the things in the heavens but *in their simplicity supposed
that the surest evidence in these matters is that of the
eye.*'

But it is not merely, or even principally, the use of the
senses that Plato protests against in the *Timaeus*. In quarrel-
ling with the philosophy of the old Ionians he is also concerned to dismiss the modes of explanation of natural
phenomena which, as we have seen, they had drawn from
techniques, and to substitute for them modes of explanation
drawn from Pythagorean mathematics and Parmenidean
logic. The kind of concepts Plato will not admit are solidifica-
tion, liquefaction, inflammation, coalescence, condensation
and so forth, that is to say, physical processes which men
control in techniques. What he substituted for them can be
seen in the following typical passage.

'When the ordering of the universe was set about, God
first began by laying out by figure and number the patterns
of fire and water and earth and air, which heretofore, though
showing some vestiges of their structure, were altogether in
such a state as might be expected when God is absent. *That
He shaped them to be, as they had not been before, wholly
beauteous and good, so far as might be, we must assume
throughout as our standing principle.* What I have now to
disclose to you is the particular structure and origin of them
each and all. The argument will be novel, but you have been
schooled in the branches of knowledge needed for the explanation of my propositions and so will be able to follow. First,
then, it must be obvious to anyone that fire, earth, water, and

air are bodies, and all body has volume. Volume, again, is necessarily enclosed by surface, and rectilinear surface is composed of triangles. All triangles are derived from two, and each of these has one right angle and two acute. One of them has, on either side, half a right angle, subtended by equal sides. The other has, on either side, unequal parts of a right angle subtended by unequal sides. *So we postulate this as the source of fire and of the other bodies, as we pursue our argument which combines necessity with probability.* What still more recondite sources there may be of these bodies is known to God and such men as God loves.' Thus the nature of fire is explained by the properties of the scalene triangle. The argument is famous in history. Nevertheless its importance would seem to be less than that of the elder Pliny's description of the rôle of fire in techniques.

'The safest general characterization of the European philosophical tradition,' says Whitehead, 'is that it consists of a series of footnotes to Plato.' As we are not here concerned, except incidentally, with philosophy, it is not our intention to discuss this dictum. We merely wish to enter a caution against the mistake of regarding Plato as being equally important for the history of science. From the scientific point of view the *Timaeus* is an aberration.

Aristotle, who was born about the time the *Republic* was composed, was a student at the Academy in his twenties when the *Timaeus* was being written. The *Timaeus* gives us the mode of explanation of the universe in which he was systematically trained. We have already seen in our last chapter how Aristotle contributed to the elaboration of Plato's theological astronomy. The whole of his physics is also inspired, and vitiated, by the Platonic ideal. It is not contended that in these writings acute argument will not be found. Chapter 8, Book II of the *Physics*, in which nature is proved to be teleological, may be recommended to the attention of the reader. If not convincing, it is at least interesting.

Nor is criticism of his predecessors absent. Even Parmenides and Plato come in for their share of it. Still it is their spirit that presides over the work. It is what Bacon called disputatious. The modern reader cries out for evidence, not argument.

> Nur das Beispiel führt zum Licht;
> Vieles Reden thut es nicht.

It is the same with other physical treatises. Plato had assumed throughout as his standing principle that God had shaped things to be, so far as might be, wholly beauteous and good. With the substitution of Nature for God, it is precisely the same teleology that informs, for instance, Aristotle's treatise *On the Heavens*. The heaven is a sphere, *because* a sphere is the perfect figure ; it rotates in a circle, *because* only circular motion, having no beginning and no end, is eternal, and so on. *On the Heavens* is an exercise in the manner of the *Timaeus*.

But, as we have already seen, Aristotle became gradually more and more convinced of the necessity of observation, and of the primacy of clear sense-evidence over any argument, however plausible. ' I decided to take refuge from the confusion of the senses in argument and by means of argument to determine the truth of reality,' Socrates is made to say in the *Phaedo*. Not without hesitation Aristotle reversed this course and decided to give sense-evidence the primacy where it promised greater accuracy. Accordingly, the element of observation shows a steady tendency to increase in his physical treatises. The *Meteorologica* comes late among the physical writings, as is clear from the fact that Book I begins with a *résumé* of what is in the earlier works – the *Physics,* the treatise *On the Heavens*, and that *On Generation and Corruption*. Ross, while observing that the information, even in this late treatise, is ' rendered to a large extent nugatory by *a priori* theorizing ', rightly stresses the fact that ' throughout there is evidence of a very considerable amount of close observation '.

We quote some of his remarks on the moon rainbow in support of this contention. 'The rainbow is seen by day, and it was formerly thought that it never appeared by night as a moon rainbow. This opinion was due to the rarity of the occurrence: it was not observed, for, though it does happen, it does so rarely. The reason is that the colours are not easy to see in the dark and that many other conditions must coincide, and all that in a single day in the month. For if there is to be a moon rainbow it must be at full moon, and then as the moon is either rising or setting. So we have met with only two instances of a moon rainbow in more than fifty years.'

As we have already indicated, the problem of the rival claims of sense and reason had occupied the attention of Plato throughout his life, and in his dialogues, *Theaetetus* and *Sophistes*, he had made a notable contribution to its solution. The problem continued to trouble Aristotle throughout the whole of his work on physical topics. It was, in fact, the driving-force of his developing thought, and in the next great division of his writings, his metaphysical and logical treatises, we find his answer to it.

It is perhaps natural that those mainly interested in the growth of positive scientific knowledge should regard this problem with some impatience. The impatience is un-justified, for the emergence of the idea of positive science necessarily brings with it the problem of the validity of know-ledge. As soon as men consciously consider the problem of Being, of existence, they inevitably raise for themselves the new problem of Knowing, of consciousness. What is appre-hended by thought is not an immediate datum of sensation. If we call a hundred objects present to our sight by the one name of star, we do so in virtue of something they share in common, though they are all different. As soon as we try to define what they have in common, we have begun to philosophize. If we say, with Thales, that everything that exists is Water, we are plunging still deeper into metaphysics. Stars differ in position, but they are more or less the same sort of thing. But what have Water, Earth, Fire, and Air in common, that we should seek to establish an identity in such manifest difference? In pursuit of such problems, the mind soon creates for itself a whole apparatus of concepts by means of which it seeks to understand nature. The problem of Being has called into existence the problem of Knowing.

The Ideal Theory, which we associate with the name of the Platonic Socrates, was an attempt to solve the problem of knowing. Knowing things means bringing things under classes. To classify things you must define what is essential to them, what is their Idea or Form. This Idea or Form is the permanent and intelligible aspect of things. Everything, as Heraclitus taught, is in a state of flux. But what flows, what changes, is the sensible element in things. The intelligible aspect, the Idea, remains. The Idea alone has validity for thought. Plato accorded the Idea a separate existence of its own – he hypostatized the Idea, as the technical expression goes – and taught that the only valid science was knowledge of the Ideas. Of the changing world of sense we could never hope, he taught, to have more than 'correct opinion'. This Ideal theory had its *religious* aspect. It was knit up with the belief in the immortality of the soul. The immortal soul, before incorporation in a man's body at birth, had knowledge of the eternal patterns or archetypes of things. The body, with its obscure sensations, gave knowledge only of the flux of the phenomenal world. The Ideal Theory, as the writer of this book contends, had also its *social* aspect. It was a leisure-class theory. It was a theory only possible to men who only thought about things and did not act upon them. The Idea became separated from the thing, when the thinker became separated from the doer. Bacon saw the point and put it clearly. He called the Forms of things 'the laws of simple action', and sought for such a science as would enable men to act upon matter.

Now, the desire to *act* upon matter is rarely evident in Aristotle's writings if we except two writings, *Mechanics* and *Meteorology* IV, both discussed later, which, by reason of their practical bent, have often been considered not genuine. From the practical point of view the Ideal theory held no inconvenience for him. The difficulty about the Ideal theory, which to some extent bothered Plato and which gave Aristotle no rest, was that it implied the abandonment of the attempt to establish a science of nature, and itself constituted an insuperable obstacle to it. The eye of the soul might suffice to inform one about the world of Forms. Only the eye of the body could bring the necessary data for a science of nature. The result of Plato's later thought about this problem was a tacit abandonment of the Ideal Theory and the substitution for it of a distinction between matter and mind. Plato had a picture of a material universe that was either motionless or disorderly. Over against this he set Mind, which was the source of life and orderly motion, and which brought harmony, proportion, and intelligibility into matter. To the division of the universe into matter and mind corresponded the division of man into body and soul.

This whole enquiry Aristotle took up again in his *Metaphysics*. The book is an enquiry into the nature of reality, and, as Aristotle was executing a 'progressive withdrawal from Plato's influence', the main problem to be considered is whether the Platonic Forms exist and, if so, in what sense. His answer, to put it briefly, is that the Forms do exist, but always in inseparable association with matter. The hypostatization of the Ideas is openly and decisively set aside. Matter and Form appear as two aspects of existence.

This is a great advance on the Ideal Theory. The problem is brought further towards a solution by being merged in a larger question, the general question of cause. Aristotle differs from Plato in making more allusion to his Ionian predecessors, not avoiding even the dreaded name of Democritus. He seeks to put the doctrine of the Academy, and his own development of that doctrine, in its historical setting. Out of the whole movement of thought on the nature of things from Thales to himself he sees developing a fourfold theory of cause. The early Ionians, with their quest for a First Principle, had been looking for the *material* cause of things. The Pythagoreans, with their emphasis on number, had hinted at the *formal* cause. Heraclitus, with the active rôle he assigns to Fire, Empedocles, with his doctrine of Love and Hate, had been concerned to find the *efficient* cause. Socrates, in insisting that the reason for things being *so* rather than *so* is because it is best that they should be as they are, had suggested the *final* cause. An adequate explanation of nature must recognize the fourfold nature of cause.

This new doctrine of cause hardly did justice to the rich experiential content of the teachings of the older philosophers, but it cleared the ground for a fresh advance in another field. Aristotle created almost *ab initio* a new science, or technique, that of logic. The object of this science was to determine the limits of validity of the exercise of reason in arriving at a knowledge of reality and in communicating it. So long as the Platonic doctrine of Ideas held the field it was not possible that the science of logic should develop. For Plato could not bridge the gap between the Ideas, which were the only objects of true science, and the phenomenal world, which lay beyond the reach of science. Plato's Logic could not give knowledge of the natural world. But Aristotle had advanced to the view that the Idea had no separate existence, that what really exists is the concrete individual thing, a union of matter and form. The only reality is ‘immattered form’. Form, since it has no separate existence. cannot be

apprehended except by the study of the thing. To arrive at
the universal we must study the particulars. But this is the
very problem of logic. What are the valid processes by which
we arrive at the universal by the study of the particulars?
How can we find the Form in Matter? And, having found it,
how can we validly discuss it, utilize it, and draw conclusions
from it? The Aristotelian doctrines of Induction, Definition,
and Deduction, with all the various forms of the Syllogism,
were the answer to these newly created demands. Aristotle's
logic did promote knowledge of the natural world *as it
exists*. It gave no help in *changing* it.

A parallel development was made in psychology. As Matter
and Form were no longer allowed separate existence in the
universe at large, so in the little world of man, body and soul
were not allowed separate existence either. The soul was no
longer looked upon as a stranger temporarily imprisoned in
the body. Soul and body were two aspects of a living thing.
The activity of the mind was not distinct from, or opposed
to, the activity of the senses, but continuous with it, a part
of the same living process. In his treatise *On the Soul* Aristotle analyses very penetratingly the physiological basis of the
various movements of the soul – imagination, memory,
dreaming, the passions. Mental processes become for him
psycho-physical. This development should have carried with
it the denial of the doctrine of the immortality of the soul.
But here Aristotle exhibits a characteristic recoil. One
activity of the soul remained for him purely psychical. The
teaching of his *Metaphysics* and his *Logic* had vindicated the
claim that there could be a true science of nature, that valid
thinking was possible about things. But it was also possible
to think about thought. Thought about thought had no
material content, only a formal one. This, then, taught
Aristotle, is the highest exercise of mind ; man, in so far as
he is capable of this exercise, may claim immortality. In
thinking about thought the eternal part of man is concerned

with the eternal. The part of the soul that thinks about thought cannot die. In a noble, and pathetic, sentence in his *Ethics* Aristotle admonishes mortal man to 'be as immortal as possible'. The phrase, at least, is immortal, as we mortals reckon immortality.

The effect of Aristotle's criticism of the Theory of Ideas was that he had again made possible a science of nature. By refusing any separate existence to the Idea, by teaching that the Idea existed only as it was embodied in the material world, he had made the Idea capable of yielding knowledge of appearances. The task of the researcher became to find the Forms in the material world. This new conception of the relations of Being and Knowing provided the basis for the biological work which occupied the last twelve years of his life. He produced a great series of works – the most important are the *History of Animals, On the Parts of Animals, On the Generation of Animals* – based partly on second-hand information, partly on original research. He mentions some 500 different kinds of animals, he personally dissected some fifty different types. His newly created logic came into its own. The task of classifying the animal kingdom according to its genera and species was the task of finding the Forms in Matter. Biology was the pre-ordained field for the application of Aristotle's logic. Nobody was proposing to change plants or animals. His logic had no fruitful application to chemical practices, unless *Meteorology* IV (see pp. 185, 186) is his.

In embarking on his biological researches Aristotle again reveals his awareness of the fact that he is departing from the tradition of the Academy which he had followed so closely in his Physical treatises. He feels the need of defending his innovation, but his defence is now confident and firm in tone. 'Natural objects,' he writes, 'fall into two great classes, the immortal ones that are without beginning or end, and those that are subject to generation and decay. The former are worthy of honour, for they are divine, but they are less within the reach of our observation. All our speculations about them and our aspirations after knowledge of them can only in the rarest instances be confirmed by direct perception. But when we turn to the plants and animals that perish, we find ourselves better able to come to a knowledge of them, for we are inhabitants of the same earth. Anyone who is willing to take the necessary trouble can learn a great deal about all the species that exist. Both enquiries have their charm. In the case of the heavenly bodies we can achieve little owing to their being out of our reach, yet the veneration in which they are held imparts to our knowledge of them a degree of pleasure greater than appertains to any of the things that are within our reach, as a lover would rather catch a chance glimpse of his beloved than have a complete view of many other precious things. But terrestrial objects, owing to our better and fuller acquaintance with them, have the advantage from the scientific point of view. Indeed their nearness to us and their kinship with us may be said to counterbalance the claims of divine philosophy. And, as I have already expressed my views on the former subject, it remains for me to treat biology, omitting nothing so far as I can avoid it, however little or great be the honour in which it is held' (*The Parts of Animals*, I, 5). This interesting passage, of which space alone prevents us from quoting more, confirms the view that the biological works are later than the physical and that they are the result of a new attitude to nature and to observation.

At the same time, in searching for the Forms in nature, Aristotle maintained the teleological method of interpretation, a method not in favour with most modern biologists. Aristotle had carefully distinguished the Formal from the Final cause. In fact the two concepts lie very close together. The Forms represent the intelligible side of nature, the design in nature. They also represent the active element.

Matter is inert, passive. The Forms are active and compel nature to take their shape. The whole activity of nature consists in the bringing of order out of chaos by stamping Form on Matter. The Forms are, in short, merely an alias for Providence or God. The Final is ultimately indistinguishable from the Formal cause. The old Socratic mode of explanation, that things are as they are because it is for the best that they should be so, reappears in a more sophisticated dress. An illustration of this point will be helpful. We shall choose one that will again bring to light the great divergence between the Ionian and the Socratic view of nature.

We have already referred to the opinion of Anaxagoras, that it was the possession of hands that had made man the most intelligent of the animals, an opinion itself dependent on an understanding of the rôle of techniques in the development of man. Let us now hear the argument by which Aristotle rejects this opinion. 'Man alone of all the animals is erect, because his nature and his substance are divine. To think, to exercise intelligence, is the characteristic of that which is most divine. This is not easy if much of the body is situated in the upper part. For weight renders the exercise of thought and perception sluggish. Accordingly, if the weight and the bodily element increase, bodies must bow down to earth ; then, for security, nature must substitute forelegs for hands and arms, and we get quadrupeds. ... But man being erect has no need of forelegs ; instead of them nature has given him hands and arms. Now Anaxagoras has said that it is the possession of hands that has made man the most intelligent of the animals. The probability is that it was because he was the most intelligent that he got hands. For hands are a tool, and nature, like an intelligent man, always distributes tools to those that can use them. The proper thing is to give a genuine flute-player a flute rather than to give a man who happens to have a flute the skill to play ; for that is to add the lesser to the greater and more august instead of adding the

E

greater and more precious to the lesser. If, then, it is best
that it should be so, and if nature, out of what is possible,
always does the best, it is not because he has hands that man is
wise, but because he is the wisest of the animals he has hands'
(*Parts of Animals*, IV, 10). This is nothing but the *Timaeus*
over again. It is astonishing to find this passage embedded in
the biological works of the closing years of his life. Very
probably it was written early. But there is no part of Aristotle's writings in which the outlook of the *Timaeus* may
not recur.

This question of hands serves also to introduce our last
topic. Following the subdivision we made in our chapter on
Plato, we have now discussed Aristotle's attitude to astronomy, and to what the ancients called *physics,* and have
found that here he achieves only a slight and hesitant
advance on Plato. Secondly we have examined his attitude to
observational research, and found that in his biological
studies he makes an immense step forward. What was his
attitude to our third topic, that of the rôle of techniques in
the development of society and in supplying concepts for
the interpretation of nature?

Our earliest, and in many ways our best, account of the
pioneers of Greek science comes from Aristotle, from the
first book of his *Metaphysics*, or *Theology*, as he himself
called it. Here it is amusing to observe his anxiety to dissoci-
ate the origins of this branch of philosophy from production,
from the techniques. 'That it is not a productive science is
clear,' he writes, ' even from the consideration of the earliest
philosophies. For men were first led to study philosophy, as
indeed they are to-day, by wonder. At first they felt wonder
about the more superficial problems ; afterwards they advanced gradually by perplexing themselves over greater difficulties ; e.g., the behaviour of the moon, the phenomena of
the sun, and the origination of the universe. Now he who is
perplexed and wonders believes himself to be ignorant.

Hence even the lover of myths is, in a sense, a philosopher, for a myth is a tissue of wonders. Thus if they took to philosophy to escape ignorance, it is patent that they were pursuing science for the sake of knowledge itself, and not for any utilitarian applications. This is confirmed by the course of the historical development itself. For nearly all the requisites both of comfort and social refinement had been secured before the quest for this form of enlightenment began. So it is clear that we do not seek it for the sake of any ulterior application. Just as we call a man free who exists for his own ends and not for those of another, so it is with this, which is the only free man's science: it alone of the sciences exists for its own sake.' His main point is clear. As a free man is to his slaves, so is philosophy to the practical sciences.

Again, in the same connection, he writes: 'It was natural that in the earliest times the inventor of any Art which goes beyond the common sense-perceptions of mankind should be universally admired, not merely for any utility to be found in his inventions, but for the wisdom by which he was distinguished from other men. But when a variety of arts had been invented, some of them being concerned with the necessities and others with the social refinements of life, the inventors of the latter were naturally always considered wiser than the former because their knowledge was not directed to immediate utility. Hence when everything of these kinds had been already provided, those sciences were discovered which deal neither with the necessities nor with the enjoyments of life, and this took place earliest in regions where men had leisure. This is why the mathematical arts were first put together in Egypt, for in that country the priestly caste were indulged with leisure.' Again the main point deserves emphasis. We owe the beginning of a true knowledge of reality to the leisured priests of Egypt, not to the technicians who found out how to do things.

The importance Aristotle attaches to this new leisure-class

mode of thinking about nature, which he calls either First Philosophy or Theology, leads him, however, to some un-historical judgements which contradict the opinions of older thinkers. (1) Aristotle asserts that the mathematical arts were first invented in Egypt because there the priests were in-dulged with leisure. The opinion of Herodotus (II, 109), universally accepted in modern times, is that geometry arose in Egypt owing to the necessity of resurveying the land after the inundations of the Nile. (2) Aristotle tells us that the inventors of the *refinements* of life were always considered wiser than the inventors of the *utilities* because their inven-tions were not useful. Plato makes it clear that the outlook of the Ionian thinkers was very different. He tells us that they regarded as the most important of the arts those that helped man by supplementing and imitating nature, like medicine and agriculture. (3) But the most arresting feature about the whole passage is this, that, in his concern to ascribe the origin of true Philosophy to the faculty of wonder in man, and not to utility, *Aristotle makes it clear that he regards applied science as something which has already completed its task*. Metaphysics is only possible because 'nearly all the requisites of comfort and social refinement have been secured', because 'everything of these kinds has already been provided'. The whole idea of a more effective exploitation of nature in the interests of mankind is dead for Aristotle. The fact that the comforts and refinements are available only for the few is not discussed. This outlook is reflected not only in his philo-sophical and scientific works, but informs the whole of his political philosophy, which is solely concerned with the man-agement of men. The fundamental problem is that of secur-ing a docile labouring class. He hopes for the disappearance of the free labourer and the universalization of the master-and-slave relationship. This, he says, is what nature intends. It is only because nature is not 100 per cent reliable that she does not produce two distinct physical types. When the statesman, instructed in the Aristotelian point of view, helps nature to realize her intention, when men really are unmistakably born Masters and Slaves, or divided by society into these two classes, the leisured class will be free for the noblest exercise of the intelligence, to wit, Metaphysics, First Philosophy, Theology. Thus, by virtue of the existence of the slave class, will the Master be enabled to fulfil the injunction to 'be as immortal as possible', to think about thought, not about things. Immortality itself becomes a class privilege.

The failure of Aristotle, the tutor of Alexander, to allow for further decisive progress in techniques, is a reflection of the general failure of the society of the age. Rostovtzeff, in his *Hellenistic World* (pp. 1166ff.) discusses this phenomenon. He speaks of the failure to acclimatize plants and animals, the failure to use the Mesopotamian oilfields and the Dead-Sea bitumen, the absence of technical advances in agriculture and in metallurgy, the failure to devise any improvement in methods of extracting mineral ores other than forced labour in ever larger quantities, the arrest of the textile industry at a pre-Hellenistic level. It is a sad picture, but it is the precise counterpart of the teaching of the *Republic* and the *Laws* of Plato and of the *Metaphysics* of Aristotle. The arrest of Greek science is only one aspect of the arrest of Greek society.

Note. For Aristotle's views on slavery see especially his *Politics*, Bk. I, chaps. iv–vii.

CHAPTER NINE

Résumé and Conclusion

★

IN THE preceding chapters an effort has been made to think out afresh the meaning of the history of science in the ancient world, and especially in the formative period of Greek thought. The subject is difficult. Opinions on it differ. Our effort in this chapter will be to make as clear as we can what precisely are the lessons we see in it for the modern world.

In the first place, we claim that the human activity we call science did not originate as a mode of thinking about things in order to be able to give verbally satisfying answers on any question that may be raised, but as a mode of thinking about things so as to be able to manipulate them to desired ends. Scientific thought is distinguished from other modes of thought by being proved valid in action. Our opinion on this matter may be expressed in the words of a French writer whose work appears to have missed recognition in this country.

'At the same time as the religious idea,' writes Félix Sartiaux, 'but much more slowly, because it requires much greater effort, the idea of science separates itself out from the magico-mystical mentality of primitive man. By handling tools, by making objects for a predetermined end, man, in spite of his inclination to represent things in his own image, seizes distinctions, forms ideas of classes, observes relations which do not depend upon his imagination. He comes to see that things do not happen as the rites represent, that they do not behave in the manner of spirits. If he had kept to his magico-religious and his religious dreams, he could never have *done* anything. But in fact, from remotest times he really kills animals and soon domesticates them, he cultivates plants, he extracts metals from ores, he makes objects for ends which he sets before himself. These actions, whatever be the representations which accompany them, succeed. Accordingly, consciously or not, man grasps true relations and submits himself to them. The existence of techniques, which go right back to the palaeolithic age, shows that there exist in the most primitive thought traces of the scientific spirit.'[1]

In the ancient civilizations of the Near East this scientific mode of thought hardly succeeded in extending itself beyond the sphere of the techniques themselves, but coexisted with a mythological interpretation of the universe. This mythological interpretation of the universe was developed and handed down in priestly corporations, and served very largely a political purpose. The technicians, whose practice contained the germ of science, were engaged in manipulating matter. The priests, on whose shoulders rested the maintenance of the social structure, were mainly occupied in controlling men. In particular the need to control men necessitated the maintenance of mythological interpretations of the major phenomena of nature – the motions of the heavenly bodies, the changes of the seasons, vegetation, irregularities or violences in nature.

The specific originality of the Ionian thinkers was that they applied to the interpretation of the motions of the heavenly bodies and all the major phenomena of nature modes of thought derived from their control of techniques. Fortunate political circumstances made it possible for them to do this. They represented a new element in society, a new class of manufacturers and merchants which brought a temporary peace and prosperity to communities worn out with the struggle between the landed aristocracy and dispossessed peasants. Being dominant in society, they made their mode of thought dominant. While feeling still secure in their

1. *Morale Kantienne et Morale Humaine*. Paris, 1917, p. 254.

possession of political power, they did not hesitate to ridicule the old mythological explanations of nature and attempt to substitute for them explanations of 'the things above' derived from their practical experience of 'the things below'.

The economic basis of this way of looking at the world was introduced into Attica at the beginning of the sixth century by Solon. Solon was a merchant who was called upon to rescue Athens from a desperate *impasse* into which it had fallen in the course of the usual struggle between the landlords and the peasants. He provided an economic alternative to the land by the introduction of the industrial techniques, and tried to secure that every Athenian should teach his son a trade. Athens was an industrial and trading town in the centre of an agricultural area when it became a democracy.

'It is interesting to note,' writes W. H. S. Jones, 'that the arts were distinguished from the sciences only when Greek thought was past its zenith.'[1] In the middle of the great fifth century, at the height of the Periclean Age, this distinction had not yet been made at Athens. This was the age when a working sculptor like Pheidias, or a working architect like Ictinus, were ornaments in the best society. This is the outlook which is reflected in the finest products of the literary art of the time.

Aeschylus, for instance, writing just before the middle of the century, puts into the mouth of the fire-bringer Prometheus a splendidly imaginative account of the rôle of techniques in the development of human society. Man, he makes Prometheus say, was in the beginning as witless as a babe. He had eyes but could not see, ears but could not hear, and lived in a dream-world of illusion, until Prometheus planted in him mind and the gift of understanding. In what did the gift of understanding consist? In this, that whereas man had before lived like an insect in sunless subterranean

1. Hippocrates (Loeb Library), IV, p. xxiii.

caves without knowledge of brick-making or carpentry, he now lived in well-built houses facing the sun. Previously he could not anticipate the coming of winter, spring, or summer ; now he had learned to read the stars, and had made himself a calendar. Previously he could neither reckon nor write ; now he had a system of numerals and an alphabet. Previously he had had himself to toil as a beast of burden ; now he had subdued wild animals to bear pack and harness. Previously he had not known how to cross the seas, cure himself when ill, or read the future ; now he had linen sails, herbal remedies, and an art of divination. To crown all, he had brought up from their hiding place in earth those buried treasures, gold, silver, bronze, iron.[1] Such is the account of the growth of civilization given by Aeschylus. Plainly for him the conquest of the techniques is identical with the growth of intelligence. The idea of a science except as applied does not occur to him.

A few years later Sophocles, in a famous chorus of his *Antigone* (332 ff.), again takes up the theme of the technical inventiveness of man. Wonders are many, he sings, but nothing is more wonderful than man. He is the power that crosses the white sea. He makes use of the storm-winds to bear him along under surges that threaten to engulf him. From year to year, the mule, the new strong animal he has bred from the horse, drags his ploughshares through the soil of Earth, oldest of the gods. In his toils, by his superior wit, he snares the birds, the beasts, the fishes of the deep. The shaggy-maned horse and the tireless mountain bull he tames and puts beneath the yoke. He has taught himself how to speak. He has taught himself how to think. He has taught himself the modes of civilized behaviour. He has made himself houses to escape the frost and the rain. For everything except death he has found a remedy. He can even cure disease. His technical ingenuity, though it brings him now to

1. Aeschylus, *Prometheus Bound*, 436ff.

evil now to good, shows a wisdom which defies imagination.

These are but pedestrian paraphrases of the untranslatable poetry of these great tributes to the inventive genius of man, but they will serve to indicate their content. The list of man's achievements in Sophocles is much the same as that in Aeschylus, but whereas the exigencies of his plot compel Aeschylus to refer the invention of all the techniques to Prometheus, Sophocles openly states what, of course, Aeschylus does not intend to deny, that all these are the achievements of man himself. Such, of course, was the opinion of their contemporary, the philosopher Anaxagoras, also a resident in Periclean Athens, who taught that it was through the possession of a capable pair of hands that man became wise.

In the wreck of the ancient literature it is not easy to illustrate as abundantly as one could wish the method of the philosopher-scientists who saw in the techniques the clue to the understanding of the operations of nature. One treatise, however, which we have examined at some length, stressed the contribution made by the cook to the understanding of human nature and of nature in general. And, amid numerous other examples, we have seen the attempt of Empedocles to throw light on the relation of the external atmosphere and the movement of the blood in the human body by an experiment with the water-clock. This experiment also established the conclusion that the fundamental operations of nature, the interaction between the elements, takes place on a level below the apprehension of our senses. It became a problem for the scientist to infer the hidden operations from observation of the visible ones.

There is extant another Hippocratic writing[1] which shows us how one scientist attempted to put this method into use. The treatise seems to be the work of the director of a gymnasium who lived about the end of the fifth century.

1. *Regimen*, I, chapters xi–xxiv.

His belief was that human nature was a blend of fire and water. His difficulty was that these elements, on which depend the vital activities of man, are, in their ultimate nature, like the air investigated by Empedocles, too subtle for man to perceive directly. How does he get over his difficulty? From internal evidence it is clear that he was a student of Heraclitus, of Empedocles, of Anaxagoras, in whose thought about the universe we have found many traces of the influence of techniques. As these cosmologists had used ideas derived from techniques to explain the nature of the universe, so our physician turns to techniques for his explanation of the nature of man. He talks a lot of nonsense in doing so, as his predecessors who employed the same method also did. But the point we are concerned with for the moment is the method, not the results.

First he enunciates his general principle. The invisible processes of human nature, he says, may be observed by attending to the visible processes of the techniques. Men miss this point, for they do not understand that the technical processes they consciously control are imitations of unconscious processes in man. The mind of the gods, he explains, has taught men to copy in their arts the functions of their bodies. Men understand the arts (i.e., employ them successfully), but they fail to understand what the arts are copies of. They should realize that the arts are a clue to the obscure operations of nature.

Here it is important to consider what the writer means by 'understanding'. He does not mean the ability to give a verbal explanation. He means the ability to act consciously to achieve a desired end. He wants to act upon the human body with a view to promoting and preserving its health. He thinks he can derive hints from the already established arts for the new art of health he is trying to create. The arts to which he directs attention are those of the seer, the blacksmith, the fuller, the cobbler, the carpenter, the builder, the musician, the cook, the currier, the basket-maker, the gold-smith, the statuary, the potter, the scribe. His master idea seems to be that, if we act rightly in regard to the visible aspect of things, the invisible processes we desire will inevitably follow.

It is in this sense that he sees an analogy between certain physiological processes and seercraft. The seer, by observing the visible, *i.e.,* present events, is able to foretell the invisible, *i.e.,* future events. So a man and a woman by a present act of intercourse begin the process which results in the future in the birth of a baby. In the same way, he implies, we may hope to discover the course of present action which will result in future health.

He tries to get closer to answering this question by consideration of the manufacture of iron tools. In his view of things man is a mixture of fire and water, but fire and water are also constituent elements of steel. The smith, by blowing fire on iron, takes 'nourishment' out of the iron, which becomes 'rare' and pliable. He then beats it, welds it, and tempers it with water. The tempering with water is a way of putting the nourishment back. The same happens to a man when he is trained. His breath fans the fire in him which consumes the nourishment. When he has been made 'rare' he is struck, rubbed, and purged. Then the application of water (*i.e.,* nourishment) makes him strong.

We shall not here follow out the analogies he draws between his regimen of health and the long list of other arts mentioned. They are fantastic enough, but it would be a mistake to regard them as devoid of all scientific value. Only those unfamiliar with the prodigious difficulty of the first steps in any science, and with the tentative and groping thoughts that accompany these steps, will fall into this error. Our author is proposing to *do* various things to men's bodies. His prescriptions of exercises, baths, massage, purgings, and dietings are far from useless. By comparison with other arts he tries to get a clearer understanding of what he is doing. But our main point here is not the value of the results but the nature of the method. The more fantastic the analogies between physiological processes and industrial techniques, the more significant is the fact that our author should have had recourse to this method. At a more primitive level he would have supposed the body to be the abode of spirits and would have prescribed accordingly. Now he thinks human physiology to be like the operations of the smith, cobbler, and potter, and prescribes accordingly. The primitive conception of nature has been transformed by the same force as had transformed primitive society itself, the practice of the techniques of production.

In the earlier period of Greek thought, then, when the sciences were not distinguished from the techniques, science was plainly a way of *doing* something. With Plato it became a way of *knowing*, which, in the absence of any practical test, meant only talking consistently. This new kind of ' science ', like its predecessor the technical mode of explanation, resulted from a change in the character of society. Historians of society are still disputing the precise degree to which the industrial techniques had, by Plato's time, passed into the hands of slaves. For our purpose it is not necessary to give a more precise answer to this question than to say that for Plato, and for Aristotle, the normal and desirable thing was that the citizen should be exempted from the burden of manual work and even from direct control of the workers. The kind of science they aimed at creating was a science for citizens who would not directly engage in the operational control of the physical environment. Their modes of explanation necessarily excluded ideas derived from the techniques. Their science consisted in being able to give the right answers to any questions that might be asked. The rightness of the answer mainly depended on its logical consistency. This was not all loss. The enormous advances that were made in mathematics largely through the encouragement of Plato and the influence of the Academy transformed the conception of the universe. Whereas the Ionians had such incorrect ideas of the sizes and distances of the heavenly bodies that their astronomy is not to be distinguished from meteorology, the mathematicians soon began to make it clear that our world is but a speck in a vast universe of space. Again, the Ionians, fertile in ideas, had but little developed the capacity to analyse their logical implications. A page of good Aristotelian logic can make their world of discourse seem as primitive as the mathematicians made their world of sun, moon, and stars. But, in spite of these advances in mathematics and logic, the separation of science from the fertilizing and controlling contact with techniques dealt it a crippling blow from which throughout the whole period of antiquity and the Middle Ages it failed to recover.

The new conception of science which came in with Plato and Aristotle demonstrably had its origin in the new form of society which rested on the division between citizen and slave. There is no aspect of Plato's thought which does not reflect a fundamental dichotomy derived from this division in society. In the developed theory of slavery the slave was not regarded as a rational being. The master alone was capable of reason, the slave might hold 'correct opinion' if he strictly followed the directions of his master. This master-and-slave relation became fundamental for Plato's thought in every sphere.

First the political sphere. Here Plato conceives of the relation of ruler and ruled in terms of master and slave. He intends government to be for the good of the governed, but it does not require their consent. His golden men, the fully enlightened aristocrats who are to rule, are a small minority of the population. All the rest are in some degree slaves, whose only chance of doing good is to obey mechanically the commands of their superiors. The manual labourer if left to himself could not rule himself, he would be ruled by his appetites. Plato oddly conceived the main activities of the worker to be concentrated, not in his hands, but in his belly and his loins. Artisans are to stand to philosophers in the relation of slaves to masters. There is no difference between the art of the slave-owner and that of the king except the size of their respective establishments. This is the doctrine Plato preached in the city the basis of whose democratic life had been the implanting of the arts by Solon.

Plato's psychology, physiology, and ethics are all three made to conform to this master plan. In the State Plato had conceived of three classes – the Rulers, their Auxiliaries (the soldiers and police), and the Producers. The introduction of a third class does not involve any fundamental departure from the master-and-slave relationship, for the main function of the Auxiliaries is to secure the control of the Producers by the Rulers. On this analogy the soul is made to consist of three parts, the reason, the spirit, and the appetites – the reason corresponding to the rulers, the spirit to the police, and the appetites to the workers. Here we perceive the *social* significance of the rejection of the view of Anaxagoras, that the hand had been the chief instrument in the creation of intelligence. The workers are not embodiments of manual skill, but of *appetite*. Compare Plato with Aeschylus and Sophocles and realize the greatness of the change.

The physiological counterpart of this class-psychology is worked out in detail in the *Timaeus*. The head is separated from the trunk by the neck, because the divine part of the soul, which is located in the head, must be saved from pollution by the mortal part, which is situated in the trunk. Then the trunk itself is divided by the diaphragm, so that the womanish and servile elements in the soul may be lodged apart in the lower chamber, while the manly and spirited element is lodged above, ' within earshot ', as he says, ' of the discourse ' of reason which goes on in the head, so that it may combine with reason in suppressing any rebellion of the appetites. The ethical system which flowed from this psychology was harsh and puritanical. There is a sharp cleavage between soul and body. Soul stands to body in the relation of master to slave. The notion that the bodily sensations of pleasure and pain should be attended to by the mind as a basis for ethical action is viewed with the same suspicion as the political proposal that the mob should have a voice in the making of the laws.

To his interpretation of the system of the universe the same key was applied. Mind and matter stand opposed to one another as master and slave. If there is any regularity or beauty in Nature, it is because mind imposes order on matter, which is essentially disorderly. It follows that reason, not sense-evidence, is the true path to science. Reason brings us directly into contact with the mind which imposes order on matter. In the *phenomenal* world, with which the senses hold converse, this order is but imperfectly achieved.

This new view of the relation of mind and matter implies a radical departure from the first premiss of the older school of natural philosophers. The older view had been that there is a necessary order in the material world, and that the human mind grasps truth in so far as it grasps this necessary order. This order could only be apprehended by sense-evidence. To the interpretation of this evidence human experience in the exercise of techniques lent the necessary clue. For Plato, however, true science is teleological. It consists in interpreting phenomena in the light of the ends at which the Mind which strives to direct all things is presumed to aim. These ends are discovered, not by observation, but by reason. Not by trying to act upon nature but by argument about ends will the truth be discovered.

This strange new view of matter as a principle of disorder underlies also the philosophy of Aristotle. 'Matter is made responsible for most irregularities', as one of the latest puzzled enquirer puts it,[1] noting at the same time that this involves a radical departure from the Ionian point of view. To the puzzle which he raises this enquirer can give no answer, nor is he likely to be able to do so while he continues to look in the wrong place. The clue to Aristotle's strange view of matter is not to be found in his physical treatises but in his *Politics*. As with Plato, the master-and-slave relation provides the basic pattern for his thought in every sphere.

Aristotle, as is well known, was a defender of slavery on the ground that slavery is natural. By calling it natural he meant, as a recent authority has reminded us, that 'it follows a pattern that pervades all nature'.[2] In Aristotle's own words: 'In every composite thing, there is always found a ruling and a subject factor, and this characteristic of living things is present in them as an outcome of the whole of nature.'[3] One must not be put off here by the bad logic. It is difficult to suppose that Aristotle really regarded master and slave as forming a 'composite thing'. But all the logic of Aristotle's justification of slavery is bad. As Montesquieu long ago observed, 'Aristotle undertakes to prove that slavery is natural and what he says does not prove it'. What concerns us now is not his attempted justification of slavery, but the effect of the attempted justification on his science. Seeing the master-and-slave relation as a pattern that pervades all nature, he regards matter as being refractory, disorderly, and resistant, and Nature, or Mind, as imposing on matter the working out of definite ends. The attributes which Aristotle applies to matter are puzzling until one understands that they are the same attributes as he applies to the slave.

1. D. M. Balme, *Greek Science and Mechanism*, Cl. Q. xxxiii, p. 132.

2. Gregory Vlastos, 'Slavery in Plato's Thought'. *Philosophical Review*, May 1941. This very valuable paper gives the references to Plato's text on which the argument of the preceding paragraphs rests.

3. *Politics*, 1254a.

His famous fourfold theory of causation derives from this conception of the relation of Nature to matter. According to Aristotle, the earlier thinkers, the Ionian natural philosophers, had considered only the material cause and constituted thereby only a primitive, 'stammering' kind of science. This was all that could be expected since they considered only the subject, slavish element in any product of Nature. Aristotle himself proposes to add three additional types of cause, the Efficient, the Formal, and the Final. These are the types of cause which explain how Nature imposes ends on refractory matter. This is Aristotle's dominant conception of science – the understanding of the way in which Nature, which resembles a Master in having ends at which it aims, imposes its will on matter, which sometimes resists those ends, and, like the slave, can achieve nothing except under the direction of a superior will. He even goes so far as to claim that the difficulty in distinguishing a natural slave from a natural master is due to a failure of Nature to impose her will on matter. Nature intends, he says, to produce a type of man who will be immediately recognizable as devoid of reason, 'a living implement', but fails to do so because matter is refractory. Part of his art of politics is designed to make good this failure of Nature. When men are natural slaves and do not know it, it is, he says, the business of the natural masters to bring it home to them.

In an earlier chapter we saw how the importation of ideas from the politico-religious sphere had affected the development of astronomy. Here we have a further illustration of the same point. The older Ionian conception of an objective order in Nature had been derived from the necessity of conforming oneself to the regular behaviour of matter if one was to be successful in the performance of technical processes. It was not the orderly motion of the heavenly bodies that gave man his first idea of regularity in nature, but the experience, endlessly repeated, that things have their own ways of behav-

ing — that you cannot gather figs of thistles, nor make the
hardest bronze unless you put one portion of tin to ten of
copper, nor get the octave higher unless you halve the string.
The conception of Nature as infinitely various and ingenious
but inexorable in its laws is the conception of technicians
who attempt to exercise over matter an operational control.
The new conception of Nature, as a power with ends in
view, which enforces its will on a subordinate but refractory
matter, is the conception of a master who governs slaves.

We have now completed our brief survey of the earlier
period. We set ourselves a limited objective, and are all too
painfully aware how imperfectly we have attained it. We
have passed in review the contributions to science of a number of outstanding men: Thales, Anaximander, Anaximenes,
Heraclitus, Pythagoras, Parmenides, Empedocles, Anaxagoras, Democritus, Socrates, Plato, Aristotle, not to mention
the nameless contributors to the Hippocratic corpus. The
fascination of their thoughts has not been weakened by the
passage of time. But our purpose has not been achieved, nor
the meaning for us of Greek science revealed, unless we have
also brought to light what historians have too little considered, the intimate connection between the development
of that body of theory and that practical activity we call
science and the total life of the society in which it takes
shape. Better histories of Greek science will soon be written
than the world has yet seen. But the necessary pre-requisite
is the acquisition of a better knowledge of the technical
history of Classical antiquity and of its interaction with the
total life of the time. The understanding of Greek science is
not going to be advanced if historians, instead of revealing
the historical genesis of the theories of the Greeks, spend
their energies wondering whether the Greeks, by some extraordinary gift of speculative genius, had not been able to leap
the centuries and anticipate the findings of modern science.
If Aristotle, for instance, talks of the irregular behaviour of

matter, it is not wise to attempt to explain this by suggesting that he had anticipated the modern theory of indeterminacy. Better explanations lie nearer to hand. The history of science must be really historical.

BIBLIOGRAPHICAL NOTE

1. Ancient Writers. The fragmentary remains of the Greek thinkers from Thales to Democritus can best be studied in Hermann Diels, *Die Fragmente der Vorsokratiker* (5th ed. by Walther Kranz, 1934). Two recent works by Kathleen Freeman, *Companion to the Pre-Socratic Philosophers* and *Ancilla to the Pre-Socratic Philosophers* (Basil Blackwell, Oxford), now offer the English reader a scholarly and full account of all the pre-Socratics and an extensive collection of their remains in translation. Burnet's *Early Greek Philosophy*, a standard work, should also be consulted. For the writings which survive in their entirety readers are referred to the various volumes of the Loeb Classical Library (Heinemann, London).

2. Modern Writers. To the references given in the text I wish to add two: — (*a*) Harold Cherniss, *Aristotle's Criticism of Presocratic Philosophy* (Johns Hopkins Press, 1935), and (*b*) Rudolfo Mondolfo's *Sugestiones de la Tecnica en las Concepciones de los Naturalistas Presocraticos* (*Archeion*, Nueva Serie T. ii. Vol. xxiii, N. i.). The first of these writers illustrates with an overwhelming display of proof the *fact* of Aristotle's failure to give a true report of the teaching of the Presocratics. The *reason* for this failure is better explained by Mondolfo. It is that the writings of the older thinkers were packed with references to techniques which, in a changed society, seemed beneath the dignity of philosophy.

PART TWO

FOREWORD

PART One of this book told the story of Greek Science from Thales to Aristotle and sought to define its significance for the modern world.

The period covered was from 600 to 322 B.C. This period is divided by the career of Socrates. The Presocratic period, it was argued, was the formative period of Greek science. It was the fruit in the intellectual field of a reasonably happy society which had launched a vigorous attack upon nature and had the picture in its mind of man as an ingenious and resourceful creature capable of indefinitely improving his conditions of life. As a sympathetic reviewer put it, 'the great theoretical advances were made by men who were well acquainted with the technical attack on nature, who developed therefrom a positive, enquiring, and to some extent experimental, attitude.'

The name of Socrates is associated with a shift of interest from natural philosophy to politics and ethics. This shift of interest represented a change in the condition of society. The confident picture of man as engaged in an attack on his natural environment had come to an end because of a social crisis. The crisis had been produced by the growth of the institution of slavery. The level of technical mastery over nature achieved at this time offered the Greeks the possibility of a cultivated leisure for a minority, and at the same time their geographical expansion offered them the possibility of enslaving weaker and more backward peoples. Slavery changed from a domestic and innocuous institution into an organized attempt to shift such heavy burdens as porterage, mining, and many agricultural and industrial processes on to the backs of alien chattel slaves. The ideal was established of the citizen as one who did not engage in manual work, and this carried with it the convenient theory that nature had intended other races of mankind to be unfit for citizenship and capable only of manual work.

One evil consequence of this was that control of techniques, knowledge of the processes of which is essential for many branches of science, was felt to be work for slaves, and an ideal of science was formed which was largely verbal and unrelated to practice. The *word* was the concern of the citizen, the *deed* the concern of the slave. As Sir Clifford Allbutt said of Plato, who is the great exponent of this phase of thought : 'Plato unfortunately despised the applications of science to the technical arts of man, not perceiving that from these arise some of the most luminous principles of academic science, nature being more ingenious and multiform and unexpected in operation than any laboratory.' (*Greek Medicine in Rome*, p. 84.)

Other evil consequences also followed. Slavery operated to make the rich richer and the poor poorer, concentrating wealth in the hands of those who had the money to invest in slaves, while it robbed the poor man as well as the rich of all initiative and enterprise in the face of nature. As a citizen the poor man too had his ideal of avoidance of manual labour. The poor citizen, therefore, constituted a proletariat that, unlike the modern proletariat, was divorced from the labour process. Too often he lived an idle parasitic life. Society had failed to organize him for the attack on nature or to give him the conditions under which he could pursue it for himself. Dispossessed and aimless, he too wanted to be carried on the back of the slave. Society tended to lose its character as an organization of citizens for common production, and become instead the arena within which rich and poor citizens fought for what was produced by the slave. Such were the social conditions under which interest shifted from natural philosophy to politics and ethics, that is, from the organization of society for the attack on nature to the attempt to prevent society from wearing itself out in a perpetual and futile civil war.

Lord Acton has a terrible phrase in his essays on *Freedom* about classical society: 'The issue of ancient politics was an absolute state planted on slavery.' Such is the ideal sketched in Plato's *Laws*. The oligarchy, reacting to the insecurity and instability of the times, became obsessed with the problem of providing sanctions by which the existing form of society might be maintained. The idea that increased control over nature could be won by human effort and could benefit mankind – the characteristic outlook of an earlier age – became less distinct: as how should it not, seeing that in the slow course of history more than a thousand years were to pass before the pattern of slave society was dissolved and technical progress became possible and fruitful for men? Accordingly the positive, enquiring, experimental attitude, which had accompanied the expansion of Greek civilization in the sixth and early fifth century, was abandoned as that civilization declined, and the desideratum became a code of laws buttressed by divine sanctions which should be unshakable. Sir Clifford Allbutt delights to find nature 'ingenious, multiform and unexpected'. But he is not stating the position quite accurately when he says that Plato did not perceive this. The unexpectedness of nature Plato perceived only too well. But since what he was looking for in nature was a pattern for the citizens of regularity, order, and stability, nature on the whole filled Plato with dismay. Astronomy was the only natural science for which he had any enthusiasm, and, as we saw in our first part, he could tolerate astronomy only on terms. These were that the behaviour of the heavenly bodies, so far from being multiform and unexpected, should be uniform and absolutely incapable throughout all eternity of springing any surprise on us whatsoever.

The formulation of an elaborate astral theology, which he knit into the fabric of his state, and belief in which he imposed by law, was the final outcome of Plato's thought. This point of view powerfully impressed Plato's pupil Aristotle in his youth, and he contributed greatly to elaborate and popularize it in his earlier writings. But later, after the foundation of his own school, he wrestled with success to restore a philosophy based on observation and experience of nature to a dominant position in the thought of his day. The degree of his success in this effort and, in particular, his tremendous achievement in the field of the biological sciences, were the last topics discussed in our first volume.

In this second part of our book we shall carry the story on from Theophrastus to Galen, that is to say, we shall begin again in the Lyceum of Athens after the death of Aristotle in 322 B.C. and end in Rome about A.D. 200. Our first task will be to describe the exciting advances in science made by Theophrastus and Strato, the immediate successors of Aristotle in the headship of the Lyceum. These advances one would certainly describe as epoch-making were it not that they failed to establish an epoch. That failure will be of as great interest to us as the achievement. Then we shall pass, with Strato, to Alexandria and follow the fate of science for some two hundred years under the Ptolemies, after which we shall shift our attention to Rome, the new mistress of the Mediterranean world.

But since we shall be vitally concerned in this second part of our book as in the first with *the meaning for us* of Greek science, we shall not be able to conclude with the death of ancient science but must also briefly consider its rebirth in the modern world. For this second birth of Greek science is a very extraordinary thing. It is only quite recently, according to the time-scale of the historian of civilization, that modern developments have made Greek science a matter of past history. When modern science began to show signs of vigorous life in the sixteenth century many of the pioneers felt, and rightly felt, that they were but resuming the old Greek tradition which had been interrupted for over a thousand years. Their new science was, in their eyes, a continuation of Greek science. The old Greek books, which the invention of printing and the birth of modern scholarship were putting into their hands, were the best available, were, in fact, the most up-to-date books in various departments of knowledge. For Vesalius and Stevin in the sixteenth century the works of Galen and Archimedes were not historical curiosities. They were the best anatomical and mechanical treatises in existence. Even in the eighteenth century for Ramazzini, the founder of industrial medicine, Hippocratic medicine was still a living tradition, just as for Vico, the most profoundly original of all sociologists before Marx, Lucretius, with his Epicurean philosophy, could supply a basis for the new science of society. In one striking example the validity of a Greek text-book remained virtually unchallenged till our own century. A generation ago Euclid and geometry were still synonymous terms in English schools.

Why did Greek science die if it had still such vitality that it was capable of a second birth? This death and rebirth, or sleep and reawakening, constitute our problem. In the attempt at a solution of this problem we shall find the meaning for us of Greek science. Accordingly, after our journey from Athens via Alexandria to Rome, we shall ask why science, which had folded its hands for sleep, sprang to life again in the Low Countries, in Germany, in Italy, in France, in England.

In raising this question and seeking to answer it we shall pursue the same method as in our earlier enquiry. We shall not treat science in isolation but in its relation to the technical, social, and political developments in the midst of which it grew.

BIBLIOGRAPHICAL NOTE

On the question of the causes of the general decline of ancient Society and its connection with the history of thought see F. Walbank, *The Causes of Greek Decline* (Journal of Hellenic Studies, Vol. LXIV, 1944), and *The Decline of the Roman Empire in the West*, Henry Schuman, New York, 1953.

CHAPTER ONE

The Academy after Plato — The Lyceum after Aristotle — Theophrastus and the criticism of teleology — Strato and experimental research — Chemistry — Mechanics — Music

★

THE ACADEMY AFTER PLATO

WHEN Plato died in 348/7 B.C. he left behind him a mystical view of the universe set forth in his dialogues in a unique combination of logic and drama. Its weakness was not that it lacked support in argument but that it was not open to correction from experience. It was not irrational so much as unscientific. Its general character was dualistic, involving a strong contrast between mind and matter, body and soul, god and the world, time and eternity. The fundamental ideas were derived from the religious doctrines of the Orphics as refined and rationalized by the Pythagorean school. A doctrine derived from the Parsis, of an evil world-soul, appears in the last dialogue, the *Laws*. This forerunner of the Christian devil is made responsible, among other things, for the false doctrines of Plato's great rivals, the atomists. In opposition to their doctrines Plato himself teaches (1) a teleological conception of nature, (2) belief in the transmigration of souls, (3) a theory of a progressive deterioration of creation (women being derived from inferior men and all the lower animals from various types of human degeneracy), and (4) the worship of the stars, especially the planets, as the highest type of life.

Inside his own school his successors preserved his writings but could do nothing to develop his thought. The mystical beliefs we have enumerated were not susceptible of development. Neither, indeed, was the Theory of Ideas. The great Cambridge scholar, Henry Jackson, writes: 'Metaphysics was, as has been well said, no more than a brief interlude in the history of Greek thought. It began with Plato and it ended with Plato.' It may be added that the hope, which modern scholarship has indulged, that Plato taught orally in the Academy a systematic philosophy different from that popularly expounded in the dialogues and recoverable by us from the study of Aristotle and other disciples, seems about to be abandoned as delusive. The one branch of teaching in the Academy really susceptible of development was mathematics, and here distinguished work continued to be done. Otherwise there is little or nothing. Plato was succeeded in the headship of the Academy by his nephew Speusippus (347–339). Jackson reminds us that he was a biologist with no taste for metaphysics. He is not a big figure in biology either. The next head was Xenocrates (339–314). Of him Jackson remarks : 'He was an amiable moralist who out of piety taught Plato's philosophy but did not understand it.' History has shown this to be the most persistent and prolific type of Platonist. Jackson proceeds : 'Then came other moralists, and after them epistemologists sceptically inclined. Thus within the school there was no one to preserve an intelligent tradition.' It is important to understand that throughout antiquity (and the school had a life of some nine hundred years) there was no real development, only a survival, of Platonism.

THE LYCEUM AFTER ARISTOTLE

The fortunes of the Lyceum, which Aristotle had founded as a break-away from the Academy, and where in the last thirteen years of his life (335–322) he achieved such amazing results in biological and historical research, were very different from those of the Academy. Aristotle's immediate successors, Theophrastus and Strato, were giants comparable with himself, and, though the school in Athens has no real history after them, it did not expire before it had handed on the torch to the Museum of Alexandria which kept it glowing pretty brightly at least for another hundred and fifty years. From the Lyceum and its offshoot, the Museum of Alexandria, proceed in the two hundred years which separate Aristotle from Hipparchus a succession of great organized treatises [1] on various branches of science – botany, physics, anatomy, physiology, mathematics, astronomy, geography, mechanics, music, grammar – which, largely modelled on the works of Aristotle himself and embodying and developing their spirit, constitute, with the addition of a few later contributions from men such as Dioscorides,[2] Ptolemy, and Galen, the high water mark of the achievement of antiquity and the starting-point of the science of the modern world.

When Aristotle died he bequeathed to his followers a vast collection of material on physics, metaphysics, ethics, logic, politics, and biology. These writings have been preserved to us, but they are not easy reading. We are told by an ancient writer that Aristotle gave two kinds of instruction. He gave formal instruction in the morning to regular students who had given proof of aptitude, attainment, zeal, and industry. In the afternoon there were more popular lectures for a wider public. When Alexander the Great, whose tutor Aristotle had been, heard a report that the subject matter of the morning lectures had been published he wrote to his teacher to protest. 'If you have made public what we have learned

1. The Greek historian Polybius, who died 122 B.C. at the age of 82, remarked (*History* X, 47, 12): 'All branches of science have with us now made such progress that instruction in most of them has been systematized.'

2. As Dioscorides will not be mentioned again it may be noted here that he was the author (about A.D. 50) of a work *De Materia Medica* which lists and describes some 600 medicinal plants. The standard edition is in 3 vols. in the Teubner ed. by Max Wellman.

from you, how shall we be any better than the rest? Yet I
had rather excel in learning than in power and wealth.'
Aristotle told him not to worry. 'The private lessons,' he
wrote, 'are both published and not published. Nobody
will be able to understand them except those who have
had the oral instruction.' This makes clear the general
character of Aristotle's surviving writings. They constitute a body of formal doctrine in technical or semi-technical
language demanding a determined apprenticeship. In style
they are only occasionally fully polished. More often
they are in the form of more or less elaborate lecture-
notes.

Together with this body of material Aristotle bequeathed
to his school a tradition of organized research. A library and
laboratories were part of the equipment of his school and
the objective, fact-finding character of the programme of
research made possible, perhaps for the first time in history,
a combination of direction of studies, of team-work, and of
freedom of thought. That many hands collaborated in the
compilation of the 158 constitutions of city-states which were
to form a factual basis for his political philosophy is known.
That many hands also contributed to the collection of
materials for the biological treatises may be safely inferred.
The freedom of thought which characterized the Lyceum is
shown both by the rapid developments which took place
there as well as by the divergent views of those who worked
there at the same time. In the generation after Aristotle there
was division of opinion in the school as to whether the active
life or the theoretical was the better. An example both of
division of work and of a new sense for the importance of the
history of thought, however imperfectly developed as yet, is
the assignment to various members of the school of the composition of histories of various branches of knowledge. To
Theophrastus was assigned natural philosophy, to Eudemus
mathematics and astronomy, to Xenocrates geometry, to

Menon medicine. Dicaearchus wrote a history of Greek culture. Such was the institution which moulded the two great men with whom we shall be concerned in the rest of this chapter.

THEOPHRASTUS AND THE CRITICISM OF TELEOLOGY

Theophrastus was born at Eresos in the island of Lesbos about 373 B.C., being thus about twelve years Aristotle's junior. He was the son of a fuller, an important profession in those days. The fact is worth mentioning, just as it is worth mentioning that Aristotle's father was a doctor. Children born into the rentier's background, where the father derived his revenues from estates run by a slave bailiff, had not so good a chance of understanding the practical aspect of science. Theophrastus, in fact, showed considerable under-standing of the fact that science ought not only to give logical answers to puzzling questions but also lead to desired results in practice. He began his higher education, as Aristotle had done, under Plato at the Academy. After Plato's death he joined Aristotle at the Lyceum, where he was his pupil and friend and finally his successor. Since Aristotle died in his sixties while Theophrastus lived to be eighty-five, he outlived his teacher by some thirty-five years. The years (322–287) during which Theophrastus was head of the Lyceum were extraordinarily fruitful for science. This is a fact which has not always been recognized. Indeed, until the researches of the last fifty years had advanced sufficiently to reverse the established opinion, Theophrastus remained in the shadow of his great teacher. Now it is certain that we must see in him an independent figure as original as he was industrious. He had the advantage of living and working till he was about fifty with one of the greatest figures in the history of science. He repaid the debt by making striking advances on his teacher. If all his works had survived they would, on a rough estimate, have made a collection of about fifty volumes of fifty thousand words each. What now survives would make four or five such volumes. It will serve to enable us to indicate the advances he made in three main spheres – metaphysics, biology, and the doctrine of the four elements.

Among the surviving works of Theophrastus is a short writing bearing the title *Metaphysics*. Its length – it occupies only nineteen pages in the edition of Ross and Forbes – is no indication of its importance or its difficulty. It is difficult because it belongs to that class of technical writings which could only be fully understood by those thoroughly conversant with the teaching of the Lyceum. It is important because it raises questions fundamental for the constitution of a science of nature based on observation. Theophrastus distinguishes the study of First Principles, that is Metaphysics, from the study of nature, which the Greeks called Physics, and seeks to define the limitations and connections of these two enquiries. Nature, he tells us, is more multifarious and disorderly and its study depends on the evidence of the senses. First Principles are definite and unchanging as being concerned with the objects of reason, which are without motion or change. Theophrastus adds that men regard the latter as a greater and more dignified study. Obviously he is not satisfied with this conclusion, his purpose being to clear the way for a new advance in observational science.

It will be remembered that Aristotle, in his *Metaphysics*, had prepared the way for his biological studies by his doctrine of 'immattered form' (cf. pp. 124ff). The general notion which this doctrine yields is that organic nature is the result of a process in which a power called Nature or God imposes on Matter, so far as possible, certain Forms conceived of as being somehow good. The human form, for instance, provided it be masculine, Greek, and free, is some-

thing good. But Nature cannot always impose anything so
fine on Matter. Hence the less perfect forms of women, non-
Greeks, and slaves, and, at a greater remove, of animals
and even plants. But, though Nature is not all-powerful,
it is legitimate and necessary to ask always in the study of
her works *at what good she was aiming* and to assume as a
principle that *she does nothing in vain*.

It is this whole conception that Theophrastus wishes to
subject to fresh analysis. First he asks whether there are any
First Principles, any objects of reason, apart from mathematics. He has none to adduce. But this leaves him with the
further question whether the principles of mathematics are
adequate also to explain Nature. This he denies, for two very
interesting reasons. First he says that mathematical principles
themselves seem to be a human contrivance. They have been
invented by men in the process of investing things with
figures, shapes, and ratios, and have no independent existence. Secondly the principles of mathematics seem incapable
of imparting life and motion to things.

This second objection leads him to an interesting speculation which goes to the root of idealist philosophy. In the
Presocratic materialist philosophy motion had been regarded
as the mode of existence of matter. Plato, however, had
taught the view that matter is essentially inert and that
its motion requires explanation. This explanation he had
attempted to give by assigning Soul as the cause of motion,
thus introducing the dualistic conception on which all idealism ultimately rests. Aristotle had wrestled with the problem
bequeathed to philosophy by Plato, namely how Soul, itself
unmoved, can be the source of motion in other things. He
had answered it by an analogy. Soul attracts Matter in the
way in which a beloved person attracts a lover. The whole
motion and activity of nature, in particular the revolution of
the heavens, is nothing but a striving of Matter to approximate to Soul. Theophrastus now raises this whole question,

F

mentions Aristotle's solution only to reject it, and asks in his turn whether any explanation for the motion of the heavens is really necessary. He goes back in effect to the Presocratic position. 'To be moved,' he writes, 'is proper both to nature in general and to the celestial system in particular. Hence also, if activity is of the essence of each natural object, and a particular thing when it is active is also in movement, as in the case of animals and plants (which if they are not in movement are animals and plants only in name), it is clear that *the celestial system also in its rotation is in accordance with its essence, and if it were divorced from this and were at rest it would be a celestial system only in name*; for the rotation is a sort of life of the universe. Surely, then, if the life in animals does not need explanation or is to be explained only in this way, may it not be the case that in the heavens too, and in the heavenly bodies, movement does not need explanation or is to be explained in a special way?'

Having in this way swept aside the whole effort to create a theology, in the manner of Plato and Aristotle, from what they thought they knew (or chose to believe) about the motions of the heavenly bodies, Theophrastus proceeds in his last chapter to lay hands on the Ark of the Covenant, the teleological principle itself. 'With regard to the view that all things are for the sake of an end and nothing is in vain, the assignation of ends is in general not easy, as it is usually stated to be.' This protest against the glib assertion of the universality of purpose and the rashness with which some philosophers assign ends to things, he backs up with powerful arguments. What is the purpose, he asks, of inundations and refluxes of the sea, of droughts and floods? In animals, what is the use of the breasts in the male or of hair in certain parts of the body? But the most important and most conspicuous failure of purpose in Nature is in connection with the nutrition and birth of animals. The presence or absence of the conditions under which either can occur are due to mere coincidences. If Nature means to provide them for animals she should do so uniformly and always. Then, without mention of Aristotle's name, he selects from him examples of the teleological mode of explanation only to reject them. His final opinion is that if science is to make progress this reckless teleology must be checked. He concludes with these words: 'We must try to set a limit to the assigning of final causes. This is the prerequisite of all scientific enquiry into the universe, that is into the conditions of existence of real things and their relations with one another.'

It was the opinion of the Swiss botanist and historian of science, Senn, that the critique of teleology which Theophrastus conducts with such firmness in his *Metaphysics* could be applied with confidence to the dating of the various parts of his botanical treatises which have been preserved for us. The botanical works which have come down to us are two, the *History of Plants* in nine books, and the *Causes of Plants* in six. Senn's opinion, in which he has the support of Brunet and Mieli, is that this division of the botanical writings is not due to the author but represents the work of editors in the Museum of Alexandria, who, distinguishing in the writings of Theophrastus passages in which he employs the teleological principle from passages in which he carefully avoids it, grouped them in separate volumes. The *Causes of Plants* would thus represent a collection of the earlier writings of Theophrastus in which, being still under the influence of Aristotle, who 'surpassed all other natural philosophers in the discovery of causes' (Diogenes Laertius, V, 32), he acquiesced in the teleological mode of explanation, while the *History of Plants* would represent the works composed after the critique of teleology we have just examined in the *Metaphysics*.

Senn's emphasis on the Theophrastan critique of teleology

is to be commended but the conclusions he bases on it cannot be accepted. As the latest enquirer, Regenbogen, has pointed out, Theophrastus proposed only to set a limit to the use of the teleological principle, not to dispense with it entirely. What he wants is not a blunt rejection of the principle but a sceptical reserve in its application. He would seem, indeed, to have arrived at the very modern conclusion that the assumption of purpose in order to explain phenomena is inadmissible, while the collection of any evidence that might seem to point to design is a legitimate activity of science. That this is the truer account of the attitude of Theophrastus is borne out by the fact that the idea of purpose is not completely excluded from the *History*, nor indeed is the criticism of teleology absent from the *Causes*. There is no sufficient reason to reverse the tradition, which makes of the *History* the earlier work. Senn had had to reverse this order to maintain his thesis. The truth would appear to be that criticism of teleology, which is not absent even from the pages of Aristotle,[1] becomes freer and bolder in Theophrastus but is to be regarded rather as a sign of his sceptical scientific temper, operative throughout his career, than of a crisis of thought occurring some years after the death of Aristotle, a crisis which found him a teleologist and left him an empiric. There is no evidence of a crisis. There is evidence, everywhere, of his sceptical reserve.

So much for the critique of teleology as it shows itself in the biological treatises. We cannot discuss these treatises in any detail, but before we leave them we should indicate what was probably the greatest contribution to knowledge made by Theophrastus. This consists in his firm drawing of the distinction between the animal and the vegetable kingdom. In the first part (pp. 129-30) we drew attention to the famous passage in Aristotle (*Parts of Animals*, IV, 10) in which, following Plato, he had advanced the theory that

1. *Parts of Animals*, IV, 2, 8.

animals were descended from men. If we had there followed
Aristotle further we should have found that he went on to
derive plants from animals. He held a theory not of evolution but of degeneration, from man through animals to
plants. All that concerns us in that theory now is that it
contains no clear differentiation between animals and plants.
Aristotle had not succeeded in defining the difference. In
the organization of research in the Lyceum Aristotle had
charged himself with the task of bringing order into the
animal kingdom and had left the plants to his disciple.
He had, however, unwittingly created an initial obstacle to
the establishment of a sound science of botany by drawing
too close a parallel between the parts of animals and
of plants. Correctly observing the *functional* analogies
between various parts of animals and plants he deduced
therefrom a *morphological* analogy which does not
hold.

It is with the clearing up of this confusion that the first
chapter of the first book of the *History* is concerned. Theophrastus fastens at once on the fundamental difference between the parts of animals and of plants. In animals we
mean by a part something that is permanent when once it
has appeared, unless it be lost by disease, age, or injury. But
in plants many parts – flower, catkin, leaf, and fruit – are
renewed and die every year. The new shoot must also be
included in this category, for plants make fresh growth both
above and below ground every year. If we accept all these as
parts of the plant, as in fact we must, then the number of
parts in a plant (unlike the parts of animals) is both indeterminate and constantly changing. Perhaps, then, he
continues, introducing his divergence from his master again
without mention of his name, we should not expect to find
a complete correspondence between the parts of plants and
animals and should even make bold to include their fruits as
parts of plants although we do not include their young as

parts of animals. He rounds off his exposition with these strong words: 'It is a waste of time to force comparisons where they do not exist and constitutes an obstacle to our special branch of knowledge.' In this masterly but unobtrusive style did Theophrastus separate the animal from the vegetable kingdom and establish the science of botany at a level above which it was not destined to rise till modern times.

Equally masterly is his criticism of the traditional doctrine of the four elements. For all the ancient schools it was accepted doctrine that, whatever the ultimate structure of matter might be, it presented itself to human observation under four primary forms, Earth, Water, Air, and Fire, each distinguished from the rest by the possession of certain qualities. In the Aristotelian doctrine Earth was dry and cold, Water wet and cold, Air wet and hot, Fire dry and hot. The Dry, the Wet, the Hot, the Cold were Forms, which being impressed in pairs on undifferentiated Matter brought into existence the four primary substances out of which the universe was made. Each of the elements had one of its qualities in common with another, and this sharing of a quality was held to facilitate their transformation into one another – a process supposed to be continually going on in nature. Such was the traditional view as shaped by Aristotle. The capacity of Theophrastus to transcend and deepen this view is proved by a fragment, twenty-three pages in length, part of a treatise *On Fire*. The opening passage is of greatest importance for us. A translation, in slightly condensed form, follows:

Of all the elements Fire has the most remarkable properties. Air, Water, and Earth can only change into one another, none of them can generate itself. Fire can not only generate itself but extinguish itself. A small fire can generate a large one, a large one can put out a small one. (Theophrastus explains what he means by this later. A lamp held over a fire goes out.) Furthermore most ways of generating fire seem to involve force. Examples are the striking of flint on steel, the rubbing together of fire-sticks, and the generation of fire from air by the gathering and collision of clouds. The contrast between the forcible generation of fire and the natural change of the other three elements into one another involves a remarkable consequence for us. We can generate fire, we cannot generate the other three. Even when we dig a well we do not bring water into being, we merely make it visible by collecting it from a scattered state. But the greatest and most important difference has yet to be mentioned. The other elements are self-subsistent, they do not require a substratum. Fire does — at least such fire as is perceptible by our senses. This is true whether we include light in our concept of fire or not. If we include light, then light requires air or water as a medium. If we do not include light, still both the fire of flame and that of a glowing coal exist in a substratum. Flame is burning smoke. A coal is an earthy solid. It makes no difference whether the fire is in the sky or on earth. In the first case fire is burning air, in the second case it is either all the three other elements burning or two of them. Speaking generally fire is always coming into being. It is a form of motion. It perishes as it comes into being. As it leaves its substratum it perishes itself. That is what the ancients meant when they said that fire is always in search of nutriment. They saw that it could not subsist of itself without its material. What is the sense then of calling Fire a First Principle if it cannot subsist without some material? For, as we have seen, it is not a simple thing nor can it exist before its substrate and material. One might of course assert that in the outermost sphere there exists a kind of fire which is pure and unmixed heat. If so it could not burn, and burning is the nature of fire.

It is difficult to bring the scientific advance registered in this passage home to the reader without a long quotation from Aristotle, for which we have no room. It derives its special character from its accumulation of careful observations of both natural and artificial processes and the closeness with which the reasoning clings to the observed facts.

The great novelty of this will be apparent to anyone who will go to Aristotle's treatise *On Coming To Be and Passing Away* and read the first four or five chapters of Book II. There he will find a great deal of logic and very little observation. The comparison of the two passages will bring home to him the difference between studying natural philosophy through the eye of reason or the eye of sense. It is clear that great changes are being effected in the Lyceum, but changes which are in the line of Aristotle's own development. The practice of observation which he had himself employed with such success in the field of biology (see above, pp. 127, 128) is now being extended by his disciple to the study of inorganic and inanimate matter. It is clear also that the new observational method is not destined to be long in sweeping away the physical conceptions which Aristotle had brought with him from the Academy. The observation that fire cannot exist without a substratum, that fire is something burning, leads at once to the theory that fire is not an element but rather a compound, and then to the further suggestion that the Hot and the Cold are not really principles but attributes. These new developments mark the end of the Aristotelian physics and prepare the way for Strato.

In his *Metaphysics* Theophrastus drops the remark that in our endeavour to understand the behaviour of matter 'we must in general proceed by making reference to the crafts and drawing analogies between natural and artificial processes' (8*a*, 19, 20). In the first part we have written at length on the importance of this approach for the Greek pioneers of science. What Theophrastus means by it is abundantly illustrated by his fragment *On Fire* as well as by others of his writings. In the twenty-odd pages of this treatise there are hundreds of observations both of natural and artificial processes. When we study them closely we see that attention to the artificial processes involved in the crafts sharpens his observation of natural processes and suggests their explanation. Thus, above, in making his point that fire generally requires force or violence for its generation, he groups in one sentence the artificial means by which men make fire and the natural phenomenon of lightning, which gets its explanation thereby. Later on he compares the red colour sometimes assumed by the light of the sun with the red flame of fresh green logs and decides that the flame from green logs gets its colour from the extra moist and earthy element contained in green logs as compared with seasoned ones and that the sun gets its reddish hue whenever 'the air is thick'.

STRATO AND THE EXPERIMENTAL
METHOD OF RESEARCH

This constant reference back and forwards between observations of natural and artificial phenomena is the root from which the technique of experiment has grown. It does not yet, of course, constitute such a technique. But with the name of Strato we reach the point at which Greek science fully establishes a technique of experiment, and we may pause for a moment to retrace some of the steps by which such a decided and important advance in scientific method was achieved. The Swiss botanist, Senn, who has made such important contributions to the history of scientific thought, can also help us here. In an examination of the Hippocratic writings he makes a distinction between two types of comparison found there. Very commonly we find comparisons drawn between the physiological processes being investigated and common occurrences of practical life. The writer, for instance, makes a remark like this : 'It is just as when cold water is added to boiling water, the water stops boiling.' Here a phenomenon in medicine which the writer is trying to understand is illustrated by reference to a common experience, but there is no suggestion that the pupil should go and try the experiment. Less frequently, however, we come upon a formula of this kind: 'If you do so and so you will find that such and such is the case,' where it seems clear that the student is invited and expected to repeat the experiment for himself.

A good example of experiment of this sort is found in *Ancient Medicine* (chap. xxii). The writer is there impressing on the student that there is a relation between the structure of the internal organs of the body and the functions they perform. He lays down the general principle that the functioning of the internal organs, being hidden, can best be studied by examination of unenclosed objects of similar shape. 'Now which structure is best adapted to draw and attract to itself fluid from the rest of the body, the hollow with the wide opening, the solid and round, or the hollow and tapering? I take it the best adapted is a wide hollow vessel with a tapering mouth. These principles must be learned from external and visible objects. For example, if you open the mouth wide you will not draw in any fluid; but if you protrude and purse your lips, or if you press your lips together and insert a tube you could easily suck up anything you like. Again, cupping instruments, which are broad and tapering, are so designed on purpose to draw and suck up blood from the flesh. There are many other examples of the same kind. Now of the parts within the human frame, the bladder, the head, and the womb are of this shape. There obviously attract powerfully and are always full of fluid from without.'

Here is something which is plainly different from a mere reference to a familiar occurrence used by way of illustration in the course of an argument. Here a confirmatory action is demanded of the listener, a repetition of the experience. It is still rudimentary in development but it is genuine experiment. This method, which among the earlier schools is most clearly to be detected with the Pythagoreans, is only occasionally employed by the other Presocratics, or the Academy, or even the Peripatetics down to and including Theophrastus. It is with the successor of Theophrastus, Strato, that it comes to sudden flower.

Considering the importance of this man we know miserably little about him. We know that he was born in Lampsacus, that he lived some time in the King's palace at Alexandria before being summoned to the headship of the Lyceum at Athens, and that he was head of the institution from 287 to 269. He must already have been a famous man before he became head of Aristotle's school, otherwise he would not have been summoned by the first Ptolemy (Soter) to supervise the education of his son, the second Ptolemy (Philadelphus), which was the occasion of his residence in Alexandria. He can hardly have been under forty years of age and may have been fifty when he took up his post in Athens. The names of about forty of his writings are listed for us by Diogenes Laertius, but time has robbed us of them all, and modern scholarship has yet to complete the task of giving us a scientific edition of the fragments of his works that can be gleaned from later writers.

We learn, however, from Polybius the historian, who lived about a hundred years later, that he was known in antiquity by the special name of The Physicist (of course in the old Greek meaning of the term, i.e. the natural philosopher). Cicero explains the choice of this title when he tells us that Strato 'abandoned ethics, which is the most necessary part of philosophy, and devoted himself to the investigation of nature'. It is unlikely that Cicero would be the only one to condemn such a choice, and that it brought Strato under criticism in his own day is rendered pretty certain by the further statement of Polybius that 'his critical and polemical writings were brilliant, but his exposition of his own ideas dull'. The reader will probably agree, when we have finished our account of the work of Strato, that Polybius's last word 'dull' should be interpreted 'too severely scientific to suit the temper of the age'. The concluding words of the brief notice of Diogenes appear to throw a little more light on this point. He tells us that Strato 'excelled in every branch of learning but most of all in that which is styled the philosophy of nature, *a branch of philosophy more ancient and serious than the others*'. We shall surely not be wrong in seeing in these remarkable words Strato's own defence of his preference for natural philosophy over ethics and politics. Strato would call natural philosophy more ancient as being characteristic of the older schools before Socrates turned philosophy away from nature to man. He would call it more serious as being connected rather with the basic arts on which life itself depends than with the arts which are the adornment of a decadent civilization. We have quoted in our first part (p. 93) the opinion of the Presocratics that 'the arts which make the most serious contribution to human life are those which blend their own power with that of nature, like medicine, agriculture and gymnastics'. This description is intended to contrast them with those arts that merely imitate nature without altering her, like painting or music. No doubt we have struck here something fundamental in the outlook of Strato whose experimental attitude to science involved not merely passive observation of, but active interference with, the processes of nature. Strato was fully conscious of the practical applications of his physical theories. The ancient writer who preserves the best account of them introduces them with the words: 'They can provide us with the most fundamental requisites of a civilized existence.'

In the wreck of Strato's writings it was difficult to prove the completeness with which he had conceived the idea and established the practice of experimental research until a great discovery was made in 1893 by the penetrating genius of

Hermann Diels. Among the surviving works of Greek science a prominent place is occupied by the *Pneumatics* of Hero of Alexandria, a work which dates from the second half of the first century of our era. In the opening pages of this text-book is contained a scientific theory of the nature of the vacuum of an obviously advanced kind. It is empirical in method, has a fixed terminology, and implies a unified physical system. Diels, who was the first to analyse the special qualities of this opening section of the work, also successfully claimed the bulk of it for Strato. Of this passage we proceed to offer the reader a somewhat condensed translation. It forms the best introduction to the genius of Strato.

The science of pneumatics was held in high regard of old by philosophers and engineers, the former logically deducing its principles, the latter determining them by experimental tests. What we have felt constrained to do in this book is to give an orderly exposition of the established principles of the science and add thereto our own discoveries. We hope in this way to be of service to future students of the subject.

Before we come, however, to the particulars of our exposition there is a general topic to be discussed, namely the nature of the vacuum. Some writers emphatically deny its existence. Others say that under normal conditions there is no such thing as a continuous vacuum, but that small vacuums exist in a scattered state in the air, water, fire, and other bodies. This is the opinion to which we should adhere. We now proceed to show by experimental tests that this is a true account of the matter.

We must first correct a popular illusion. It must be clearly grasped that vessels which are generally believed to be empty are not really empty but are full of air. Now air, in the opinion of the natural philosophers, consists of minute particles of matter for the most part invisible to us. Accordingly if one pours water into an apparently empty vessel, a volume of air comes out equal to the volume of water poured in. To prove this make the following experiment. Take a seemingly empty vessel. Turn it upside-down, taking care to keep it vertical, and plunge it into a dish of water. Even if you depress it until it is completely covered no water will enter. This proves that air is a material thing which prevents the water entering the vessel because it has previously occupied all the available space. Now bore a hole in the bottom of the vessel. The water will then enter at the mouth while the air escapes by the hole. But if before you bore the hole you lift the vessel vertically out of the water and turn it up and examine it you will see that the interior of the vessel has remained perfectly dry. This constitutes the demonstration that air is a bodily substance.

Air becomes wind by being set in motion. Wind is simply air in motion. If after boring a hole in the bottom of the vessel and plunging the vessel into the water you keep your hand near the hole you will feel the wind streaming out of the vessel. This is simply the air being driven out by the water. You must not then suppose that a continuous vacuum is among the things that exist, but that small vacuums exist in a scattered state in air, water, and other bodies. This must be understood in the sense that the particles of air, while in contact with one another, do not completely fit into one another. They leave empty spaces between, as does the sand on the beach. The grains of sand may be compared to the particles of air, and the air between the grains of sand is to be compared to the vacuum between the particles of air.

The consequence of this physical structure of the air is that if an external force be applied air is capable of being compressed and of settling into the empty spaces, its particles being crushed together in a way contrary to nature. On the relaxation of the pressure, owing to the elasticity of the particles, it resumes its former state. Similarly, if the application of any force results in the separation of the particles from one another and the creation of larger empty spaces between them than is natural under normal conditions, then their tendency is to draw together again. The reason for this is that the motion of the particles becomes rapid through the void, there being nothing to impede or resist it until the particles get into contact with one another again.

The following is an experimental demonstration of the above theory. Take a light vessel with a narrow mouth, suck the air out and take your hands away. The vessel will remain suspended from your lips because the void will tend to pull the flesh in to occupy the empty space. This makes it clear that a continuous void had been created in the vessel. Here is another proof of this. Medical doctors have glass vessels with narrow mouths which they call ' eggs '. When they wish to fill them with a liquid they suck the air out, put their fingers over the mouth and invert the vessel in the liquid. The liquid is then drawn in to fill the empty space, although an upward motion is unnatural for a liquid.

Let us now return to those who absolutely deny the existence of the void. It is of course possible for them to discover many arguments in reply to what has been said and in the absence of any experimental demonstration their logic may appear to have an easy victory. We shall therefore show them, by phenomena which can be brought under observation, two facts : (1) that there is such a thing as a continuous void, but that it exists only contrary to nature, and (2) that in accordance with nature void also exists, though only in small scattered quantities. We will further show them that under pressure bodies fill up these scattered vacuums. These demonstrations will allow no loophole of escape for these verbal gymnasts.

For our demonstration we shall require a metal sphere, of a capacity of about four pints, made of metal sheeting of such thickness as to resist any tendency to collapse. The sphere must be air-proof. A copper tube, a pipe with a narrow bore, must be inserted in the sphere in such a way that it does not touch the spot diametrically opposite the point of entry but leaves room for the passage of water. The pipe should project about three inches from the sphere. The part of the sphere around the point of insertion of the pipe must be strengthened with tin solder so that the pipe and the sphere present a continuous surface. There must be no possibility that air forced into the sphere by blowing can escape by any crack.

Now let us analyse in detail the implications of the experiment. There is air in the sphere from the beginning as in all vessels popularly called empty, and the air fills the whole of the enclosed space and presses continuously against the containing wall. Now according to the logicians, since there is absolutely no unoccupied space, it should be impossible to introduce water or more air unless some of the air already contained in the vessel be displaced. Further, if the attempt were made to force air or water in, the vessel being full should burst before admitting it. Very well. What in fact happens? One who puts his lips to the pipe can blow a great quantity of air into the sphere without any of the contained air escaping. This happens as often as the experiment is repeated, and it constitutes a clear proof that the particles of air in the sphere are compressed into the vacuums between the particles. This contraction is contrary to nature, being the consequence of the forcible intrusion of air. Again if, after blowing, one stops the pipe quickly with one's finger, the air remains the whole time compressed in the sphere. But on the removal of the finger the air that was forced in rushes out noisily and violently, being expelled by the expansion of the air within owing to its elasticity.

If the reverse experiment be tried, a great quantity of air in the sphere can be sucked out without any other air getting in to replace it, as we saw before in the case of the 'egg'. This experiment conclusively demonstrates that the formation of a continuous vacuum takes place in the sphere. From this it follows that vacuums are interspersed in the interstices of the particles of air and that when force is applied the air suffers a compression contrary to nature into the vacuums. The existence of a continuous vacuum contrary to nature has already been shown by the adherence of the light vessel to the lip and by the example of the doctor's 'egg'. Many other experiments about the nature of the void might be adduced, but these may suffice, for they depend on the evidence of observable phenomena. Summing up then we may say that every body consists of tiny particles of its material between which are interspersed vacuums smaller than its parts. It is only by an abuse of language that it can be maintained that, in the absence of force, there is absolutely no void but everything is full of air or water or some other substance, and that it is only in so far as one of these substances departs that another can enter in to occupy the empty space.

A reviewer of one of my books writing in *The Journal of Roman Studies* (Vol. XXXI, 1941, p. 149) categorically states 'experimentalism as a systematic theory was unknown to Antiquity : it is a product of the Renaissance'. In face of the quotation we have given, and the quotation of course does not stand alone, this writer's pronouncement must be declared unfounded. In Strato we find the exponent of a systematic experimentalism which represents the culmination of a practice occasionally observed earlier with the Pythagoreans, with Empedocles, with Anaxagoras, with some doctors of the Hippocratic school, an experimentalism which has got so far that it involves the construction of special apparatus for the solution of a special type of problem, and which is backed up by the explicit assertion of the primacy of experiment over logical demonstration.

Among the disciples of Strato was an Alexandrian physician, Erasistratus, of whom we shall have something more to say later on. Among the fragments of his writings we find a striking expression of the zeal for natural philosophy which consumed the men of this age who came under the influence of the Lyceum. The passage is from Galen's *Scripta Minora* (II, 17, ed. Müller) and is quoted in Heidel's *Heroic Age of Science* (p. 53): 'Those who are altogether unaccustomed to research are at the first exercise of their intelligence befogged and blinded and quickly desist owing to fatigue and failure of intellectual power, like those who without training attempt a race. But one who is accustomed to investigation, worming his way through and turning in all directions, does not give up the search, I will not say day or night, but his whole life long. He will not rest, but will turn his attention to one thing after another which he considers relevant to the subject under investigation until he arrives at the solution of his problem.'

Lest anybody should suppose that the research envisaged by Erasistratus in this exquisite passage was of the kind that can be carried on entirely in the head, as Parmenides recommended and Plato practised, let us quote *en passant* one of the experiments of this great physiologist. Remember he is attempting to investigate the processes of life and is concerned with the significance of respiration, as Empedocles was long before him in his experiment with the toddy-lifter (see Part I, p. 58). But how marvellous a development the technique of experiment has undergone! Worming his way through his problem and turning in all directions Erasistratus has arrived at an experiment which anticipates the famous achievement of Sanctorius (1561–1636). Sanctorius, in an experiment finely described by Singer (*A Short History of Medicine*, p. 108), lived some time suspended in a balance of his own devising in order to investigate changes of weight in the human body. Similarly Erasistratus put a bird in a cage and weighed it, left it without food and weighed it again together with the droppings only to find a considerable loss of weight. He recommends the repetition of this as a stock experiment (Diels, *Anonymi Londinensis*, p. 62ff.).[1] Here the exact measurement implied by the weighing should be noted. So perfect, and so various in its applications, has the experimental method become.

If we return now to Strato we shall find abundant evidence of how he too wormed his way through and turned in every direction in his efforts to solve his problems. In the passage which I quoted above I used a shortened version in order

1. See also the new edition, *The Medical Writings of Anonymous Londinensis,* by W. H. S. Jones, C.U.P. 1947 (p. 127).

to concentrate attention on the main experiment with the sphere. But if we turn to the full text we shall find the record of many supplementary experiments. In advancing the theory of the presence in all substances of vacuums dispersed between the particles, Strato hazards the suggestion that the 'diamond' may be the one substance which does not contain void. He says it is indestructible by fire and offers such resistance to blows as to embed itself in the hammer or the anvil. A diamond, of course, will split under the blow of a hammer along the planes of its crystal. One would like a longer account of what tests Strato had here employed. Possibly he had found small particles of emery or corundum embedded in hammer or anvil. The word translated 'diamond' above would be equally applicable to these. When he mentions the elasticity of the air he illustrates his meaning by comparison with the behaviour of horn shavings and a dry sponge. The evidence derived from light vessels which hang from the lip when the air has been sucked out is reinforced by the example of the heavier cupping-glass in which rarefaction has been produced not by suction but by heat.

This leads on to a striking section in which the action of heat on various bodies is discussed. It is pointed out that if heat is applied to coal so as to produce coke, the coke appears to the eye to be of the same bulk as the coal but is found on weighing to be lighter. Here again is evidence of the exact measurement of phenomena. The loss of weight is ascribed to the transformation of coal under the action of fire into three substances of differing densities, classed as fire, air, and earth. There follows an interesting comment on the action of fire on water. In order to keep our historical perspective right it may be well to remind the reader that it was not until 1615 that air and steam were specifically distinguished and the practical conclusion drawn that there were potentialities in steam pressure of much greater magnitude than were to be found in air pressure. It was the work of Cardan (1501–1576) and Porta (1538–1615) that led to the decisive pronouncement of Solomon de Caus (1576–1630) that steam is evaporated water and that upon cooling the vapour returns to its original condition. Now Strato did not succeed in drawing the distinction between steam and air, but he does record explicitly the conclusion that 'the steam from a heated cauldron is simply rarefied water passing into "air"'. He could not have known how much this vapour differs from the air we breathe.

Strato used his theory of the discontinuous void in things to help in the interpretation of many phenomena. It has an obvious bearing on the problem of differences in density of various substances. It is invoked by him to assist in the interpretation of the action of the sun's rays in the evaporation of moisture and the phenomena of dew and hot springs. But perhaps its most suggestive application is to the problem of the propagation of light. 'If vacuums did not exist neither light nor heat nor any other material force would be able to penetrate the substance of water or air or any other body. How, for instance, could the sun's rays get to the bottom of a bucket full of water? If there were no interstices in the water, but the sun's rays had forcibly to part the water, full vessels would overflow. But this is not seen to occur. Here is another proof. If the rays forcibly parted the water they would all reach the bottom, instead of some being reflected and some reaching the bottom. What actually happens is that the rays that hit particles of water are reflected, those that find vacuums or encounter only a few particles of water get to the bottom.' Further proof of the porosity of water is found in the fact that if wine be poured into water it visibly disperses itself throughout the whole body of the water. A similar conclusion is drawn from the interpenetration of light by light. 'When more lamps are lighted the whole place shares in the increased illumination, since the rays of

light are able to propagate themselves through one another.'
Of course there are innumerable weaknesses in these demonstrations, but everywhere we are in the presence of a man
who, where physical facts are in question, prefers a demonstration to an argument. We find further confirmation of
Strato's habit of appealing to facts in a passage from another
writer, Simplicius (659, 22). He tells us that Strato, con-
fronted with the endless debate as to whether change of
position is possible without the supposition of a continuous vacuum, settled the matter by a simple demonstration. He put a stone into a closed vessel full of water,
inverted the vessel, and showed that the stone changed its
place.

Not only was he fertile in devising experiments, but he
made also the most penetrating applications of his principles
in many new fields. Here for example, in a few sentences
from an anonymous treatise which has come down to us in
the Aristotelian corpus – sentences now confidently claimed
for his – we find him laying the foundation of a correct
theory of sound. 'All sounds, vocal or otherwise, arise from
bodies falling on bodies or air falling on bodies. The propagation of sound is not due to the air taking on a shape, as
some suppose, but to its being an elastic medium which
contracts and expands in accordance with the impulse imparted to it ... For when the impact of the breath strikes the
air, the air is violently moved and imparts the same motion
to the air next to it with the result that the same sound is
carried out in every direction as far as the movement of the
air extends.'

These examples are enough to show that Strato had fully
established the experimental method and that he had given
it a wonderfully wide application. It is important for us also
to realize the independence of mind that he displayed in
doing so. It has already been said that Theophrastus had
thrown overboard the Aristotelian conception of matter.

Strato is prepared to go much further. He throws overboard also Aristotle's doctrine of weight. Aristotle had taught that two of the elements, Earth and Water, have a natural tendency to move downwards, which he called gravity, while the other two, Air and Fire, have a natural tendency to move upwards, which he called levity. That is to say, Aristotle attempted to relate his doctrine of weight to a theory of 'natural place', each element in the universe having a place to which it naturally tended. For this Strato substituted the view of Democritus that weight is motion towards the centre, that all the elements have gravity and none levity, but that the lighter rest on the heavier, and that mass depends on the greater or less amount of matter in a given volume. But it must not be supposed from this that Strato had abjured Aristotle only to swear allegiance to Democritus and his atoms. Not so. For though he accepts from Democritus the idea of void within bodies he rejects the idea of an external continuous void. Though he believes that matter consists of minute invisible particles he rejects the idea that all the qualities of things depend on the size, shape and position of the atoms, as we have just seen, for instance, in his theory of sound. There is evidence also that he sought to escape from the mechanistic outlook of Democritus.

At this point it becomes appropriate to consider what the general world-view of this great experimentalist was. It is clear that with him all anthropomorphic and teleological ideas have been finally cast aside. Cicero tells us (*On the Nature of the Gods*, I, 13, 35) that 'Strato the physicist was of opinion that all divine power resides in nature, and that nature, which is a power without shape or capacity to feel, contains in itself all the causes of coming to be, of growth, and of decay.' In another passage (*Academics*, II, 38, 121) which seems to reflect Strato's lively controversial style, Cicero records his views at slightly greater length. 'Strato of Lampsacus gives god a dispensation from his arduous task, opining that if the priests of the gods get holidays it is only fair that the gods should have them too. He says he does not use the help of the gods to make the world. Everything that exists, he says, is the work of nature, but adds that he does not mean that in the sense of the great man who said that all things are concretions of atoms, rough and smooth, hooked and barbed, with an admixture of void. These views he called the dreams of Democritus who could not prove them but only desired them. He himself goes through the parts of the universe one by one and proves that whatever exists or comes to be has been made or is made by purely natural forces and movements.' The standpoint of Strato is clear. His wish is to identify the divine with nature and at the same time to regard the whole of nature as the legitimate field of scientific enquiry. It is a bold effort to eliminate the idea of the supernatural, but it is not the first time we have met it in our study of the history of Greek thought. The view was characteristic also of some of the Hippocratic doctors (see Part I, pp. 81 and 82).

As was usual with Strato, who, unlike Theophrastus, does not seem to have wished to hesitate between two opinions, he worked his principles out to their logical conclusion in every branch of science. We shall conclude our account of him by an indication of his views on the nature of man and his place in the scheme of things.

Psychology already had a long and honourable history among the Greeks in the two hundred years which separate Alcmaeon from Aristotle. But Strato was able here also to register a remarkable advance. When faced with the old debate as to whether all knowledge originates in experience or whether, as Plato taught, true knowledge is independent of experience, being a possession of the soul before it is housed in the mortal body, Strato could not hesitate. He must place its source in experience. He accepted, of course, the now familiar distinction between the sense-organs and the mind. His originality, and the signal advance he made over the brilliant psychological work of Aristotle, lay in the way in which he conceived the relation between the senses and the mind. He was, with the possible exception of Diogenes of Apollonia, the first Greek to say clearly that it is not in the sense-organ but in the mind that an objective stimulus is transformed into a sensation. This is a piece of analysis of truly fundamental importance.

The recognition of the activity of the mind in sensation enables Strato to assert firmly the idea of the unity of the soul. With him both perception and thought become activities of the same soul. This not only rules out the Platonic notion of the soul as a strange immaterial visitant temporarily lodged in its house of clay. It cuts the ground also from under Aristotle's attempt to teach the mortality of the soul (*psyche*) and the immortality of the intellect (*nous*). Strato's doctrine has the further effect of permitting the recognition of the kinship of man with the animals. If we think and perceive with the same organ, the mind, it follows that the animals, who have sense-organs and perceive, have also in some degree mind. It was the opinion of Strato that every living thing can be in some degree the bearer of mind. Plutarch (961 *b*) preserves his opinion on this point. 'It follows', Strato argued, 'that everything that has perception has also intelligence, if it is by the exercise of intelligence that nature makes us able to perceive.' Rodier, the first of the moderns to make a systematic investigation into the physical opinions of Strato, was of the opinion that the influence of the philosopher Epicurus upon him was great. This may very well be true. In any case there is no room for doubt that Strato held the view of the Epicureans, the best anthropologists of the ancient world, that man is a superior kind of animal, not the view that animals are a degenerate kind of man.

For the small size of our volume we have given rather full

accounts of the work of Theophrastus and Strato. Lest, however, the impression should be created that only the heads of the institution did any work, we shall include mention of three other scientific works produced by the Lyceum, one on chemistry, one on mechanics, one on music. The first two are anonymous, the third is by Aristoxenus.

CHEMISTRY

What I have called the work on chemistry has come down to us as Book IV of the *Meteorology* of Aristotle. Ross describes the contents of the whole treatise in these terms: 'Its subject (that is, of Books I–III) is in the main weather phenomena such as wind and rain, thunder and lightning, together with certain astronomical phenomena (such as comets and the milky way) which Aristotle wrongly believed to be not astronomical but meteorological. But the fourth book deals with quite a different set of facts – with composite bodies such as metals, and their sensible qualities.' This fourth book has been often regarded as not by Aristotle, it is so intimately concerned with a multiplicity of practical activities connected with the crafts. If accepted as the work of Aristotle it forms, with the *Mechanics*, a surprising exception to Aristotle's general indifference to productive techniques. For this treatise, the purpose of which is (I again quote Ross) 'to consider in detail the operation of the active qualities heat and cold and the modifications of the passive qualities dryness and fluidity', contains, among much else of interest, an extraordinary programme of research into the nature of various substances with a view to classifying them in accordance with their ability or inability to be acted upon. I translate a short passage: 'Let us begin by enumerating those qualities expressing the aptitude or inaptitude of a thing to be affected in a certain way. They are as follows: to be apt or inapt to solidify, melt, be softened by heat, be softened by water, bend, break, be comminuted, impressed, moulded, squeezed, to be tractile, malleable, fissile, be cut, be viscous or friable, compressible or incompressible, combustible or incombustible, apt or inapt to give off fumes.' The programme of experiments here envisaged is worthy of Francis Bacon. It has been pointed out to me[1] that in two undoubtedly genuine works (*Parts of Animals,* 649*a* and *Generation of Animals*, 784*b*) Aristotle accepts the conclusions established in *Meteorology*, IV, as the considered statement of his own views. It would follow from this that such chemical researches as are here described – which are of the same kind as those in Theophrastus's work *On Fire* – were already in vogue in the Lyceum in Aristotle's day. The latest editor of the treatise (Ingemar Düring, Göteborg, 1944) accepts it as genuine and selects from its teaching, which is of course not all of equal value, the definition of a chemical combination 'as being perhaps Aristotle's most important achievement in this branch of science'. The definition is indeed brilliant, being given in a sentence of seven words impossible to render accurately with equal neatness in English. It is worth quoting as one example among others of the logical perfection of Greek science at this epoch. 'Chemical combination is a union of several bodies capable of such combination involving a transformation of the properties of the bodies combined.'

MECHANICS

The book on Mechanics is thought by Ross to belong to the early Peripatetic school, 'perhaps to Strato or one of his pupils'. Its best translator, Professor E. S. Forster, remarks of it : 'Whilst the scientific standpoint is certainly Peripatetic, the writer's interest in the practical applications of the problems involved is quite un-Aristotelian.' But we have already

1. By Mr. David Eichholz of Bristol University.

seen reason to doubt the validity of this argument. Its opening general statement, before it gets down to particular problems, is as follows: 'Things may occur either in accordance with nature or contrary to nature. Events in the former class excite our wonder when we do not know their cause. What excites our wonder in the second class is the ingenuity with which man pursues his advantage. Nature does many things in a way opposite to what we require. This results from the fact that the action of nature is uniform and simple, while human requirements are various and changing. When we require an effect contrary to nature, we are in difficulties and at a loss and require technical skill. The skilled invention which gets us out of our difficulty we call a device or a mechanism. It was the poet Antiphon who wrote:

By skill victorious nature we defeat,

and he was right. Examples of what he meant are where smaller things control greater, or where small forces move great weights, or in general everything we include under the term mechanical problem. Mechanical problems are neither identical with physical problems nor entirely distinct from them. They rest upon a combination of mathematical and physical theory. The general principle is disclosed by mathematics, the application belongs to physics.'

There follows a brilliant attempt to bring a great range of human activities within the scope of mathematical explanation. These activities are concerned with the lever, the balance, the position of rowers in a boat, the steering-oar, arrangement of sails, the varieties of circular movement in the cart-wheel, the pulley and the potter's wheel, the sling, the strengths of varying lengths of wood, the wedge, the steelyard, the advantage of the forceps over the bare hand in the extraction of teeth, cracking nuts, the proper proportions in the construction of beds, the transport of long timbers, swing-beams at wells, the motion of wagons (involving the problem of inertia). Two questions are touched on that concern natural rather than human agency – the shaping of pebbles on a beach and the eddies in water. The whole constitutes an admirable essay in applied mathematics. Some of the main principles of statics are expounded with surprising success, namely the law of virtual velocities, the parallelogram of forces, the law of inertia.

Nothing is more astonishing in the genius of the age we have under discussion than the capacity of the great founders of the sciences to bring order out of chaos by delimiting the true field of particular branches of knowledge. Aristotle himself had done this with superb mastery, his comprehensive grasp of the whole field of human knowledge being matched by his capacity to draw firm boundaries between the various parts. The conception was formed of an organic body of scientific knowledge, covering the whole field of human experience, in which the separate parts which made up the whole should be clearly separated from one another yet seen in their mutual relations. With this master plan before them his disciples continued his work, now reconsidering the basic principles of the whole structure (as when Theophrastus raised the whole problem of the validity of the teleological principle), now defining the limits of the particular sciences more clearly (as when Theophrastus, by his analysis of the nature of the parts of animals and plants, separated the sciences of zoology and botany). So too we have seen Strato reconstituting two branches of science – the theory of the fundamental structure of matter and the theory of the nature of the soul. We have seen two other members of the school, whose names are uncertain – an indication of the teamwork which was practised there – constituting branches of chemistry and of applied mathematics. We have now to turn to another great man, Aristoxenus, who brought order into the interpretation of one of the major branches of art, namely music.

MUSIC

Aristoxenus, a contemporary of Theophrastus, was born at Tarentum, an ancient seat of varied culture. He was the son of a distinguished musician, Spintharus, who had travelled much and been in contact with many of the great men of the day. It was almost inevitable that the scion of this powerful and intellectual family should be enrolled sooner or later at the Lyceum. Aristoxenus, in fact, not only became a Peripatetic and a pupil of Aristotle, he held such a position in the school that he entertained hopes of succeeding his master. We cannot say that Aristoxenus would have made a better head than Theophrastus. It is worth recording, however, that besides his work on musical theory he wrote philosophy and biography.

The special achievement of this man, with his wide, practical knowledge of music and his deep philosophical training, was eminently characteristic of the school to which he belonged. It consisted in the accurate determination of the scope of musical science and the establishment of a truer conception of the real nature of music itself. Up to the time of Aristoxenus music in Greece had been in the position of an Art, a Techne. There were, of course, schools of musical art. There was conscious preference of one style of composition to another. There were musical competitions in abundance, where a wide public learned an exquisite discrimination in the style and talents of various performers. Makers of instruments were famous for their skill. All the habits formed by these preferences were transmitted by instruction from generation to generation of craftsmen, composers, and executants. But nowhere in all this do we perceive any apprehension of the basic principles of a science of music as such.

How were such principles to be come by? The only school that had seriously concerned itself with the endeavour to establish a science of music was the Pythagorean. But, though the Pythagoreans spoke of music, they had not risen above the level of acoustics. They reduced sound to air vibrations. Where the ear hears high and low, they detected mathematical relations which appeal to the intellect. These were remarkable scientific achievements, but they do not constitute a science of *music*. The mere principles of sound do not supply any basis for the criticism or appreciation of music. Aristoxenus, who was of course aware of what the Pythagoreans had done, understood that they had not yet got to the point. He saw that true musical science must accept, as elements requiring no further explanation, such conceptions as voice, interval, high, low, concord, discord. Its task must be to reduce the more complex phenomena of music to these simple forms and to ascertain the general laws of their connection.

Here was a clear definition of the scope of musical science which brought with it a deeper conception of music itself. The essence of music lies in the dynamical relations of sounds to one another, not in the physical and mathematical antecedents of sounds. Aristoxenus had now found a definition of music which made possible the understanding of the essential nature of a musical composition as a system of sounds, in which no sound has a meaning by itself but in which every sound acquires a meaning by virtue of its relation to all the rest. Here is a key sentence: 'Our method rests in the last resort on an appeal to the two faculties of hearing and intellect; by the former we judge the magnitudes of the intervals, by the latter we contemplate the functions of the notes.'

This achievement of Aristoxenus finds its nearest parallel in the *Poetics* of Aristotle where for the first time science had been successfully applied to the analysis of a great branch of art. With the *Poetics* of Aristotle and the *Harmonics* of Aristoxenus the basis had been laid for an intelligent and conscious criticism of the nature and function of art. The human spirit had made immense gains in its consciousness of itself.

With this we end our recital of the scientific achievement of the Lyceum. It only remains to admit that at the death of Strato the popularity of the institution was in full decline. Under the eloquent Theophrastus, who maintained all the manifold activities, cultural and scientific, which had characterized the work of the school under its founder, we are told (Diogenes Laertius, V, 37) that as many as two thousand students were in the habit of attending the lectures. These days were no more. The education most required and desired by the citizen was a knowledge of men and affairs, and the gift of speech. Something plausible to say and the ability to say it with effect was the supreme necessity for a public man. Strato, in shifting the main emphasis of the institution onto scientific research, failed to meet the popular demand, and the numbers of students fell. His choice of a successor fell upon Lyco, a man who had no capacity as a scientist but was distinguished for his cultural attainments. The appointment was made by Strato in his will, the text of which has been preserved for us. It suggests that the school was in difficulties. 'I leave the school to Lyco, since the others are either too old or too busy.' This is a back-handed compliment. 'It would be well if the others would co-operate with him.' Obviously there is dissension. 'I bequeath to him all my books, *except those of which I am the author.*' Does this mean that Lyco had no use for them? The facts, at least, are that Lyco shifted the weight of interest from natural philosophy to ethics and rhetoric and sought to revive the more popular features of the school, particularly the afternoon lectures. We may perhaps draw the conclusion that a programme of physical research, with a strong bias towards the practical applications of science, such as we find in Theophrastus *On Fire,* in Strato *On the Vacuum,* in

Meteorology IV, and *On Mechanical Problems*, had become functionless in a city such as Athens, which had lost the leadership in Greek affairs and was materially in a state of decay.

The Lyceum had always owed much to Macedonian patronage. Aristotle was a Macedonian. His father had been physician at the court of Philip, the Macedonian king. Aristotle had been tutor to Philip's son, Alexander the Great. The Lyceum was, in a very definite sense, a centre of Macedonian influence in Athens. Strato, before he had been called to Athens to be made head of the school, had been appointed by the founder of the new Macedonian dynasty in Egypt to be tutor to his son. We have evidence that the career of the Lyceum had not always been untroubled by the shifts and changes of Athenian politics. There was arising in Egypt a new Macedonian power with aspirations to be the strongest power in the Mediterranean world. The Ptolemies have left the clearest proof that they were acutely aware of the service that science could be made to render to government. There is therefore nothing to be surprised at in the fact that they exerted their powerful influence to transfer from Athens to Alexandria every activity of the Lyceum which they thought could be of use to them. The scientific future lay, not with Lyco and his inconspicuous successors in Athens, but with the Museum of Alexandria and the brilliant band of scholars and scientists gathered and maintained there by the magic of Ptolemaic gold.

BIBLIOGRAPHICAL NOTE

The articles in Pauly-Wissowa, *Real-Encyklopädie*, on Peripatos (by K. O. Brink), on Theophrastus (by O. Regenbogen), on Strato (by Capelle) give a comprehensive and up-to-date review of the history of the Lyceum after Aristotle. For the opportunity to consult the first two I am indebted to Dr Brink. Brunet et Mieli, *Histoire des Sciences : Antiquité* are valuable for the whole period, but where they follow Senn's lead on Theophrastus do not carry conviction against the criticism of Regenbogen. The *Metaphysics* of Theophrastus was edited with translation by Ross and Forbes, Oxford, 1929. *Meteorology* IV and *Mechanics* will be found in the *Works of Aristotle translated into English*, Oxford. In the Loeb Library will be found a translation by Sir Arthur Hort of *The Enquiry into Plants* (i.e. *The History of Plants*) of Theophrastus.

CHAPTER TWO

History and organization of the Museum – Planned religion and planned science – Engineers – Doctors – Mathematicians – Astronomers – Geographers – Astronomy Again – The organization of learning – Grammar

★

HISTORY AND ORGANIZATION OF THE MUSEUM

THERE was a sort of American opulence about the new centre of learning in the Egyptian capital. Formally the Museum was, what its name implies, a Temple of the Muses, and its head was a high priest. But its real purpose was to be a research institute which also went in for teaching. In both these respects it was modelled on the Lyceum, but on a vastly larger scale. Its library, which incorporated that of Aristotle, had about half a million rolls, and the direction of research and teaching seems to have lain with the librarian. There were about a hundred professors whose salaries were provided by the king. There were rooms for research, for lectures and for study. The Lyceum had studied astronomy, biology, and botany. For the prosecution of these studies the Museum supplied an observatory, a zoo, a botanical garden. There were also dissecting rooms. Such opportunities for research and scholarship had never existed before. Good use was made of them.

It is not possible to give an exact date for the foundation of the Museum. Alexander had conquered Egypt in 332 B.C. His general Ptolemy, son of Lagus, who had been appointed satrap, took control when Alexander died in 323. When he proclaimed himself king in 305 he assumed the cognomen Soter (Saviour). Two years before his death he had been succeeded by his son Philadelphus, whose tutor Strato had been. Philadelphus reigned from 285 to 247. It was under these first two Ptolemies that the Museum took shape. It had in all a history of some six hundred years, but the first couple of centuries, from Euclid to Hipparchus, are the all-important ones. Then the various branches of ancient science were systematized. Then was established the fashion and the art of writing those orderly treatises, expounding a subject from its first principles to its latest conclusions, which entitled this period to be called the Age of the Text-book. It marks a real stage in human progress.

The Macedonian monarchs who founded and maintained the Museum were the successors of a ruling family which had long shown that it understood the connection between science and government. Philip and Alexander owed their military success largely to engineers. They did not allow themselves to be stopped by walls. Alexander showed that he knew also how to build and organize. The Ptolemies, in charge of Egypt, would have been neglecting an obvious duty if they had not made provision for the training of engineers, doctors, astronomers, mathematicians, geographers. In a more haphazard way the chief Greek city-states had long provided such men for their more limited needs. Vast territories were now to be organized and scientists and technicians had to be secured in a more systematic way. The fame of the Athenian schools had also resulted in the growth of a new pride in every branch of literary culture.

The new conditions in Egypt, however, provided a novel environment for Greek science and culture, which were traditionally national and local. The Academy and the Lyceum were personal ventures. But Alexandria was the Greek capital of a great Egyptian territory and the State was behind the organization of the Museum. Greek science was required to take root in a new soil and play an altered rôle. The cosmopolitan character of the huge city was a new thing. The court and the army were Greek, and for the capital he required the first Ptolemy relied on Greek business men. These constituted the ruling class. In the cities there was an international proletariat, mainly Greek, consisting of petty traders, artisans, and the like. Of the city-dwellers the Jews, after the Greeks, were culturally and socially the most important. The population of the country at large was Egyptian, and, though there is evidence that some Greeks intermarried with Egyptians, the mass of the natives remained untouched by the advent of a Macedonian government and its imported Greek culture.

For the wealthy ruling-class Greek the familiar master-slave relation was still the dominant feature in the structure of society and in the structure of his thought. Life was still inconceivable without the personal attendance of the chattel slave. But Egyptian, Jewish, and other cultures now made a direct impact upon his own, and the Ptolemies had succeeded to the problems of government of the Pharaohs, with the additional complication of being foreigners. Various sources recently explored throw some light on the composition of Egyptian society. At the base of the social pyramid was a depressed and numerous population, performing among other exacting functions one that was demanded by the very nature of the soil. Egypt is called the gift of the Nile. But without the incessant toil of myriads of hands, maintained generation after generation, the gift would have been a barren one. The Nile does not irrigate the land of Egypt without human aid. There was an enormous network of irrigation canals, including long underground passages giving access to subterranean springs, to be kept in order. To be born into the class of those who did this work was regarded as a hopeless doom. The 'toil-worn water-leaders, burdened water-carriers, burrowers into underground passages, earning a miserly wage which gave them no prospect of ever owning anything of their own as a fruit of their toil' were held by the ancient astrologers to have been born under a disastrous conjunction of planetary influences. Along with them we learn of the workers in other humble trades – the bakers, for instance, whose affliction, then as in all later ages, was the necessity of working by night in order that others might eat by day; the porters, with burdens on their backs like dumb beasts; the quarrymen and those who carried away the cut stones, not to speak of the children who shifted the rubble; the divers for sponges and the bath attendants who 'died in early youth', since theirs were dangerous trades. According to the latest evidence these poor Egyptians were wage-earners, not slaves. Their lot was none the less wretched. It was the traditional old poverty-stricken Egypt which the Ptolemies had undertaken to govern, and needless to say their efforts were not directed to transforming their conditions of life. The inventive genius of the scientists and mechanists called into existence by the Museum could not, at this date in the world's history, be applied in the Russian manner to the relief of mass misery. On the contrary, except for certain necessities of the State (chiefly the provision of engines of war) and certain amenities of the rich (like garden-fountains) science tended more and more to retreat from its function as man's weapon in the fight against nature and confine itself to its function of being a mental discipline for the contemplative. For the relief of the needs of the poor government continued to cater by religion.

PLANNED RELIGION AND PLANNED SCIENCE

Before the advent of the Ptolemies the Egyptians had not lacked this commodity. But with the establishment of a Greek government in an Egyptian population new problems had arisen. A god pointed the way to a solution. The first Ptolemy learned in a vision of the night that a new worship was required and was advised to fetch a statue of Pluto from a temple of Jupiter in Sinope to help furnish a centre for the new cult. The proper execution of this divine intimation required care and elaboration. A combination of native Egyptian with imported Greek theology proved equal to the task. The Egyptian priest Manetho and the Greek priest Timotheus worked out the attributes of the new god and decided on his name. He was to be called Serapis. His temple, the Serapeum, was one of the most sumptuous monuments of the ancient world. A statue by the sculptor Bryaxis, of the school of Scopas in the middle of the fourth century, was selected for the cult image. The liturgical language was Greek. The new cult, says Loisy,[1] was 'a carefully thought out adaptation of the religion of Egypt to the spirit and habits of the Greeks'.

The new god showed immediate signs of vitality. Among his other attributes he was a god of healing and he performed miracles from the first. The Athenian philosopher, Demetrius of Phalerum, a member of the Peripatetic school and a pupil of Theophrastus, being cured by him of blindness, composed paeans in his honour which were still being sung centuries later. Such blessings could not be confined to the capital. By the second century A.D. there were forty-two Serapeums in Egypt. But the god had still wider ambitions. His worship very early spread to Cyprus, Sicily, Antioch, Athens. Later it reached the coasts of Syria, Asia Minor, and Greece, the islands of the Aegean, the Hellespont, and Thrace. At Delos, the centre also of the slave trade, the Roman merchants were rivals, in their devotion to the god, of the Greek aristocrats who maintained the cult. The cult lasted till the end of paganism and beyond it. It penetrated Italy, where it is attested at Puteoli before the end of the second century B.C. About the same time it reached Pompeii. The senate tried to arrest its spread among the populace at Rome, choosing itself to introduce new religions rather than to tolerate those introduced by the people. But authority in the end gave way. It was probably in A.D. 38 that the emperor Caligula built his

1. *Les Mystères Païens et le Mystère Chrétien*, 1930.

great temple to Isis (who shared the worship of Serapis) in the Campus Martius.

Cumont[1] observes that the art and literature of Greece were put at the service of the new religion created by Ptolemy. He omits to mention science. But science had also its mite to contribute. For science never succeeds in remaining neutral, in remaining pure. When it lost its ambition to transform the material life of man by being applied to industry it quickly acquired fresh applications. It became the handmaid of religion and was applied to the production of miracles in the Serapeums and other temples of Egypt. Strato had proudly averred that he did not need the help of the gods to make a world. The gods did not disdain the help of Strato to run this one. Hero of Alexandria, who has preserved the record of Strato's work on pneumatics, explains to us how this and other branches of science will be found useful 'not only in providing the most fundamental requisites of civilized life but also in producing bewilderment and awe'. The bewilderment and awe refer to the effects of the temple miracles.

Most of the miracles described by Hero depend on one or other of two principles – the siphon and the expansive power of heated air. They were applications of the pneumatics of Strato. The principle of the siphon was applied in a great variety of ingenious ways to counterfeit the turning of water into wine. Water poured in at one end in a system of siphons resulted in wine coming out at the other. The expansive power of hot air produced supernatural movements. An air chamber in an altar was connected with a shrine of the deity above. When the offering was burned on the altar the expanding air opened the door of the shrine, propelled the deity forward and caused him to salute the worshipper. This principle had many other applications. From other sources we learn of the religious applications of the principles of

1. *Religious Orientales dans le Paganisme Romaine*, 1929.

another Alexandrian science, optics, to the production of apparitions. To the conscience of the age these scientific aids to devotion hardly differed in principle from the use of improved lighting effects or the introduction of organ music, which also were achievements of this age. They were intended to create a pious public, to make religion attractive and impressive, and seem to have done so.

We have, for instance, an account by the accomplished poet Claudian of an unusual type of temple miracle which conveys also the impression of the ceremonial which attended the routine performance of the pious fraud. The natural force employed in this instance was that of the magnet. The scene was a joint temple of Mars and Venus. The divine actors were a Mars made of polished iron and a loadstone Venus. Preparations were made for the marriage of the two. Myrtle wreaths adorned the portals of the marriage chamber. The couch was heaped with roses, the coverlets were of purple. The priest went through the marriage service. The choir entered singing, preceded by the nuptial torch. There were lights, music, colour, odours, and ritual. It is to be presumed that the congregation responded to these effects. Then came the miracle. The iron figure of Mars was brought within the ambit of attraction of the loadstone Venus. 'Without quitting her station, the goddess by her potent charm draws the god into her arms. She clasps him to her bosom with amorous breath', says the poet, embroidering his theme.[1] The date of this poem is about A.D. 400. The scientific production of miracles covers the whole period of the rise and fall of Alexandrian science. It is not without a bearing on it. When science began to flourish again in the modern world it had another purpose than to deceive.

1. C. E. N. Bromehead (Geology in Embryo, Proceedings of the Geologists' Association, Vol. LVI, Part 2, 1945. p. 115), while not denying that a large piece of magnetite might attract a small statuette, suspects the use of fine cords invisible in a dim religious light.

THE ENGINEER

So it had in antiquity also, but in a strangely limited degree. A quotation from Brunet and Mieli will give us a preliminary view of the character of Alexandrian science, to the study of which we must now turn. 'It is certain', they write, 'that the ancient engineers in general, not only those of Alexandria, tried only exceptionally to apply their machines to useful results. It did not occur to them, for instance, to apply the force of water, of compressed air, or of steam, as a source of power in their trades or to obtain results analogous to those which the development of modern civilization has revealed. One might even suppose that with the knowledge that they had, and availing themselves of the mechanisms they thought out for their toys, the ancient engineers might have arrived at applications analogous to those that make the glory of the eighteenth century. However, in recording their failure, sufficiently curious in itself for the modern mind, one must of course recognize that the attention of the technicians of Antiquity was not exclusively applied to toys. Some truly useful machines were constructed, like pumps for raising water or putting out fires. The ingenuity of the Alexandrians exercised itself above all in the perfecting of a great number of instruments of precision, very delicate in construction, and indispensable even for the progress of science. Such were their astronomical instruments and their water-clocks.'

It is now generally agreed that the founder of the Alexandrian school of mechanists was Ctesibius. Ctesibius, whose lifetime fell within the reigns of the second and third Ptolemies, that is between 285 and 222, was the son of an Alexandrian barber. An early achievement of his was to facilitate the raising and lowering of a mirror in the barber's shop by balancing it with a lump of lead. Suspended on a cord, this ran up and down in a pipe concealed behind a beam. Where there is mother wit one thing soon leads to another. The fact that when the lead fell rapidly down the pipe it forced the air out with a squeak suggested to the ingenious barber's son the invention of a mechanical musical instrument. This, when finally perfected, was the famous water-organ, an instrument in whose tones Cicero some two hundred years later tells us he found great delight. The power was supplied by a column of water supported on a cushion of air. The air passed through a valve into a horizontal cylinder connected with a series of vertical organ pipes into which the air could be allowed to enter through valves controlled by jacks.

The introduction of mechanical music is no mean contribution to civilization. But the hydraulis was not the only achievement of Ctesibius. Equally famous were his water-clocks. The description which follows is taken from Vitruvius (IX, viii, 4 and 5). It will be intelligible to one who studies the accompanying illustration. 'For the water-inlet he used a hole bored in a piece of gold or in a gem, finding that these neither wear nor get blocked. This secured an even flow. The water as it rose floated an inverted bowl, technically known as the cork or drum. This connected with a bar and a revolving drum. Both bar and drum had teeth at regular intervals fitting into one another. By this means the rectilinear motion of the rising cork was transformed into a series of small measured circular movements. By an elaboration of this device through a number of rods and cogs he caused a variety of movements. The little figure which pointed to the hour moved. The cylinder of the clock revolved. Stones or eggs were dropped. Trumpets were sounded, and there were other incidental effects.' The discerning reader will notice here some knowledge of materials as well as of mechanical principles. It should be observed that the construction of these clocks was unnecessarily complicated by the antique fashion of hours which varied in

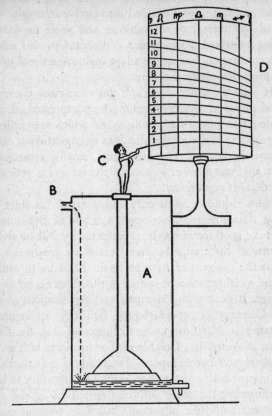

WATERCLOCK OF CTESIBIUS

A — container with float.

B — hole cut in gold or precious stone, through which water enters.

C — figure which rises with float and points to the hours.

D — drum which revolves once a year, showing the hours varying in length according to the seasons. The vertical lines indicate the months.

length according to the seasons of the year. Day and night, darkness and light, were divided into twelve intervals. The hours of day were long in summer and short in winter. Ctesibius contrived clocks which conformed to this inconvenient convention, just as we adapt instruments and tables to our primitive metrical system.

Apart from the water-organ and the water-clock Ctesibius invented pieces of artillery working by compressed air and a double-action pump for raising water which was utilized in fire-engines. Mechanical difficulties of construction made the former ineffective. The fire-engine, equally remarkable theoretically, was more of a practical success and is generally regarded as his masterpiece.

Ctesibius is known to us only by reports of his chief inventions. His younger contemporary, Philo of Byzantium, has had the good fortune to be represented by still surviving fragments of his comprehensive treatise on mechanics. A study of the contents of its nine books helps us to understand the social function of science at this time. So far as we can judge, it dealt with Principles and Applications of the Lever, Construction of Harbours, Ballistics or Artillery, Pneumatics or Machines using Compressed Air, the Construction of Automata, Defence of Towns, Siege of Towns, and probably some other aspects of war. Apparently the main application of mechanics was to war. The attention to harbours illustrates the more constructive activity of the age. The automata and the pneumatic machines without doubt found their main application to the provision of amenities and miracles. The application of mechanics to industry is lacking.

Special interest attaches to a passage from Philo's book on Ballistics translated by Cohen and Drabkin (*op. cit.* pp. 318, 319). This gives an account of extensive experimentation in the principles of artillery construction made possible by the munificence of the Ptolemies. The point of interest is that, whereas the strength of Greek science is traditionally supposed to lie in its logical, deductive character, we here see the experimental, empirical side clearly displayed, the purpose of the research being to discover an *empirical formula* needed in the construction of artillery. This is the side of Greek science which has tended to disappear from the record. Plato condemned it; and Archimedes is known to have suppressed the empirical steps by which he arrived at his conclusions once he had succeeded in setting out his findings in logical order.

THE DOCTOR

Let us turn now from mechanics to medicine. We have made some acquaintance with the work of Ctesibius and Philo who carried on the work of the Lyceum in mechanics and pneumatics. Let us leave them for Herophilus and Erasistratus who carried on the tradition of the Lyceum in biological research.

Herophilus, who came from Chalcedon in Bithynia and flourished about 300 B.C., wrote a general treatise *On Anatomy*, a special study *Of the Eyes*, and a handbook for midwives in which he gives an elementary account of the anatomy of the womb. The handbook for midwives is a refreshing example of that humanitarian zeal which again and again shines out of the pages of the history of Greek medicine. It may also be regarded as the repayment by the scientist of a debt due to the craftswoman. It is a commonplace that in his vast collection of information on biological subjects Aristotle owed a debt to fisherfolk and stockbreeders. His debt to the midwife's profession is less well known and worth quoting. In his *History of Animals* (VII, 10) we find the following passage : ' The cutting of the navel-string is the duty of the midwife and requires an alert intelligence. In a difficult labour everything depends on her skill. She must have presence of mind to deal with emergencies and to manage the tying of the string. If the afterbirth comes away with the child, the navel-string is separated from the afterbirth by a knot and is severed above the knot. Where it is tied it grows together and the continuity is broken. But if the fastening comes undone the blood flows out and the child dies. If, on the other hand, the afterbirth does not come away at once, then the navel-string is tied and severed after the birth of the child while the afterbirth is still inside. It often happens that the child seems to be stillborn, if it is a weak child, and the blood flows out into the cord and the neighbouring parts. Experienced midwives then press the blood back out of the cord, when the child, as if it had been previously drained of blood, revives. As has been said already, children like other animals come out head first, and children have their arms stretched by their sides. Immediately on being born they cry and move their hands to their mouth. Some children evacuate immediately, some after a little time, all within a day. The evacuation, which is called the meconium, is more copious than the normal evacuation of a child.' The reference to the blood flowing into the cord and causing danger of stillbirth is wrong. It seems to be a misinterpretation of *asphyxia neonatorum*. But there is no doubt, in view of the fullness and accuracy of his remarks, that Aristotle had gone to the midwives for his facts. Herophilus keeps alive the contact between biological research and midwifery.

Of the contributions Herophilus made to anatomy the most fundamental was his investigation of the seat of the intelligence. In the fifth century Alcmaeon had located it correctly in the brain. A century later Aristotle, for ten excellent, but as it proved mistaken, reasons transferred it to the heart. Herophilus returned to the view of Alcmaeon on the basis of a diligent dissection of the nervous system and the brain. Anatomists before him had made some progress in tracing the nerves of the special senses. He was the first to get a general picture of the nervous system and to effect the distinction of the motor from the sensory nerves. The nomenclature of the parts of the brain still bears many traces of his work.

His younger contemporary, Erasistratus of Chios, partly carried on his work, partly struck out a line of his own. Singer tells us that the observations of Herophilus on the lacteals were extended by Erasistratus to a point beyond which no advance was made before Gasparo Aselli (1581–1626). But the work of Erasistratus for the most part lay in a new field. If Herophilus is to be called the founder of anatomy, then Erasistratus is the founder of physiology. His work, though he did not come to the correct conclusion, has a tremendous bearing on the question of the circulation of the blood. His success in advancing the knowledge of the heart is proved by his having observed the semi-lunar valves, the tricuspid and the bicuspid valves. He traced the subdivisions of the veins and arteries to the limits of vision and was confident that they must proceed beyond this. That with all this he should have failed to arrive at the theory of the circulation illustrates a fundamental difficulty in the progress of science.

In the infinite variety and complexity of the phenomena of nature the scientist is at a loss in which direction to turn unless he is looking for something. If he is looking for something that means he has a theory. If he has a theory he tends to see what supports it and to miss other significant facts. There is no way out of this difficulty except the patience and discipline which the long tradition of science can help to supply. In this situation an ardent and enthusiastic mind is more liable to error than one that is without these attractive qualities. There is no doubt of the zeal of Erasistratus for his ideal of science. It is the tradition, and the known facts confirm it, that Erasistratus and Strato profoundly influenced one another. Almost certainly the two men were personally acquainted. The similarity of their outlook was such that we have already felt justified in quoting from Erasistratus to illustrate the experimental technique of Strato. But they not only shared the experimental temper. They were working on the same problem in different fields. Erasistratus was a firm adherent of the theories of Strato on the vacuum and they provided the basis for his physiological system. This, in the end, was his undoing. Herophilus had had no doubt that the function of both veins and arteries was to carry blood. Erasistratus, fascinated by Strato's demonstration of the pull exercised on liquids by the void, found reason to conclude that the arteries are normally empty of blood. He knew, of course, that if you sever an artery in a living animal it spouts blood. But there was the contrary fact that in a dead animal the arteries are empty of blood but full of air – full of that air which, if rarefied, had the power, as Strato had shown, to suck up liquids. His observations of the minute subdivisions of veins and arteries had convinced Erasistratus that they were connected by capillary vessels. His knowledge of Stratonic pneumatics now revealed to him how he could reconcile the apparently contradictory facts that the arteries of a wounded animal spout blood while dissection of the dead animal shows them empty. He concluded that the arteries are normally filled with air, that when the artery is severed this air escapes, causing a vacuum, that the pull of this vacuum brings blood from the veins through the capillaries into the arteries, which then spouts out as it follows hard on the escaping air. This fatally ingenious explanation proved an obstacle for some time to a true view of the function of the arterial system. Four hundred and fifty years later we find Galen disproving the Erasistratan view by careful experiments in vivisection. Nearly fourteen hundred years after Galen Vesalius repeated these experiments before his classes in Padua. These demonstrations of the presence of blood in the arteries became traditional and in another eighty years or so led Harvey, who had been a student at Padua, to his great discovery. The success of Harvey was not due to the fact that he had no false theories in his head. He had as many as Erasistratus but he paid no attention to them. The essential progress had consisted in the acquisition of the gift of patient observation.

MATHEMATICIANS

Mechanics and medicine are the two branches of Alexandrian science which exhibit most clearly the historical connection with the Lyceum. Mathematics, which in the opinion of many is the greatest achievement of Greek science, reflects rather the influence of the Academy. Not, of course, that the Lyceum was indifferent to this study. We have already mentioned the fact that one of Aristotle's pupils, Eudemus, wrote a history of mathematics. That work, written before 300 B.C., could not, even if it were extant, give us any information about the founder of Alexandrian geometry, Euclid, whose *Elements*, in thirteen books, is generally regarded as the greatest text-book in the whole history of science. But some seven hundred years after Eudemus a Neo-Platonic philosopher, Proclus (A.D. 410–485), engaged on the composition of a Commentary to Book I of Euclid, borrowed from Eudemus a sketch of the earlier history of geometry and proceeded against this background to sketch the special achievement of Euclid. This Commentary of Proclus is extant, and we shall summarize its opening pages. By this summary we hope to achieve three things – first, to bring out some facts about the earlier history of Greek mathematical science for which we have not yet found space; second, to define the qualities in Euclid which have been so much admired both in ancient and modern times; and third, to give an example from a writer as late as Proclus of the care the Greeks devoted to the preservation of their great heritage even when they had lost the capacity to add to it. One of the chief glories of the Museum is that it established the tradition of scholarship, without which the creations of genius have little chance of survival.

Geometry, says Proclus, had its origin in Egypt, taking its rise from the perpetual necessity of resurveying the land after the Nile floods had removed the boundaries. This and every other science naturally have their origin in practical needs. Arithmetic similarly arose among the Phoenicians out of the requirements of commerce and contracts. Thales was the first to fetch the study out of Egypt to Greece. He had made progress in generalization which served as an example to his successors. But the man who transformed the study into a liberal education was Pythagoras. He endeavoured to base the science on fundamental principles, investigating his theorems by means of the pure intellect in abstraction from matter. He discovered the theory of proportionals and the construction of the cosmic figures. Distinguished men after him were Anaxagoras of Clazomenae, Oenopides of Chios, Hippocrates of Chios, who discovered the quadrature of the lune, and Theodorus of Cyrene. Hippocrates was the first to write *Elements*. Plato who came next gave a tremendous impetus to geometry by his enthusiasm for it. He filled his dialogues with references to mathematics and inspired all lovers of philosophy with respect for the subject. Contemporaries of his were Leodamas of Thasos, Archytas of Tarentum, and Theaetetus of Athens. A pupil of Leodamas, one Leon, wrote an improved *Elements*. Another to compose an excellently arranged *Elements* was Theudius. He, like Eudoxus of Cnidos, Amyclas of Heraclea, Menaechmus and his brother Dinostratus, Athenaeus of Cyzicus, Hermotimus of Colophon, and Philip of Medma, were all members of the Academy.

Those who have compiled histories, continues Proclus,

carry the development of the science up to this point. Shortly after this came Euclid, the author of the *Elements*, who gave irrefutable proofs of the looser demonstrations of his predecessors. That he lived in the time of the first Ptolemy is proved by the fact that Archimedes refers to him. There is also his famous saying that *there is no royal road to geometry*. This was his reply when Ptolemy enquired whether there was no shorter path to geometry than by the elements. He was an adept in the Platonic philosophy and set as the end of the *Elements* the construction of the Platonic, or cosmic, figures. He wrote many other admirable scientific works, like his *Optics* and *Elements of Music*. But his great title to fame is his *Elements of Geometry*, which is notable not only for its order but for the selection of the material, for he did not put in all he could but only what could strictly be regarded as belonging to the elements. The *Elements* constitute an irrefutable and adequate guide to the scientific investigation of mathematical material. So much for the summary of Proclus.

English students of Greek geometry are in a fortunate position. Apart from excellent older works like Allman's *Greek Geometry* and Gow's *Short History of Greek Mathematics*, in 1921 came Sir Thomas Heath's now world-famous two-volume *History of Greek Mathematics*, which has been followed in 1939 and 1941 by Ivor Thomas's two volumes in the Loeb Library, *Greek Mathematical Works*. These cover the same ground as Heath's *History* but in a way that facilitates the study and enhances the value of the older work. While Heath offers a continuous history of his subject, Thomas has compiled a copious selection of material from the extant Greek writers, with English translation opposite and helpful introductions and notes. There is no royal road to Greek geometry, but for English readers access to the subject as a whole, or to particular parts of it, has been made easy and reliable. For those who read Greek mention should be made of Heath's annotated school edition of Euclid Book I. Heath was surely not wrong in supposing that many 'would be really interested to see the actual language in which the old Alexandrian taught the youth and pupils of maturer age in his own day, and so to put themselves in the place of their fellow-students of twenty-two centuries ago'.

With Euclid and his immediate successors, Archimedes of Syracuse and Apollonius of Perga, Alexandrian mathematics achieved such developments that they require a specialist to understand and describe them. The present writer, at any rate, has not the mathematical equipment to understand Archimedes' extant works, *On the Sphere and the Cylinder, On Conoids and Spheroids, On Spirals, On the Quadrature of the Parabola*. The subject-matter of the little treatise called *The Sand-Reckoner* is more accessible to lay apprehension. The point of it is this. The Greeks used an alphabetic notation in their arithmetical calculations which made the handling of large numbers difficult. Where we use but ten symbols and easily express the highest numbers by the significance we attach to their position, the Greeks used twenty-seven alphabetical signs and did not exploit the advantages of a positional notation. Their minds were thus haunted by the idea that the expression of very large numbers would demand the use of an immense number of symbols. Archimedes' little book, which is addressed to King Gelo of Syracuse, sets these fears at rest. He expounds a system he has invented by means of which, if the whole universe were conceived to consist of grains of sand and if that number were known, it could be simply and conveniently expressed. The highest number he expresses would in our notation be represented by 1 followed by eighty thousand million million o's.

The title of Apollonius to fame rests on his *Conic Sections*. In a dedicatory letter to a friend he describes the scope of his work. The composition of the book, he says, was suggested to him by a geometer called Naucrates who made a stay with him in Alexandria, and he finished off the eight books as quickly as he could because Naucrates had to sail, which left insufficient time for revision. He is now publishing a revised edition and begs his friend not to be surprised if some of the propositions have got about in their earlier and less perfect form. The first four books offer an orderly exposition of the elements of conics, the last four deal with a number of miscellaneous problems. The chief topics of the first books are: (1) Methods of producing the three sections; (2) Properties of the diameters and axes of the sections; (3) Theorems useful for the syntheses of solid loci and for determining limits of possibility; (4) Investigation of the number of times the sections of cones can meet one another and the circumference of a circle. He is careful to indicate what is his own contribution to the general stock of knowledge of the subject.

Our other allusions to the geometry of the Greeks will be incidental to our account of their astronomy, where they found their principal application, but before we leave the subject one general observation is necessary. The extraordinary success of Euclid in exhibiting the whole of geometry as a logical deduction from a small number of definitions, postulates, and common notions, set a standard of scientific truth which the Greeks attempted to apply not only in the field of pure mathematics but also in observational and experimental sciences like astronomy and mechanics. Here the results were not so satisfactory. The scientist tended to regard as science whatever could be included as deductions from a few self-evident principles in a logically constructed system. The readiness to question the fundamental assumptions in the light of fresh observations whether of natural phenomena or of controlled processes was discouraged by the passion for logical consistency. System-building tended to take the place of research, and what could not be made to fit into the system was left on one side. The strength and the weakness of this ideal will be apparent in what follows.

Archimedes (287–212) is very generally regarded not only as the greatest mathematician but as the greatest mechanist or engineer of antiquity. Some would claim for him also, more doubtfully, that after Strato he best understood the experimental method. We have spoken of his mathematical works. His engineering works include the construction of a planetarium, which Cicero says reproduced all the unequal and different movements of the heavenly bodies. He invented a screw for raising water which had application both to irrigation in Egypt and to raising water in mines. It is not certain how it worked, but recent information suggests that it involved exhausting labour for slaves. He moved great weights by a system of compound pulleys. The military engines he devised for the defence of Syracuse seem never to have been outdone in the ancient world. His devotion to experiment is proved by more than one passage. Most interesting, perhaps, is the account, given in the opening pages of the *Sand-Reckoner*, of his efforts to make a more accurate determination of the angle subtended at the eye by the sun's disk. His predecessor Aristarchus had given it as the seven hundred and twentieth part of the circle of the Zodiac, i.e., half a degree. To secure a more accurate estimate Archimedes observed the sun as soon as it came above the horizon, when alone it could be observed by the naked eye, by means of a carefully turned circular disk mounted at right angles on the end of a long rule. The distance of the disk from the eye could be altered. Archimedes took two kinds of readings, one when the disk completely covered the orb of the sun, the other when it just failed to do so. Tangents were drawn from the eye to the disk. The first reading necessarily gave him too big an angle, the second too small a one. The correct one lay somewhere between the two. An effort was also made to correct the error due to the fact that one sees not with a point but with an area of the eye. The experiment deserves to stand with those of Strato, exhibiting, as it does, the construction of apparatus for a specific purpose and the taking of precautions to guard against error in its use.

When we come, however, to examine from a proper perspective the character of the scientific achievement of this uniquely great man we can see that it shows a certain weakness due to the effect on it of the uncontrolled admiration for the logical consistency of geometry. We can best understand this by a comparison of Archimedes' work on *Statics* with the Aristotelian treatise on *Mechanics* already described. The Aristotelian, or rather pseudo-Aristotelian, work shows the science of mechanics at a more elementary and groping stage than that to which Archimedes brought it, but it is also more comprehensive and more enterprising. The reader will remember the great range of problems tackled by the earlier treatise, problems both of statics and dynamics. An effort was made to bring unity into this vast field of events by interpreting all of them in the light of the marvellous properties of the circle. 'Therefore, as has already been remarked, there is nothing to be surprised at in the circle being the principle behind all these wonders. The facts about the balance depend upon the circle, those about the lever depend upon the balance, and pretty well all the other problems of mechanical movement depend upon the lever.' (*Mechanical Problems,* 848a.) No such boldness characterizes the attempt of Archimedes. He had invented many weight-throwing engines, but he does not study ballistics. He had too wholesome an awareness of the logical difficulties that beset the idea of motion. He was about to constitute a science, and a science as he conceived it required to be presented as an orderly logical deduction from a limited number of clearly intelligible postulates. Archimedes accordingly put dynamics on one side and confined his attention to statics. Thus he produced his justly admired masterpiece. But Pierre Duhem (*Origines de la Statique,* Vol. I, p. 11) was right to observe, and Arnold Reymond, in an excellently argued chapter

(*Science in Greco-Roman Antiquity*, p. 195), was right to
repeat, that 'The path followed by Archimedes in mechanics,
though an admirable method of demonstration, is not a
method of investigation. The certainty and lucidity of his
principles are largely due to the fact that they are gathered,
so to speak, from the surface of phenomena and not dug out
from the depths.'

This excessive admiration for the purely logical in science
must, if it is to be understood, be connected with the whole
character of the society in which it grew. The reverse of the
medal was contempt for the practical applications of science.
Archimedes was the greatest engineer in antiquity, but when
he was asked to write a handbook on engineering he refused
(Plutarch, *Life of Marcellus*, chap. xvii). 'He looked upon
the work of an engineer and everything that ministers to the
needs of life as ignoble and vulgar', and wished his renown
with posterity to rest entirely on his contribution to pure
theory. It is an ironical judgement of history that his logically
perfect treatise on statics should come to be regarded as less
profound and less rich in promise of fruitful developments
than the immature and disorderly work in the Aristotelian
corpus.

ASTRONOMERS

The brilliant work of the Alexandrian astronomers also will
reveal to us certain deficiencies not unconnected with the
social conditions of the age. In our first volume we traced the
history of Plato's famous formulation of the chief problem
of astronomy. Whatever the *apparent* movements of the
heavenly bodies might be Plato was convinced on religious
grounds that the *true* movements must be revolutions at uniform speed in perfect circles. The problem was accordingly
formulated in these terms: 'What are the uniform and
ordered circular movements by the assumption of which the
apparent movements of the planets can be accounted for?'

We have told how the solution of this problem by Eudoxus, Callipus, and Aristotle led to a view of the universe as consisting of fifty-nine concentric spheres, with the earth at the centre and the heaven of the fixed stars in the outermost place.

We have now to consider what the apparent irregularities were that required to be accounted for on Plato's assumptions. They affected more than the planets, as Plato knew. In his *Laws* (vii, 822a) he says that it is impious to use the term ' planets ' (wanderers or vagabonds) of the gods in heaven, as if the so-called planets *and the sun and moon* never kept to one uniform course, but wandered hither and thither. More is therefore involved than the fact that the planets seem to vary in their speed, to stop and to regress. The further facts are that both the *moon* and the planets appear to vary in their distance from the ecliptic ; and that even the *sun's* speed is not uniform. If the sun moves in a circle at uniform speed the four seasons ought to be exactly equal. But so soon as it became possible to determine the sun's arrival at the two solstices and the two equinoxes with approximate accuracy it became apparent that the seasons vary notably in length. This variation had been established by the Athenian astronomer Meton a few years before the birth of Plato in 428, the phenomenon continued to be the subject of anxious investigation, and a hundred years later, in 330 B.C., we have on record an observation of the lengths of the seasons for that year which is within half a day the same as our modern calculation. Such were the observed irregularities which the contrivers of the ever more complicated system of homocentric spheres were forced to take into account. These were the phenomena which they had to save, as the phrase went. The inner tension produced by the contradiction between the observed facts and the mathematico-religious basis of their world-outlook resembles that produced in the nineteenth century by the contradiction between the narrative of the creation in Genesis and the new geological and biological knowledge.

Plato in his *Timaeus* (39 B–D) speaks of the 'wanderings' of the planets as 'incalculable in multitude and marvellously intricate'. On this Heath comments (*Aristarchus of Samos,* p. 171), this admission 'is in sharp contrast to the assumption of the spirals regularly described on spheres of which the independent orbits are great circles, and still more to the assertion in the *Laws* that it is wrong and even impious to speak of the planets as "wandering" at all, since "each of them traverses the same path, not many paths, but always one circular path". For the moment,' continues Heath, 'Plato condescends to use the language of *apparent* astronomy, the astronomy of observation; and this may remind us that Plato's astronomy, even in its latest form as expounded in the *Timaeus* and the *Laws,* is consciously and intentionally ideal.'

It is an odd compliment to Plato's pre-eminence as an idealist to describe as 'ideal' his obstinate adherence on religious grounds to an unworkable hypothesis. Heath (*Op. cit.,* p. 200) is less ceremonious with Eudoxus, who first worked the homocentric system out. 'Eudoxus,' he writes, 'supposed the annual motion of the sun to be perfectly uniform; he must therefore have deliberately ignored the discovery made by Meton and Euctemon sixty or seventy years before, that the sun does not take the same time to describe the four quadrants of its orbit between the equinoctial and solstitial points.' But when inconvenient discoveries continued to multiply, a breach was at last made in the conception of a geocentric universe with the heavenly bodies moving round a stationary earth in homocentric spheres. The daring innovator was an associate of the Academy, Heraclides of Pontus (388–310). He introduced two revolutionary ideas. Taking account of the fact that the planets Venus and Mercury are never observed to be at any great angular distance from the sun, he suggested (1) the explanation that they revolve not about the earth, but about the sun. He added (2) that the appearance of a daily revolution of the heavens about the earth could equally well be explained on the assumption of a daily rotation of the earth about its axis. These were two very disturbing suggestions. They shook the foundations of the universe in two ways, first by making the sun into a second centre, and then by making the old fixed centre, the earth, rotate.

These were difficult concessions to make to the science of observation. Readers should remember that the mathematico-religious conception of the universe, based on the properties of the circle and the sphere, had fought a tough battle to establish itself against a rival view. The atomists believed in an infinity of worlds coming into existence and passing away in boundless space. The Pythagoreans and Platonists believed in the uniqueness, the eternity, and the finiteness of our universe. The innovations of Heraclides seemed like dangerous concessions to the atomistic view. Such was the state of the science of astronomy when the work of the Alexandrian astronomers began.

Heraclides of Pontus was a resident at Athens. The first of the great Alexandrian astronomers was Aristarchus of Samos, a pupil of Strato of Lampsacus. His probable dates are 310–230, which makes him about seventy-five years younger than Heraclides and twenty-five years older than Archimedes. He will be for ever remembered as the first to put forward the heliocentric hypothesis. Copernicus, in the sixteenth century, was aware that he was reviving the hypothesis of Aristarchus. Though the treatise in which Aristarchus developed his hypothesis is lost, we have the most reliable testimony to its existence. His younger contemporary Archimedes, in that interesting work to which we have made so much reference, the *Sand-reckoner,* tells us that Aristarchus published a book containing a number of hypotheses, among which was the following : *the fixed stars and the sun remain unmoved, but the earth revolves about the sun in the circumference of a circle, the sun lying in the middle of the orbit.* Though Aristarchus still adhered to circular motion, and though it is improbable that his suggestion was put forward as more than a mathematical hypothesis, we have evidence of the shock it caused. Cleanthes, the head of the Stoic school at Athens, a man devoutly attached to star-worship, who was his almost exact contemporary (the two men died old within a year or two of one another), expressed the opinion that the Greeks ought to indict Aristarchus on a charge of impiety. These threats of the philosophic schools (Cleanthes was only reasserting the argument of Plato in the *Laws*) appear to have involved a real danger to the scientist. Such is the opinion of sober historians like Paul Tannéry and Pierre Duhem (Duhem, *Système du Monde* I, 425). In all antiquity only one astronomer, Seleucus, a Babylonian, who lived about a hundred years after Aristarchus, was found to support his hypothesis. He, indeed, went further, and apparently asserted his belief in it not only as a mathematical hypothesis but as a physical fact. But one swallow does not make a summer. The conception of a heliocentric universe was still-born.

The treatise in which Aristarchus developed this hypothesis is, as we have said, lost. But another of his writings, *On the Sizes and Distances of the Sun and Moon,* is still extant. It is judged to be an earlier work by reason of the fact that it contains no allusion to the heliocentric hypothesis and bases part of its argument on a very faulty estimate of the angle subtended at the eye by the orb of the sun, an estimate corrected by Aristarchus himself elsewhere. But it offers such an admirable and typical example of Alexandrian science that we shall give a brief description of it. T. L. Heath's edition of the text in his *Aristarchus of Samos* is one of the modern classics in the history of science.

The book begins in the orderly Alexandrian fashion with

a list of six hypotheses which form the basis of the whole argument.

1. That the moon receives its light from the sun.

2. That the earth is in the relation of a point and centre to the sphere in which the moon moves.

3. That when the moon appears to us halved, the great circle which divides the dark and the bright portions of the moon is in the direction of our eye. (That is, the centres of the sun, earth, and moon form a right-angled triangle, with the right angle at the centre of the moon.)

4. That when the moon appears to us halved, its distance from the sun is then less than a quadrant by one thirtieth of a quadrant. (This estimate of the moon's angular distance from the sun, 87 degrees, is very much out. The true angle is over 89 degrees.)

5. That the breadth of the earth's shadow is that of two moons.

6. That the moon subtends one-fifteenth part of a sign of the zodiac. (This again is wrong. As we have already seen, Archimedes reports a later, and pretty accurate, estimate of Aristarchus, reducing his estimate of 2 degrees to half a degree.)

Aristarchus then proceeds to establish eighteen propositions, the most important of which are these:

1. The distance of the sun from the earth is greater than eighteen times, but less than twenty times, the distance of the moon from the earth.

2. The diameter of the sun is greater than eighteen times, but less than twenty times, the diameter of the moon.

3. The diameter of the sun has to the diameter of the earth a ratio greater than 19:3 but less than 43:6.

Aristarchus had attempted only comparisons between the sizes of sun, moon, and earth. Estimates in standard units of measurement were still lacking, or, if not wholly lacking, inadequate. The next great Alexandrian astronomer and

geographer, Eratosthenes (about 284–192), supplied the lack.
He observed that at Syene (the modern Assuan) at noon at
the summer solstice, the sun is directly overhead, while at
Alexandria, roughly 5,000 stades away and roughly on the
same meridian, the sun-dial showed the sun at a distance
from the zenith of one-fiftieth of the meridian circle. This
gives a length of 250,000 stades for the earth's circumference,
and if we give Eratosthenes the benefit of the doubt as to
which particular measurement called the stade he was working with, his polar diameter of the earth works out at only
about fifty miles short of our modern estimate.

GEOGRAPHERS

With Eratosthenes the science of mathematical and astronomical geography was constituted. In its rise from its
humble beginnings geography had shared the rapidity
which characterizes the development of other Greek sciences.
No doubt there had been much preparatory work done by
nameless, or all but nameless, men in many parts of the
Greek world. Astronomy itself had been advanced in this
way. In a work on *Weather Signs* Theophrastus writes:
'Good heed must be taken of the local conditions of the
region in which one is placed. It is, however, always possible
to find a local observer, and the signs learnt from such persons are the most trustworthy. Thus good astronomers have
been found in some parts – for instance, Matricetas at Meth-
ymna observed the solstices from Mount Lepetymnos, Cleo-
stratus in Tenedos from Mount Ida, Phaeinos at Athens
from Mount Lycabettus. Meton, who made the calendar
cycle of nineteen years, was the pupil of the last named.
Phaeinos was a resident alien at Athens. Other examples of
local astronomers could be given.'[1] Similarly the harbours
and coasts of the Mediterranean must have been described

1. Theophrastus, Loeb ed., vol. II, p. 393.

and mapped in a crude way by generations of mariners before the scientific works began. Anaximander, as we have related in our first volume, was the first to make a map *of the world*. He is very unlikely to have been the first to make a map of a harbour or a stretch of coast. In later times Greek geographers refer frequently to documents called *Harbours* and *Coasting Voyages* (*limenes* and *periploi*). Richard Uhden (*Imago Mundi*, vol. i, pp. 2 and 3) argues convincingly for these being not books but maps.

However this may be, and however early we may suppose such local map-making to have begun, from the time of Anaximander on Greek geography has a distinguished history of rapid development. The younger contemporary and fellow-townsman of Anaximander, Hecataeus, wrote a *Description of the World*. The history of Herodotus is full of geographical information. Eudoxus wrote a second *Description of the World*. Aristotle's *Meteorology* contains much of geographical interest, and his pupil Dicaearchus was famous for a map of the inhabited earth and for reasonable estimates of the heights of mountains.

Out of all this activity gradually emerged a picture of a geographical globe with poles, equator, ecliptic, tropics, meridians of longitude and parallels of latitude. Five zones were recognized – frigid zones at the poles, a torrid zone about the equator and two temperate zones, though the extent of these zones was at first variable, being fixed rather by meteorological than by astronomical indications. The progress of astronomical geography was furthered both by the invention of astronomical instruments – Aristarchus, for instance, is credited with an improved sun-dial – and, at least in one famous instance, by the voyage of a sailor who combined scientific and commercial enthusiasm. Between the years 310 and 306, when the Carthaginians, who normally controlled the western end of the Mediterranean, were locked in a deadly struggle with the Sicilian Greeks, Pytheas, a Greek sailor of Marseilles, slipped through the Pillars of Hercules and made for Cornwall to investigate the possibilities of the tin-trade. His voyage probably took him as far as Norway and the Baltic, and he seized the opportunity to calculate a number of fresh latitudes. There is no doubt that his achievement had its effect on the geographical science of Eratosthenes.

From now on a general acquaintance with astronomical geography was part of the education of the citizen, and geographical science in its two main divisions – descriptive and mathematical – was necessary to the successful administration of states. The best ancient geographical treatise we possess, that by Strabo (eight vols. in the Loeb Library), was composed between 9 and 5 B.C., probably in the interest of Pythodoris, Queen of Pontus. An earlier residence of some four or five years in Alexandria had given him access to the best sources of material, from which (wherever he read them) he quotes abundantly. After explaining that his work will be mainly descriptive, Strabo expresses himself as follows: 'The reader, however, should not be so unsophisticated or idle as never to have studied a globe and its circles, some parallel, others at right angles to the parallels, others again oblique. He should know the position of the tropics, equator and zodiac. With a matriculation knowledge of these things – the horizons, arctic circles and so forth – he will be able to follow the book. But if he doesn't even know what a straight line is, or a curve or a circle, or the difference between a spherical and a plane surface, and cannot even pick out the seven stars of the Bear in the night sky, my book will be no use to him – or none just yet. He must first acquaint himself with the studies preparatory to a knowledge of geography. It is also this lack of preliminary training that makes the work of the authors of the so-called *Harbours* and *Coasting Voyages* incomplete. They fail to supply the relevant mathematical and astronomical details.' (I, 1, 21.)

ASTRONOMY AGAIN

We must now leave the contribution made by astronomy to geography and return to astronomy itself. It is not only the greatest scientific achievement of the Alexandrian age, but the special form of its development reveals best the action of the prevailing philosophy on the science of the time. We have seen the astronomers uneasily ignoring irregularities in the movements of the heavenly bodies for which they had failed to account. But their situation was more difficult than we have yet disclosed. It was not only that there were phenomena still unaccounted for, there were phenomena which on their hypothesis could never be accounted for. The blunt fact is that the homocentric hypothesis was, in its fundamental principle, unacceptable and that the reasons for its inadmissibility were generally known by those who nevertheless laboured to perfect it.

The homocentric system, if true, implied that every one of the heavenly bodies maintains an unvarying distance from the earth. They move *round* the earth, they do not approach or depart from it. But the distance of the planets from the earth in fact varies every day, as is plainly visible with Venus and Mars by the variations in their brightness. The distance of the moon varies, as is clear from the measurable variations in its apparent diameter. Such variations are also proved by the fact of eclipses of the sun being sometimes annular (when the moon is too far from the earth to cover the sun completely) and sometimes total (when the moon is nearer to the earth). Such variations also follow from the fact of the variations in speed of the heavenly bodies. If the angular speed of a heavenly body varies, it is because we are not observing it from the centre round which it revolves.

How early were these facts known? Listen to the words of an astronomer, Sosigenes, of the second century A.D. who had access to the ancient books now lost to us. 'The spheres

H

of the partisans of Eudoxus do not account for the phenomena. Not only do they not account for the phenomena which have been discovered after them, *they do not account for the phenomena which were known before them and which they themselves regarded as true.* Can Eudoxus, can Calippus, be said to have succeeded? There is one thing at least, plain to the view, that none of them succeeded in deducing from his hypotheses. I refer to the fact that certain stars are sometimes near to us and sometimes far. This can be seen in the case of Venus and Mars, which show much bigger in the middle of their retrograde path, so much so that, on moonless nights, Venus casts shadows. The same variations can be observed in the moon, if we compare it with objects invariable in size. Those who use instruments confirm this observation. At the same distance from the observer it sometimes takes a disk of eleven fingers' breadth to shut out the moon, sometimes of twelve. Observations on eclipses of the sun tell the same tale. Sometimes the sun remains for some time hidden by the moon, sometimes the moon does not completely cover the sun. The same conclusion also follows from the daily variations in the apparent speeds of the heavenly bodies. Now these appearances the followers of Eudoxus have not accounted for. They have not even tried to explain the variations in speed, although it is a problem that deserves attention. *One cannot say that they did not know the variations in the distance of the same star. Polemarchus of Cyzicus knew the variations, but dismissed them as of no importance because he had a prejudice in favour of the system which arranges all the spheres concentrically about the centre of the Universe.* It is clear also that Aristotle, in his *Physical Problems*, doubted the hypotheses of the astronomers because the size of the planets does not remain the same.'

Such is the account of Sosigenes. It records a crisis of thought at the end of the fourth century in the Academy and the Lyceum at Athens. The account of Sosigenes is based, at least in part, on the history of astronomy by Aristotle's pupil Eudemus, and the men he mentions as having discussed, or evaded, the problem – Eudoxus, Calippus, Polemarchus, Aristotle, and others whose names we have omitted in our shortened version – belong to this period. It was as the aftermath of this controversy, with its establishment of the homocentric system on the basis of ignoring inconvenient facts, that the systems of Heraclides and Aristarchus broke away from the orthodox view, and by making some planets revolve about the sun or by making the earth itself revolve about the sun, attempted to account for some at least of the unexplained phenomena. But, as we have seen, the fear of dislodging the earth from the centre of the universe was too great. Their effort failed. The heliocentric system was finally abandoned so far as the ancient world was concerned.

If we look into this question more closely we shall find much matter for wonder. The system of homocentric spheres was known to be false at the very time when it was being constituted by Eudoxus and Calippus. Nevertheless it reigned, if not unchallenged at least unshaken, for some two thousand years. What is the explanation? The explanation lies in the more general philosophical conceptions into the framework of which astronomy had to be made to fit. Aristotle had written a work *On The Heavens*. This is not an astronomical work, but a physical work, in the sense in which the *Timaeus* of Plato is a treatise on physics. That is to say, it is theological and deductive in character. In this work *On The Heavens* Aristotle argues that since the activity of God is eternal life, and since the heavens are divine, the motion of the heavens must be eternal, and therefore the heavens must be a rotating sphere. Further, since the centre of a rotating body is at rest, the earth must be at rest in the centre of the universe. The earth, which is the realm of change, consists of the elements of Earth, Air, Fire, and Water, but the heavenly bodies, which are eternal, consist of a Fifth Element, free from change, free from generation and decay, and moving not like the terrestrial elements in a straight line but in a circle.

Such in the Pythagorean, Platonic, early Aristotelian, and Stoic conceptions was the nature of the universe. The starry heavens were the visible image of the divine. As such they shared the lot of the gods and became the province of the theologian. They were called upon in a special sense to be the revelation of the divine mind to man and they played a multiple rôle in the government of cities and empires. The stability of ancient oligarchical society was bound up with a particular view of astronomy. To hold other views was not a scientific error but a heresy. Astronomy in antiquity was as thorny a subject as biblical criticism in modern times. Observational astronomy was subjected to anxious scrutiny and careful management. One had to be as indiscreet as Colenso or as stubborn as Loisy to ignore the convention. The wanderings of the planets, the variations in the lengths of the seasons, the changes in the distances of the heavenly bodies from the earth were awkward subjects, like miracles, forgeries, or persecution. The astronomers themselves were often torn between two loyalties, like modern historians of religion. They had scientific consciences, but they knew that they were trespassing on a field where opinion involved political and social consequences. Often their own personal religious convictions were at variance with the facts of observation. Belief in the star gods was sincerely and passionately held by many exalted minds.

For these reasons we need not be surprised that efforts to alter astronomical conceptions on the basis of an observational science, the authority of which was still very insecurely established in all but the rarest minds, should encounter violent resistance not only among priests, philosophers, and kings, but even among astronomers. 'The obstacles which in the seventeenth century Protestantism and then the Catholic

Church', writes Duhem, 'offered to the progress of the Copernican doctrine can only give us a feeble idea of the accusations of impiety that ancient Paganism would have levelled at the bold mortal who dared to shake the perpetual immobility of Earth, the Hearth of the Gods, and to assimilate the incorruptible and divine being of the stars to that of Earth, the lowly domain of generation and of death.' (*Op. cit.*, I, 425.) Only the Epicureans consistently maintained and uttered such blasphemies, insisting that the heavens had a beginning and would have an end, that the heavenly bodies so far from being divine were masses of dead matter. And they had difficulty in reassuring their followers that those who proposed such views were not in danger of being damned for them (Lucretius, V, 110–25). It was for such reasons as these that ancient astronomy rejected the aberrations of Heraclides and Aristarchus and returned to the conception of a geocentric universe.

This did mean a delay in the formation of truer opinions on the shape and size of the universe, and it checked mechanical and chemical speculation on the motion and substance of the heavenly bodies. It caused no interruption to the pursuit of positional astronomy and the improvement of the calendar. Here one may safely rally to the conviction of the poet Rossetti, that 'it makes not the slightest difference to anybody whether the earth goes round the sun or the sun round the earth'. On the latter hypothesis was based the work of the great astronomer, Hipparchus, in the opinion of many the greatest astronomer in the ancient world, to whose system we must now turn.

The theory of eccentrics and epicycles, which forms the basis both of the system of Hipparchus (died about 125 B.C.) and Ptolemy (died after A.D. 161), was probably the invention of late Pythagorean schools in South Italy, from where it made its way to Alexandria. The new principles can be readily understood in their simplest forms, though their complete elaboration in the Syntaxis of Ptolemy presents a formidable study. If we stick to the assumption that the sun moves in a perfect circle at uniform speed, then the only explanation of its variations in angular velocity as observed by us is that *we are not ourselves situated at the centre of the circle in which it revolves*. The sun's circle is eccentric to the earth. This theory involves the necessity of supposing that a body like the sun can revolve about a geometrical point, which was a difficult conception for the ancient astronomer, but it became the accepted explanation. The theory of the epicycle is a little more complex. Consider the movements of the planet Venus. Two movements have got to be accounted for – the synodic revolution, when Venus returns to the same position relative to the sun and earth, and the zodiacal revolution. The supposition that Venus revolves in a circle about a point which itself revolves about the earth provides an explanation of both these movements. The first circle is the *epicycle*. Venus completes her revolution in this circle in the time of the synodic revolution. The larger circle, described by the centre of the epicycle about the earth's centre, is the *deferent*. The centre of the epicycle completes this revolution in the time of the zodiacal revolution of the planet. A radius from the centre of the earth extended to the centre of the sun passes through the centre of the epicycle. The radius of the epicycle is given by the maximum distance of Venus's departure from the sun.

A similar scheme would apply to the planet Mercury, which also remains in the neighbourhood of the sun. In the case of the planets which do not remain in the neighbourhood of the sun it is no longer possible to suppose that a radius of the earth which passes through the centre of the epicycle will always pass through the centre of the sun, for each of these planets has a longer zodiacal period than the sun, thirty years for Saturn, twelve for Jupiter, two for Mars, to quote the estimates known to Eudoxus. But the hypotheses may be generalized to include all the planets as follows: To each planet corresponds a deferent circle, lying in the plane of the ecliptic, and having for centre the centre of the earth. This deferent circle is described by a point which is the centre of the epicycle in which the planet moves. The time taken to describe the deferent is the zodiacal period. The time taken to describe the epicycle is the synodic period.

Alexandrian astronomy had also its more practical side. Nowadays we take the calendar for granted, but the calendar was not an easy thing to perfect – if we can yet call it perfect when an important body of opinion is asking for its reform. The Greek astronomer Geminus who is thought to have written about 70 B.C. defines the main problem when he says: 'The ancients had before them the problem of reckoning the months by the moon but the years by the sun.' This bringing into harmony of the older method of reckoning time by the moon with the later method by means of the sun and so establishing a lunisolar calendar is one of the achievements of ancient civilization for which a share of credit goes to the Greeks, although some would maintain that they did little more than serve as a connecting link between the scientific achievement of Babylonia and the civil needs of the Roman empire. As we know, the solar year is 365¼ days approximately, while the month is approximately 29½ days. No round number of months to the year will make these two correspond. A twelve-month year will give us 354 days, which is eleven days short by the sun. The desert Arabs still get on very well with this system. The fact that they have gained nearly forty years since the date of the Hegira (622) is of no practical importance to them. But very early in the history of the civilization of the Near East efforts were made to find a cycle of years in which the lunar and solar years would correspond. In the eighth century the Greeks borrowed from the Babylonians an eight-year cycle. Three

hundred years later, in 432 B.C., the astronomer Meton introduced a nineteen-year cycle to the notice of the Athenians.
This probably also had its origin in Babylonia. It is a very
efficient system, keeping the lunar and solar calendars in
step for over two hundred years before they require adjust-
ment by a single day. But the modern evidence is that the
Athenians did not in practice observe it – one of many
indications that administration in ancient time was less
efficient than it is to-day. A hundred years later Calippus
devised a seventy-six-year cycle. Two hundred years after
that again Hipparchus came forward with a cycle of 304
years. These refinements were of more interest to astronomers
– perhaps to astrologers – than to the framers of the civil
calendar, but it must be borne in mind that when Julius
Caesar wanted to reform the civil calendar of Rome he sent
to Alexandria for an expert who made an excellent job of it.

Almost all the writings of Hipparchus are lost, but we
know from the evidence of Ptolemy that three of them had
reference to the calendar or to problems that arose out of its
improvement. These were: *Intercalary Months and Days, On
the Length of the Year, On the Movement of the Solstitial and
Equinoctial Points*. In his efforts to determine as accurately
as possible the length of the year Hipparchus disclosed the
difference between the tropic and the sidereal year and thus
discovered, and indeed measured with astonishing accuracy,
the phenomenon of the precession of the equinoxes. Modern
astronomy tells us that, owing to the bulge of the earth at the
equator, the earth oscillates slightly in its revolution about its
axis. The effect of this oscillation is that the pole of the earth
is not steady but moves in a circle, completing a revolution
once in every twenty-six thousand years. The effect of this
oscillation is to produce a slight alteration in the position of
the sun and planets as seen from the earth against the background of the fixed stars. It was this alteration that was
detected by Hipparchus. He made determinations of the

tropical year, that is the interval of time which separates two successive arrivals of the sun at the same equinoctial point. He made determinations also of the sidereal year, that is of the time it takes the sun to return to the same star. Comparing his findings with the records of earlier astronomers he noticed that an equinoctial point does not throughout the centuries retain the same relation to a fixed star but slowly moves forward along the zodiacal belt from East to West. Hence the name of the Precession of the Equinoxes. In his book on the length of the year Hipparchus says that the precession is not less than a degree in a century. In his later work on the precession he arrives at a more precise determination, given by Tannéry as 1 degree, 23 minutes, 20 seconds. The modern estimate is only 10 seconds more.

In arriving at these accurate determinations Hipparchus is thought to have had Babylonian as well as earlier Greek records to work upon. Whatever advantages he enjoyed, he had achieved results which fill us with awe, and set a standard of scientific work to which remote generations may look back with pride. So sensible was Hipparchus of the debt he owed to his predecessors, so well aware was he that only records kept over the generations make possible a conclusion so refined as that of the precession of the equinoxes, that he too determined to leave posterity in his debt and busied himself to make calculations of the positions of some eight hundred and fifty of the fixed stars, together with some record of their appearances, so that future astronomers might be able to detect changes. 'He made the heavens our common heritage', comments old Pliny, 'supposing anybody could be found great enough to enter on the inheritance.' (*Natural History*, II, 26, 95.)

It is unfortunate that the one treatise by Hipparchus which has survived should not be among the most important or interesting of his works. Nevertheless it tells us something of the time, and we shall briefly describe it. About the year

270 B.C. a versifier of great skill, Aratus, had composed a didactic poem on astronomy, which continued throughout antiquity to enjoy great popularity. A young friend wrote to Hipparchus to be informed of the degree of accuracy of this widely influential poem. Hipparchus, in reply, after complimenting his friend on the steadfastness of his interest in science, first establishes the general point that the poet Aratus had relied for his facts on the astronomer Eudoxus. He then proceeds to criticize Eudoxus in the light of later knowledge. This is not without interest as an example will show. 'Eudoxus displays ignorance about the North Pole in the following passage. "There is a star which remains always motionless. This star is the pole of the world." In fact there is no star at the pole but an empty space close to which lie three stars, which, taken together with the point at the pole, make a rough quadrangle, as Pytheas of Marseilles tells us.' (*Commentary on Aratus*, I, iv, 1.)

THE ORGANIZATION OF LEARNING

The mention of this commentary on a poem which had been written about a hundred and thirty years before serves as a reminder of a function of the Museum which must by no means be omitted from our account. We have spoken of the fact that the Library connected with the Museum contained about half a million rolls. This might easily lead to an exaggerated notion of the extent of the world's literature at this time. It must be remembered that a Homer, which with us can be made up into a compact volume that will fit in the pocket, would then occupy fifty or more rolls. But, if there is danger of exaggerating the number of books that then existed, there is no likelihood that we shall exaggerate the rôle of the Museum in creating the whole technique, apparatus, and tradition of scholarship. A famous modern scholar, Boeckh, described the ideal of what the Germans call Phil-

ology as 'the systematic knowledge of what has been known'
– *Erkenntnis des Erkannten, cogniti cognitio*. This task of
scholarship, which is of priceless importance to the human race,
as being the indispensable foundation of historical knowledge,
was first adequately cared for by the Museum. The British
public at the present day is probably much better fitted to
understand the importance of the natural sciences than the
historical. It is better fitted to understand what science means
than to understand what scholarship means. Many have felt
in their own minds the transforming power of scientific
conceptions and of a scientific attitude to life. They know by
their own experience that a man who has learned the technique of scientific investigation has added a new power to
his mind. Far fewer they are who have been touched by
any similar attitude to scholarship, who have felt that the
systematic knowledge of what has been known is not a dead
thing but the most living of all things, raising human consciousness, as it were, to a new dimension. The rub is that so
few of the scholars have any sense of this truth themselves.
Collingwood was not talking idly when he said (*Autobiography*, Pelican ed., p. 61): 'In the last thirty or forty years
historical thought had been achieving an acceleration in the
velocity of its progress and an enlargement in its outlook
comparable to those which natural science had achieved
about the beginning of the seventeenth century. It seemed
to me as nearly certain as anything in the future could be,
that historical thought, whose constantly increasing importance had been one of the most striking features of the nineteenth century, would increase in importance far more
rapidly during the twentieth; and that we might very well
be standing on the threshold of an age in which history
would be as important for the world as natural science had
been between 1600 and 1900.' Such an extension of the range
of human thinking as Collingwood here foreshadows could
not even have been glimpsed if the Museum had not made

distant preparation for it by inventing the technique of the preservation, criticism, and accurate transmission of texts.

GRAMMAR

Out of this care for the written record of the past emerged a great achievement of Alexandrian science, Grammar. The complicated phenomena of speech are not easy to analyse and the eventual emergence of a science of grammar had been prepared for by generations of curious enquiry and practical endeavour. The difficulty of these obscure steps escapes the casual eye. Accepting the marvel of the Phoenician invention of a phonetic alphabet, we have still to enquire how the Greeks took the measure of the problem of borrowing the script and adapting it to their own requirements. Eduard Schwyzer[1] opines that the practical phonetics implicit in the recitation of cult hymns and the Homeric poems were a necessary preparation for the application of a foreign alphabet to the writing of Greek. However that may be, we have evidence that the Ionian Greeks in the sixth century had become grammar conscious. They had begun to pay attention to the declension of nouns and had a doctrine of cases. The fifth-century philosophers thought hard on linguistic problems. All the phenomena of speech have entered into full consciousness. They are busy with letters, syllables, words, rhythm, style. There is division of opinion on the tremendous question whether languages are established by nature or by convention. Plato, in his *Cratylus*, debated the question with characteristic range and subtlety. With characteristic perversity, too, be it added, for he introduced the extravagant theory, sharply criticized by Lucretius (Bk. V, 1041ff.) that words were invented by a Lawgiver and passed as fit for current use by a Metaphysician! Aristotle, the Stoics, and the Epicureans carried on the work of linguistic

1. *Griechische Grammatik*, p. 5.

analysis. It remained for the Alexandrians in this as in other departments of knowledge to give the subject systematic form.

The earliest text-book of grammar that has come down to us is by one Denys of Thrace (or Dionysius Thrax, to give him his Latin name). It shows all the genius of the age by its clear definition of grammar as 'the practical knowledge of the usage of the writers of poetry and prose'. It is obvious from the chief divisions of the work that it has acquired its form from its function. Greek literature when Dionysius made his grammar was already six hundred years old. The language had changed with the passage of time. The literature had been created through the medium of a considerable variety of dialects. It was now being studied by non-Greeks all over the Mediterranean world. An aid to study was required. Accordingly the grammar of Dionysius, the aim of which was to give a practical knowledge of correct usage, dealt with accurate reading, explanation of figures of speech, exposition of rare words and subject-matter, etymology, doctrine of the regular grammatical forms, and finally, criticism of poetry, which is described as 'the noblest part of all'. Two specimens of the contents will be given. (1) The parts of speech are defined as: noun, verb, participle, article, pronoun, preposition, adverb, and conjunction. (2) Reading is said to be 'the delivery without stumbling of poetry or prose'. Then the instruction follows: 'In reading aloud one must attend to the manner of the delivery, to the accentuation and to the punctuation. From the manner of delivery we tell the character of the work, from the accentuation the skill in composition, from the punctuation the thought contained in it. Our aim must be to read tragedy in an heroic manner, comedy in an everyday style, elegy plaintively, epic firmly, lyric musically, laments in a subdued and tearful way. What is done in disregard of these rules defeats the intention of the poet and brings ridicule on the art of the reader.' What

an admirable grammar this is! Sure in taste, firm in doctrine, concise in presentation, clear in aim, it held its own
for some thirteen centuries, a monument both to the high
literary character of the civilization of Greece and to the
mastery of the Alexandrians over the difficult art of the text-
book. The date of its composition was about 100 B.C.

We are now coming to the end of the first period of Alexandrian science and it will be an appropriate moment to take
a general view of it. Towards the end of the third century
A.D. a Christian bishop, Anatolius of Laodicea, delivered
himself of some broad generalizations on the development of
Greek science which it will be helpful to consider. He remarked that in the time of the Pythagoreans, which we
would interpret to include Plato and his school, philosophers
thought they ought to concern themselves only with the
eternal and changeless reality, free from any other admixture.
But at a more recent date, he continued, mathematicians
changed their opinion and began to busy themselves not
only with the incorporeal and ideal, but also with the cor-
poral and sensible. 'In a word', he writes, 'the mathematician must now be skilled in the theory of the movement of
the stars, their speeds, their sizes, their constellations, their
distances. Furthermore he must instruct himself in the
various modifications of vision. He must know the reasons
why objects do not at every distance appear what they are in
reality ; why, though they keep their mutual relations, they
produce illusory appearances as to their positions and order,
whether in sky or air, or in mirrors and other polished surfaces, or seen through transparent media. Again it is now
believed that the mathematician must be an engineer and
must understand geodesy and calculation and be concerned
with the combination of sounds to form agreeable melody.'

The subjects here stressed – astronomy, optics, mechanics,
geodesy, applied arithmetic, harmonics – remind us of the
practical aspect science had assumed in its journey from

Plato's Academy via the Lyceum of Aristotle to the Museum of Ctesibius and Archimedes. It also indicates a major omission from the list of sciences we have so far described, namely optics. This very important subject, treated many times by Alexandrian scientists from Euclid to Ptolemy, was divided into four main heads: Optics proper, Catoptrics, Dioptrics, and Scenography. The first dealt with what we would now call perspective, the visual effects produced by viewing objects from various distances and angles. *Catoptrics* dealt with effects produced on rays of light by reflecting or transparent media, that is to say with reflection in mirrors, formation of rainbows, light seen through a prism, burning-glasses, and so forth. We can best understand what was included in *Dioptrics* by an examination of the treatise of Hero of Alexandria on the surveyor's instrument called the Dioptra, which took the place with the ancients of our theodolite. It deals with such problems as: to determine the difference of level between two given points; to bore a tunnel through a mountain beginning from both ends; to construct a harbour on the model of a given segment of a circle, given the two ends. The fourth, *Scenography*, is the application of perspective whether to genuine architecture or to stage scenery. It dealt with the whole fascinating subject which is opened up to us by these words of an eighth-century writer: 'The object of the architect is to produce a work which is well-proportioned in appearance and, so far as possible, to contrive correctives for ocular illusions, setting before himself as his goal symmetry and proportion not in reality but as judged by the eye.' As is well known, this correction of ocular illusions was a practice of Greek architects, the secret of their wonderful results. Doubtless the traditional practice was systematized into a treatise in Alexandria, but no such treatise has come down to us.

We have said that the first two hundred years of the existence of the Museum were the most important. In fact, within less than that period from the foundation of Alexandria itself in 330, a crisis had overtaken the Museum with the description of which we shall bring this long chapter to a close. The ninth Ptolemy, who called himself Euergetes (or Benefactor) II but who was called by the Alexandrian Greeks Malefactor or Fat Belly, had a long and mysterious reign, from 146 to 117. From the monuments which survive it would appear that he did much good to Egypt in his long reign, but his career has suggested to the modern historian that he preferred to spend money on promoting Egyptian institutions rather than on financing foreign professors. The historian Polybius visited Alexandria during the reign of this king. He was disgusted with its state. He draws a sharp distinction between three elements in the population, the Egyptians, the now mongrel Greek ruling class, and the mercenary foreign soldiers. Polybius calls the native Egyptians an intelligent and civilized race. He says that the mercenary soldiers were out of hand and had forgotten how to obey. Of the third element in the population, he says that they, being originally Greek, had retained some recollection of Greek principles, but had been corrupted by their privileged position as against the natives. Then he adds that Fat Belly had almost exterminated them.

This persecution of the Greek element in Alexandria seems to be confirmed by the report from other sources (Athenaeus, IV, 83) that there was a great revival of learning in other Greek lands during the reign of this king, for he not only massacred many Alexandrians but exiled many more. ' The result was that all the cities and islands were filled with grammarians, philosophers, geometers, musicians, painters, trainers, physicians, and other artists who being compelled by poverty to turn teachers produced many famous pupils.' It is relevant to point out that the great grammarian Dionysius appears to have written his grammar not at Alexandria but at Rhodes. He is probably to be regarded as one of the involuntary exiles. It is not to be supposed, however, that the Museum ceased to exist at this time. There is evidence, in fact, that, whatever the extent and the motive for his persecution of the Greeks, Ptolemy IX was a patron of learning and literature. Nevertheless his reign marks a turning-point. Not only were scientists, scholars, and artists scattered far and wide, but Egypt and the whole of the eastern Mediterranean world were now fallen within the shadow of Roman power and Rome itself had now for about a hundred years been busy with the creation of a literature of its own. The Romans had as yet produced no great work of science and were not ever destined to produce many. But their rulers were now cultivated men who were beginning to be interested in Greek and had the opportunity to be entertained at home by the native comedy of Plautus and Terence. Plautus and Terence, and the epic and didactic poet Ennius, had already carried over into Latin much of the sophisticated mind of Greece. Henceforth we shall be concerned not only with a Greek but a Graeco-Roman world.

And not only Graeco-Roman. When Roman political power swept the Mediterranean world into its orbit, of all the peoples it overran it found two, and only two, with literatures that were destined to survive and exercise mastery over the minds and the hearts of men – the Greeks and the Jews. Now it was in Alexandria that the penetration of the mind of Europe by the Hebrew scriptures began. There was accomplished a work which so far had no parallel in history, the translation of the literature of one civilization into that of another. Some are of opinion that the initiative in translating the Hebrew scriptures into Greek was due to the Ptolemies and the Museum. The more probable opinion is that the Alexandrian Jews, who were forgetting their native tongue, made the translation themselves for their own use in their synagogues. However that may be, first the Law and then the Prophets made their way into Greek. By the reign of Ptolemy Physcon (Fat Belly) the whole canon had been translated and the Greek Bible, the Septuagint, existed. It is not the subject of our book, but reckoned in terms of world influence it is as great and as typical a product of the first two hundred years of the existence of Alexandria as the science of Archimedes and Hipparchus. The mixture of Greek and Hebrew ideas in Alexandria supplied the background out of which Christianity was to arise. The Septuagint supplied the language in which its sacred books were to be written. Christianity was prepared for in Alexandria, it conquered Rome, it was to found Constantinople. We shall have occasion before we conclude to refer again to this all-important Alexandrian creation, the Greek Bible.

BIBLIOGRAPHICAL NOTE

On the general history of the Museum see Sandys, *History of Classical Scholarship*, Vol. I. For the science of the period T. L. Heath's two masterpieces, *History of Greek Mathematics* and *Aristarchus of Samos* are indispensable. So is Duhem, *Système du Monde*, Vols. I and II. A. de Rochas, *La Science des Philosophes et l'Art des Thaumaturges* is intelligent, clear, and full of out-of-the-way material, but neither so learned nor so reliable as Heath or Duhem. Jotham Johnson's article, *Calendars of Antiquity* (Journal of Calendar Reform, Dec. 1936), good in itself, contains valuable bibliographical indications. The best edition of the *Grammar* of Dionysius Thrax is by G. Uhlig, 1883.

CHAPTER THREE

*The Graeco-Roman Age – Bilingual culture : The Grammarian,
the Encyclopaedist, the Translator – Cicero and Lucretius –
Vitruvius, Frontinus, Celsus, Pliny – Geminus, Strabo,
Ptolemy, Galen*

★

THE GRAECO-ROMAN AGE

WHILE the first Ptolemies were consolidating their empire
over Egypt an event of even greater importance had been
taking place in the west. The city of Rome had conquered
and organized Italy. The Italian communities were separated
from their conquerors by no great cultural or racial gap, and
the Romans found in the sturdy and numerous peasantry of
Italy a vast reservoir of military power. In this they were
more fortunately placed than the Ptolemies at Alexandria
who found it necessary to hold Egypt with an army at first
exclusively and always mainly Greek, or than the Phoenicians
at Carthage whose imperial ambitions were insecurely based
on mercenary armies enrolled from Berber tribesmen.
Rome and Italy were capable of a degree of unity impossible to Alexandria and Egypt, or to Carthage and Africa.
This was the condition of Rome's becoming mistress of the
world.

The strength of the new power was soon revealed. Pyrrhus
of Epirus, who aspired to the rôle of Alexander in the west,
led an army into Italy expecting an easy conquest. If he had
been able to subdue Rome he would have led the Greeks of
Magna Graecia against Carthage. His career was checked
before it had well begun by his decisive defeat by the
Romans in 275 B.C. Hegemony, first over the Italian Greeks,
then over the Sicilian Greeks, passed to Rome. Partnership
between Romans and Greeks had begun. Before the close of

the third century Carthage had been humbled in two long and hard-fought wars. The opening of the second century found the Romans moving east, and before the century had run half its course the successors of Alexander in the east, the Antigonids of Macedon and the Seleucids of Syria, had been crushed. The Greek cities both of Asia Minor and of the mainland had taken their place with those of southern Italy and Sicily as ornaments of the Roman world. Only Egypt remained. It was incorporated into the Empire by Augustus.

These were the events which produced the cultural epoch known as the Graeco-Roman Age. The Romans who, with superb political skill, effected the unification of Italy, were not a cultured people. They had no literature. Their language, which, save for a few garrisons and colonies, was confined to the district of Latium in the neighbourhood of Rome and the Tiber, had indeed begun to be fashioned into an idiom fit for political debate and decision but had never been used for the expression of philosophical or scientific ideas. But now the Romans found themselves masters successively of the Greek cities of Magna Graecia, of Greece proper, and of Ionia. They who spoke the undeveloped language of a small district of Italy found themselves politically masters of the Mediterranean which culturally was a Greek lake. They who previous to their contacts with the Greeks had no literature found themselves masters of a people whose literature was five or six centuries old and had already become the subject of sophisticated and scholarly appreciation. Inevitably their boys began to be schooled by Greek grammarians and their statesmen by Greek politicians. Their entertainments, their learned professions, were in the hands of Greeks. Their nascent literature was modelled on the Greek. The culture of the Roman world became bilingual. Make yourself expert in the two tongues, advised Ovid in his *Art of Love*, if you wish not to bore your mistress. The advice was found valid and acted upon in other spheres. Every Roman who wanted to be at all cultured had to learn Greek, every Greek who wanted to sell his culture had to learn the language of his Roman master. It was the Greeks who had the knowledge, but the Roman mastery was not a mere political fact. It had its meaning also in the spiritual sphere. Rome had succeeded where Greece had failed and on the Romans rested the responsibility of power. Roman literature is not a mere imitation of Greek but the expression of a new era. The Romans formed themselves mentally by their effort to digest an alien culture, but they chose to digest it for their own ends. Roman culture, if less original, has a new complexity and a new maturity. Cicero imitates Plato, but discourses of actual government rather than of ideal justice. Lucretius sets up his rest in the Garden of Epicurus, but addresses the Senate and the People therefrom. Virgil follows Hesiod over his farm, but does so at an Emperor's nod. Tacitus traces the decline of oratory, but reads in it the story of a political revolution. This new consciousness which characterizes the literature of Rome corresponds to a new social and political configuration of the world. A vast area of the world, through the building of roads, the improvement of ships and harbours, the movements of armies, the invention of new political forms, and the possession of a common language, had become one. The *oikoumene*, the inhabited world, was a more complicated organism than any city state, and in the mind of its Roman masters and their Greek teachers the problems of its management begin dimly to take shape. For the most part they seem so overwhelming that man resigns himself to mysticism, to cynicism, to fate, the stars, the gods, the emperor. The companion picture to the growth of science at this time is the story of the spread of oriental religions and the relapse of the various philosophies into schools of resignation. But in the books and writers we shall now discuss we shall see some refreshing evidence of the capacity of man to take his destiny into his own hands.

BILINGUAL CULTURE: THE GRAMMARIAN, THE ENCYCLOPAEDIST, THE TRANSLATOR

The bilingualism of the Graeco-Roman world means that from about 100 B.C. European science had two tongues, but the work was unequally distributed between them. The work of advancing the now traditional branches of science continues to be done in Greek. In Latin was done a work of assimilation and adaptation to Roman needs, which involved criticism, selection, and organization, and produced a few masterpieces of a new type.

One consequence of this relation of Roman to Greek science is that grammar, one of the last sciences to be constituted by the Greeks, was the first in which the Romans achieved mastery. It remains one of their great achievements. The Romans, studying in Greek and writing in Latin, became grammar conscious in a new way. The Greeks had become grammar conscious through the necessity of interpreting old writers in their own tongue. It was the need of studying a second tongue that made the Romans grammarians. Forced by their national pride not to become culturally a Greek province and engaged in the effort to transfer into Latin speech the literary and scientific culture of Greece, they found that the first Greek science they had urgent need to adopt, and to adapt, was grammar. Their first great grammarian was Lucius Aelius Stilo (about 154-74 B.C.) who studied in Rhodes at a time when Dionysius Thrax, long expelled from Alexandria, was resident there. Stilo's greatest pupil was Marcus Terentius Varro (116-27 B.C.), author of twenty-five books on the Latin language of which we still possess six. The list of Roman grammarians is long and there is no reason to give it here. But, coming to the end of a great succession, we may mention two names. Donatus, who lived in the middle of the fourth century A.D., was so famous that, like Euclid, he gave his name to his subject. In the late Middle Ages a grammar was called a Donat. Still greater than he was Priscian whose *Institutiones Grammaticae* in eighteen books, which appeared about A.D. 500, is the most famous of all ancient grammars. In spite of its formidable length (it is about as long as the modern Latin grammar of Madvig) its popularity was once so great that no library in Europe was without a copy and it survives to this day in about one thousand MSS. The debt of culture to the Roman grammarians is immense.

Linguistic phenomena have not proved the easiest sort of material for science to analyse. An example of the way the Roman grammarians set about it may be welcome. Thus in his *Art of Grammar* Donatus begins by defining *Vox*, or Voice. 'Voice is air in vibration which is perceptible to hearing. Every vocal utterance is either articulate or confused. By articulate I mean that which can be expressed in letters, by confused that which cannot be written.' Priscian evidently feels this to be on the right lines but inadequate, and at the beginning of his Bk. I offers a more extensive analysis. 'The philosophers define voice as a small quantity of air in vibration, or its effect on the ears. The first definition is of substance, the second of accident. For hearing is something that happens to voice. There are four kinds of vocal utterance: articulate, inarticulate, literate, and illiterate. Articulate is that which is accompanied with meaning by the speaker. Inarticulate is accompanied by no meaning. Literate is what can be written, illiterate what cannot. An example of articulate literate utterance is " Arms and the man I sing ". Articulate illiterate utterances are groans, whistles, sighs. They have an intended meaning but cannot be written down. Inarticulate literate utterances are such as " coax " or " cra ". They can be written down but they mean nothing. Inarticulate illiterate vocal utterances, which neither convey a meaning nor can be written down, are chattering, or mooing.'

Varro, whom we mentioned a moment ago, is not only the author of the first Latin grammar which is extant in large part. He is also for us the best early example of an encyclopaedist. His grammar was but the first part of a great work which included also logic, rhetoric, geometry, arithmetic, astronomy, music, medicine, and architecture. The Romans had looked at first with a somewhat jaundiced eye on the culture of the Greeks. When we come to Varro we can say that they had made up their minds that it was indispensable and resolved to assimilate it. It is also clear that the form in which they assimilated it had very durable qualities. Varro's conception of an encyclopaedia of knowledge lasted through the Middle Ages and down into modern times. Only modern developments of the natural and historical sciences have made it date.

CICERO AND LUCRETIUS

But the writings of the grammarians and encyclopaedists, though by no means to be despised, pale into insignificance beside the achievement of the two men who, by endowing the work of selection, criticism, and reorganization with the brilliance of their own genius, did more than any others to bring it about that Latin should become the mediator to western Europe of the wisdom of the Greeks. Cicero and Lucretius, vastly different as their spiritual and mental endowments were, both left behind them imperishable masterpieces which, if we exclude the plays of Plautus and Terence, are the first monuments of Latin genius which still exert a living influence on the thought and style of the modern world. What is the secret of the influence of these two men?

In the last century of the pagan era two Greek schools of thought, the Stoic and the Epicurean, contended for the allegiance of Romans who aspired to philosophy. Of sects other than these the most important were the various Socratic schools; but they were so much closer to the Porch than to the Garden that it might fairly be said that the one real division was between the followers of Epicurus and the rest. The Epicureans, like their rivals, taught belief in the gods. But they limited the sphere of action of their gods to the inner personal life, teaching that good men have communion with the blessed gods while bad men terrify themselves by imaginary fears of them. They differed sharply from the other schools by banishing the gods from nature and from society. Their gods neither made worlds nor ruled them, had not taught men the rudiments of civilization nor guided them to its refinements, were not guardians of property or public morality, dropped no thunderbolts on the rebel or the perjurer. It followed that in a city like Rome, which had been founded and guided by gods, where no public act was done without consulting the will of the gods, where the gods powerfully assisted in the maintenance of order, Epicureans were hardly fit for public life. On the other hand wherever men studied nature, not as a manifestation of the mind of a benevolent providence, but as a non-human environment by the control of which men had laid the foundations of civilized life; wherever men studied history, not to trace in it the mysterious intentions of the gods, but as a record of the trials and errors of mankind; wherever human nature was studied as a basis for a rational control of the instinctive life; there the teaching of Epicurus was likely to be at the root of it. Such was the philosophical atmosphere of the world into which Cicero and Lucretius were born and in which they grew up to be the champions of such opposite points of view.

Cicero was a public man, and though he numbered many Epicureans among his private friends, in his published writings he had no good to say of their sect. His philosophy was a blend of Platonism and Stoicism. He inclined to the metaphysics of Plato and the ethics of Zeno, or rather to refinements of their teaching introduced by later generations in these schools. Nobody regards him as an original thinker nor am I among those who feel his borrowed opinions to have been held with such sincerity as to endow them with the interest of being the creed of a great man. He hardly set this value on them himself. All the same he merits our attention and our admiration. The author in politics of a *Republic* and a *Laws*, in which the teaching of Plato is applied to the history and the problems of the Roman state; in metaphysics of the *Academica* and the *Tusculan Disputations*, in which words and formulae are devised for the expression in Latin of the fundamental problems of traditional philosophy; in ethics of the *De Finibus* and the *De Officiis*, where the same is done for the domain of conduct; he gave so many examples of an adroit exploitation of Greek sources to produce new Latin works, and of an adroit solution of the innumerable problems that beset the translator, that he must take a high place in the history of the transmission of ideas. Perfunctory as his thinking is, there is charm in the eager response of his mind to the impact of new ideas, in the virtuosity with which he endows his undeveloped native idiom with all the qualities necessary to express the thought of a Plato or a Xenophon, in the inexhaustible mastery of words. He was a great man of letters as well as an orator and a politician, and the stamp of his personality rests on all his work. In that field also in which philosophy borders upon science he has left work of the greatest interest, namely, a version, extant in part, of the *Timaeus* of Plato, and a more or less original work *On Divination*, where for once he has written with sincerity and passion. This is a treatise in two books in dialogue form. In the first he assigns to his brother Quintus the task of defending the ancient practice of consulting the will of the gods by augury, haruspicy, astrology, and all the other devices known to antiquity. In the second he reserves for himself the more grateful, and the hardier, task of discrediting the whole conception. This he does with point and spirit, not hesitating even to conclude with the expression of his belief that 'he would be rendering a great service to himself and his country if he could tear this superstition up by the roots'. This revolutionary impulse in Cicero, directed against proved and established institutions which he had elsewhere defended for their utility, is a surprising phenomenon.

It is the attack on superstition which does most to bring Cicero close, if only for a moment, to his contemporary Lucretius. Lucretius was a follower of Epicurus, that is to say a member of that school which, almost alone at this time, fought to rid nature and history of the arbitrary interference of supernatural forces. His work is our best example of the capacity of Roman writers to assimilate a mass of Greek learning and create a new organic whole out of it. The basis of the philosophy of Epicurus was the atomism of Leucippus and Democritus. But atomism had come under the fire of the Socratic schools and the task of Epicurus had been to restate the atomistic position in the light of the criticism of Plato and Aristotle. Atomism as reconstructed by Epicurus was the philosophy Lucretius undertook to expound to his Roman audience; but there is no doubt that he did not confine himself to the three hundred scrolls of his master but made an independent study of the Presocratics, notably Heraclitus, Anaxagoras, and Democritus. He had studied also the Hippocratic writings and Thucydides, material from whom he uses in his sixth book; and the mistakes he has made in interpreting them are proof, if any were needed, that these were not easy studies. He directly criticizes opinions of Plato, though without mention of his name. Homer, Aeschylus, Euripides have also left their imprint on his work. Such was the Greek material he had studied and digested.

One other Greek source remains to be mentioned, the philosophical poem *On Nature* by the Presocratic philosopher, Empedocles of Acragas. Lucretius followed his example in choosing verse as the medium for the exposition of his theme. The verse form has been an obstacle to some students of Lucretius. Many agree with Shelley's protest 'Didactic poetry is my abhorrence. Nothing can be equally well expressed in prose that is not tedious and supererogatory in verse.' It is a superficial opinion. Much of the best poetry of antiquity is didactic. When an author has a great subject to expound, the importance of which he feels deeply, which stirs his emotions as well as his thought, which haunts his imagination as well as his reason, which he plans to bring home to the heart as well as the mind of his hearers, poetry has many resources of eloquence by which to engage the attention, rouse the interest and impress the memory. These qualities Lucretius found in Empedocles and he was glad to have a poet as his model, for the Latin language of his day was much better developed in verse than in prose. In philosophic verse he already had a Latin predecessor in Ennius. Philosophic prose was only being created in his own day, partly by Epicureans whose works are lost but mainly by Cicero.

A contemporary situation invested atomism in the mind of Lucretius with the attributes of an evangel. According to him the world of living men groaned under a burden of fear – fear of going under in the grinding struggle for existence, fear of disaster overtaking them as punishment for sin, fear of death, fear of punishment in the afterlife. The first of these fears Lucretius sought to exorcize by a doctrine of philosophic anarchism. He thought if men would be content to live the simple life there could not fail to be enough for all. 'A frugal life with a heart at rest is great riches, and never is there lack of a little', he sings – sufficient proof, if any were wanted, that he himself enjoyed reasonable security and comfort. To the other fears he had given more serious thought. These fears, natural to men, especially to ignorant men, were also inculcated in the masses for reasons of state. Polybius, Varro, Cicero, all advocate the use of superstition for the purpose of policing the mob. Having elsewhere [1] reported their opinions I offer here a quotation from another source. Strabo, writing about 30 B.C., says: 'Poets were not alone in giving currency to myths. Long before the poets, cities and their lawgivers had sanctioned them as a useful expedient. They had some insight into the emotional nature of the rational animal. Illiterate and uneducated men, they argued, are no better than children and, like them, are fond of stories. When, through descriptive narratives or other forms of representational art, they learn how terrible are divine punishments and threats, they are deterred from their evil courses. No philosopher by means of a reasoned exhortation can move a crowd of women or any random mob to reverence, piety and faith. He needs to play upon their superstition also, and this cannot be done without myths and marvels. It was, then, as bugbears to scare the simple-minded that founders of states gave their sanction to these things. This is the function of mythology and it accordingly came to have its recognized place in the ancient plan of civil society as well as in the explanations of the nature of reality.' (*Geography*, I, 2, 8.) [2]

Epicureanism for Lucretius meant war to the knife on this view of the plan of civil society. In the opening of his poem he proclaims that the philosophy he propounds is able to give man victory over *religio*, that is to say, the official mythology. He warns those who wish to follow him that their path will not be altogether smooth, for they will have to contend against the opposition of men whom he calls *vates* or seers, who will play upon their fears of what may happen after

1. See my *Science and Politics in the Ancient World*.
2. Strabo claims that the history and science of a later date were better, but adds at once that they were only for the *élite*.

death to unbelievers. A true philosophy of nature is the weapon with which he fights these fears. Twice in his poem he declares that the old Greek natural philosophers, and not the oracle of Apollo at Delphi, ought to be revered as the fountainhead of truth. Such was the situation Lucretius sought to influence, and such was his message.

His poem is unfinished, but the plan of the six extant books which he brought near completion is both comprehensive and clear. His first two books are concerned with the fundamental principles of the atomic explanation of the nature of the physical world. The next two books treat of man, the first expounding the nature of the soul and the way in which it is connected with the body, giving proofs of the mortality of the soul, and attempting to exorcize the fear of death; the second dealing with sensation, thought, and biological functions. Book five deals with our world and its history, describing its formation, the nature and motions of the heavenly bodies, and the beginnings of life and of civilization; book six with meteorological phenomena, curious happenings on earth, pestilences in general and in particular the great plague at Athens during the Peloponnesian War. In no other single work in the whole of antiquity, and I think I might add in the modern world either, is there to be found a comparable effort to muster all the phenomena of nature and history as joint witnesses to a unified view of things. The book is truly encyclopaedic but is the least possible like an encyclopaedia, for every item of information it contains is but part of a single argument. An intense intellectual excitement pervades every part and is even heightened by the unfinished state of the work. One feels that Lucretius must have died like Buckle, exclaiming 'My book, my book!'

Of the inexhaustible variety of matter contained in these teeming pages, one topic – the sketch of the origin and progress of civilization, which occupies the second half of book five – most concerns us here. In Part One (pp.

82–5) we gave special emphasis, as the true culmination of Presocratic science, to a brief sketch of civilization taken from Democritus[1] and preserved for us by the historian Diodorus. Lucretius, the contemporary of Diodorus, gives us, in some seven hundred lines, what looks like an elaboration of the same sketch made in the Epicurean school. In its elimination of the action of providence and its search for intelligible causes in the domain of human history it constitutes perhaps the ripest contribution of antiquity to the science of the modern world. Accordingly we shall summarize it at some length.

The earth, the poet tells us, brought forth first vegetable life and then living things. Of these the first were birds which hatched from eggs, next came animals born out of wombs rooted in the earth. Earth fed and clothed them and tempered the climate to them. But in time she grew old and ceased to bear, and living things began to propagate themselves. Before she ceased bearing earth produced many monsters now extinct. In fact all species that could not find their food or propagate their kind or protect themselves or, in the last resort, win man's protection in return for their services to him, died out.

Primitive man was hardier than men now and longer-lived. He was not a producer but a food-gatherer. He did not have fire, clothing, or houses, but dwelt in woods or mountain caves and mated promiscuously. The more dangerous wild beasts he avoided, others he hunted with sticks and stones. Civilization began after man got fire, skin-clothing and huts. Man and wife then began to mate permanently and know the tenderness of parenthood. Civil society began in friendship and compacts with neighbours.

1. The probability of the ascription of this passage to Democritus is strengthened by the latest research. See *On the Pre-history in Diodorus* by Gregory Vlastos. *American Journal of Philology*, Vol. LXVII, 1 (Jan., 1946).

Language was a product of society. It could not have been invented by one man and imparted by him to his fellows; but, just as dogs, horses, and birds express the variety of their emotions by various sounds, so did man use different sounds to designate different things until by convention language was established.

The knowledge of fire came either through a conflagration caused by lightning or the ignition of branches of trees rubbed together by the wind. The sun taught men to cook. Then gradually those whose technical inventiveness gave them the lead emerged as kings and built cities, each with a citadel as a stronghold and refuge for himself. The kings parcelled out flocks and fields to their subjects, at first according to their personal qualities of mind or body. But the invention of money and the growth of property completely altered the conditions of life. Riches now became more important than personal worth, and, in the envious and ambitious society that resulted, monarchy was overthrown and anarchy prevailed. Out of this anarchy emerged constitutional government. Magistrates were appointed, laws promulgated, and crime was held in check by legal sanctions. The poet next turns to religion. What is the cause of its universal prevalence? It is found everywhere among great peoples. It has filled the cities with altars and led to annual celebrations which strike shuddering dread into mortal men, who then spread the evil and erect new temples over the whole world with new crowds of worshippers.[1] It results from a confusion of ideas among those who have not a true philosophy of nature. Men, waking and sleeping, see the gods in all their glory and (rightly) ascribe to them blessedness and immortality. They behold also the phenomena of the heavens, majestic, regular, and incomprehensible. So they imagine that the gods dwell in heaven and guide all

1. Compare the account given above (pp. 197ff.) of the spread of the cult of Serapis.

these celestial happenings by their will. 'O hapless race of men, when they charged the gods with such acts and imagined them at the same time capable of bitter wrath! What groanings did they beget for themselves, what wounds for us, what tears for our children's children! No act is it of piety to be often seen with veiled head to turn towards a stone and approach every altar and fall prostrate on the ground and spread out the palms before the statues of the gods and sprinkle the altars with much blood of beasts and link vow on vow, but rather to be able to look on all things with a mind at peace.'

Man's first lessons in metallurgy were given when forest fires melted gold, silver, lead, copper, and iron and suggested to him the forging of weapons and instruments. Previous to his knowledge of metals man's weapons and implements had been hands, nails, teeth, stones, branches torn from trees, and flame and fire when once they were known. Horses were ridden before war-chariots were invented. The Carthaginians introduced elephants into war. Garments tied together came before woven raiment, for the loom could not be constructed before the invention of iron. Men were the first weavers, but later abandoned this craft to women and went to work in the fields. Sowing and grafting were lessons taught by nature, and the gradual extension of tilth drove the woods farther up the hills and gave us the smiling landscapes we now enjoy. Music was first an imitation of birdsong and whistling winds. Sun and moon taught man the regularity of the seasons and to adapt his work to them. Walled towns, navigation, treaties, and the celebration of great deeds in song all followed in due course. 'Ships and tillage, walls, laws, arms, roads, dress and all such like things, all the prizes, all the elegancies too of life without exception, poems, pictures, and the chiselling of fine-wrought statues, all these things practice together with the acquired knowledge of the untiring mind taught men by slow degrees

I

as they advanced on the way step by step. Thus time by degrees brings each several thing forth before men's eyes and reason raises it up into the borders of light; for things must be brought to light one after another and in due order in the different arts, until these have reached their highest point of development.'

Many of the principal features of this sketch of human progress have contributed, and are perhaps even still capable of contributing, to the growth of the science of history. We may note the fundamental importance attached to the achievement of the great technical inventions. Much history still remains to be rewritten in the light of this conception. We may note, too, the conception of science as an imitation of nature by which man learns to control the natural environment in his own interest. Very remarkable is the sense shown of the dependence of the intellectual and moral life of man on his external circumstances. Control of fire, he teaches, made man a social animal: society gave birth to language. Rudimentary architecture allowed a mating couple to share a hut; conjugal and parental love began to develop. But the process has its inherent contradictions. Fire, which makes civilization possible, weakens man physically. Or again, the invention of property and money throws society into confusion. Religion is seen to contain elements of truth, but to be tragically mingled with error arising from ignorance of science, and cruelly exploited by the rulers in order to maintain their power (compare Bk. I, 102–17). Finally there is the realization that history follows laws, in so far as 'things must be brought to light one after another and in due order in the different arts'.

The poem of Lucretius is sometimes described as a versified text-book of atomic physics. Those who hold this view of it will think that we have misrepresented it in concentrating attention on that portion of it devoted to the sketch of human progress. But our emphasis is not wrong. The poem is essentially an analysis of human history and society which, in the mind of Lucretius, were continuous with the history of the physical universe. The main theme of the poem is the social and psychological consequence of man's action upon nature, of man's knowledge or ignorance of nature, of man's lies about nature.

The poem stands in a strange isolation in Roman literature. It may be said to record the opinions of the defeated party in ancient philosophy. Its fundamental ideas, surviving from the Presocratic schools, proved incompatible with the development, or decline, of ancient society. Virgil as a youth deeply studied Epicurus and always continued to love the poem of Lucretius, but he discarded the views of these men in the process of becoming the poet of the Augustan reform. Providence then became his theme. Human history turned on miracles and oracles. The fundamental arts of life were represented as divine revelations. The hardness of man's lot was explained as a careful provision of Jove for his moral and intellectual training. But though the thoughts of Lucretius were drawn from Ionia and bore some characteristics of an age when men still had confidence in their ability to shape their own destiny, it must not be thought that he shared this confidence. His Epicureanism taught him to see in natural philosophy the means to combat the politico-religious myth ; but, like a good Epicurean, once satisfied that he had precluded supernatural agency, he was indifferent which of the various possible natural explanations of any phenomenon was the true one. Nor was this indifference corrected by the need to prove the truth of a theory in practice, for, as an Epicurean, he sought to make life tolerable rather by a return to primitive simplicity than by any great technical attack on nature. He lived in a declining civilization when all prospect of fundamental improvement lay below the horizon of thought. He believed that the world was worn out and would soon break up, sending its individual atoms raining through space. His thoughts were the echo of a nobler dead world. In his shame at the world of political contrivance in which he lived his favourite epithets for the old materialist philosophers were 'serious' and 'holy'.

VITRUVIUS

Meanwhile the world, such as it was, continued to exist, and the Romans continued to take over from the Greeks not only their philosophy but their more practical arts. The Roman work of selection and reorganization of Greek sources is particularly well represented in the treatise *On Architecture* of Vitruvius. This book, written for Octavian some time before he assumed the title of Augustus in 27 B.C., is much more comprehensive than its title suggests. Its ten books deal with the general principles of architecture, the evolution of building and the use of materials, the various temple styles (Ionic, Doric, and Corinthian), public buildings (theatres, baths, and harbours), town and country houses, interior decoration, water-supply, sun-dials and clocks, mechanical and military engineering. It is probable that such a comprehensive and orderly work was a novelty. In the Preface to his sixth book he mentions (par. 12) a dozen Greek architects who had written descriptions of masterpieces of their own design and construction, and (par. 14) a dozen names of Greek writers on mechanics. It is certain that this is not an empty display of erudition. Some or all of their works he had studied and assimilated, if not perfectly, then to the best of his ability. But the intention, and the ability, to reduce this varied and difficult material in a foreign tongue into a practical manual written 'for the foreman and the works manager' were his own. The architect, complains Briggs, is missing from history. We have the names and boastful epitaphs of Egyptian architects, not even the names of the

Mesopotamian, and nothing from the Hebrews or the Cretans. Many names of Greek architects are known but their works are lost. For us the literature of architecture begins with Vitruvius, and this is likely to be due not to an historical accident but to the merit, that is to say the comprehensiveness, orderliness, and practical usefulness, of his work.

One of the charms of Vitruvius is that he gives us many autobiographical glimpses of his own simple and sterling character. He recalls (Bk. VI, Intro. 3 and 4) that while the laws of all the Greeks required that children should maintain their parents, the Athenians added the proviso that this should only apply to parents who had educated their children in some art or craft. 'Hence', he adds, 'I am very much obliged to my parents for their approval of this Athenian law. They saw to it that I should be taught an art, and one moreover that cannot be perfectly acquired without an extensive training in the liberal arts. Thanks to my parents and my teachers I obtained a wide education, am able to appreciate art and literature, and am myself an author.' The breadth of his interests and knowledge and the fineness of his taste are apparent in his work, which is an important source for our knowledge of ancient science and civilization.

Sometimes the opinions of Vitruvius are to be read between the lines. Thus (Bk. I, 2, 7) he recommends selecting 'very healthy neighbourhoods with suitable springs of water in places where fanes are to be built, particularly in the case of those to Aesculapius and to Health, gods by whose healing powers great numbers of the sick are apparently cured. For when their diseased bodies are transferred from an unhealthy to a healthy spot, and treated with water from health-giving springs, they will the more speedily grow well. The result will be that the divinity will stand in higher esteem and find his dignity increased, all owing to the nature of his site.' A similar discreet scepticism is revealed in another passage (IX, 6, 2) where astrology, an almost universal superstition at this time, is politely cold-shouldered.

We have described in our last chapter the firmness with which Greek science at its height, with Theophrastus, Strato, and Archimedes, had grasped the idea of experiment. Vitruvius will illustrate for us both the survival of the idea and the insecurity with which it was held. Among the best-known passages of his book is the Introduction to Bk. IX where he describes the experiment which led Archimedes to the discovery of specific gravity. Elsewhere (Bk. VII, 8, 3) he himself recommends a repetition of this experiment with quicksilver. A stone weighing one hundred pounds will float upon quicksilver, a scruple of gold will sink in it. 'Hence the certain inference that the gravity of a substance depends not on the amount of the weight but on the nature of the substance.' But an appeal to experiment was more often made simply as an illustration of an already formed opinion, which might be false. Bk. I, 6, 1 and 2 offers a good example. Vitruvius is here engaged in a sensible discussion of the proper siting of a town in relation to the prevailing wind. Mytilene, he says, is magnificently built but not sensibly sited. Here 'when the South wind blows men fall ill, when the North-west blows they cough, when the North blows they are restored to health but the cold is such that they cannot stand in the alleys and streets'. These excellent observations lead him on to a disquisition on the nature of wind. He does not know that wind is simply air in motion but supposes it to be an addition to the existing air. 'It is produced when heat meets moisture, the rush of heat generating a mighty current of air. That this is a fact we may learn from bronze eolipiles, a technical invention sufficing to bring to light a divine truth hidden in the laws of the heavens. Eolipiles are hollow bronze balls with a small opening through which water is poured in. If they are set before a fire, not a breath issues from them before they get warm, but, as soon as they begin to boil, out comes a strong blast caused by the heat. From this small and easily performed experiment we may judge of the mighty and wonderful laws of the heavens and the nature of winds.' It is worth noting that this 'experimentally' established *untruth* persisted into quite modern times. In the eighteenth century the enlightened traveller, ten Rhyne, quite a reputable scientist in his day, detected in the cloud over Table Mountain at the Cape of Good Hope the source from which the mighty south-easter was being 'poured into' the atmosphere.

The 'experiment' with the eolipile is really not an experiment at all but an argument from analogy. A still more extraordinary misuse of this type of argument is found in Bk. VI, 1, 5 and 6. Vitruvius accepts without question an opinion, current in his day, that northern peoples have deep voices and southern peoples shrill ones. He imagines this human phenomenon to derive its explanation from the very structure of the universe. The Greeks were familiar with a triangular stringed instrument called the sambuca. A diagram made up of the circle of the horizon, a diameter bisecting it from north to south, and an oblique line drawn up from the south point to the Pole star 'clearly shows that the world has a triangular shape like the sambuca'. If we imagine the longest string of this world instrument to be a vertical line dropped from the Pole star to the diameter and the rest of the parallel strings to grow progressively shorter towards the south, we can understand by analogy why the human voice becomes deeper as we go north!

Two more passages may be referred to in illustration of the scope of this book, which, apart from its merits as a manual of architecture, is rich in material for historians of almost every branch of ancient science. Bk. II, 1, 1–8 gives a sketch of the cultural development of early man bringing in the discovery of fire, the origin of speech, and in

particular the evolution of architecture. The chapter is important for the early history of anthropology. Allusion is made to
contemporary building practice in Gaul, Spain, Portugal, and
Aquitaine; and the architecture of the Colchians in Pontus,
'where there are forests in plenty', is contrasted with that
of the Phrygians, 'who live in an open country, have no
forests and consequently lack timber'. In a fine passage of
the same book (chapter 9), where the information is derived
from Theophrastus, the suitability of various types of timber
for building is discussed. From this we quote a few sentences
about the preparation of seasoned timber. 'In felling a tree
cut the trunk into the very heart and leave it standing so that
the sap may drain completely out. This lets the useless liquid
run out through the sapwood and the quality of the wood
will not be corrupted. Then and not till then let the tree be
felled and it will be in the highest state of usefulness.' It is
probable that this practice is very old. In the *Odyssey* Calypso
leads Odysseus to a place where he can *cut down* seasoned
timber for his raft. The idea of seasoned timber still standing
was so strange to Samuel Butler that he took this as one
example of that ignorance of men's affairs which proved
that the *Odyssey* was written by a woman.

Evidence of Vitruvius's competence in matters of artistic
taste will be found in his chapter on The Decadence of
Fresco Painting Bk. VII, 5). Its fine sensibility is not at all
out of harmony with the unpretentious and practical character of his work.

FRONTINUS

Practicality carried even to excess distinguishes the work on
the aqueducts of Rome by Frontinus. Sextus Julius Frontinus
was an experienced man of affairs, used to the highest
responsibilities. After his first consulship he was despatched
as Governor to Britain where he triumphed over the warlike

Silures and their still more intractable habitat. In A.D. 97 he was made commissioner of waterworks by Nerva. He was already an experienced author – his *Art of War*, which is lost, and his *Stratagems*, which we have, must have been written between his return from Britain and his appointment as water commissioner – and when he had thoroughly familiarized himself with all the knowledge relevant to his new duties, in order, as he said, to make himself independent of the advice of subordinates, and when the success of his administration was clear, he digested the results of his studies and his practice into his brief and brilliant treatise on the water-supply of Rome. The absence of adornment is part of the merit of his work. His facts speak for themselves. For 441 years from the foundation of the City, he tells us, the Romans were satisfied with such waters as they drew from the Tiber. Now, however, the following aqueducts convey water from near and far to the City : The Appian, the Old Anio, the Marcia, the Tepula, the Julia, the Virgo, the Alsietina or Augusta, the Claudia, and the New Anio. There follow essential details : the lengths of the aqueducts, interesting features like the settling reservoir of the New Anio, the quality of the various sources of supply (Augusta was unwholesome and unfit for drinking), an account of the secret plundering of Julia by branch pipes and how these pipes were detected and destroyed. After a few such paragraphs, packed with telling detail, he permits himself a curt reflection. 'With such an array of indispensable structures carrying so many waters compare, if you will, the idle pyramids or the useless though famous works of the Greeks.' It is a memorable comment, though a Vitruvius would not have expressed himself with so little sympathy about the temples of the Greeks.

It is probable, as his latest editor suggests, that the composition of Frontinus's book was dictated by a political as well as an administrative purpose. It may have been a blow in

support of Nerva's policy of weakening the power of freed-
men in the administration and strengthening the power of
the senate. Whatever its purpose its testimony to the public
spirit and ability of its author remains the same. Rarely in
any ancient writing does one have the feeling of being introduced with such competence into a branch of applied science.
We read of the plans of the aqueducts drawn to assist calculations of the cost of upkeep, of the builders, dates, sources,
lengths and elevations of the aqueducts, of the size of the
supply, the number of reservoirs, the quality of the water,
and the purpose for which it was supplied. Special attention
is paid to the ajutages, the nozzles which assisted in the calculation of delivery. We hear of ajutages of wrong sizes and
of ajutages which did not bear the official stamp. Frontinus
is very sensible of the difficulty of calculation, but he dryly
adds, 'when less is found in the delivery ajutages and more
in the receiving ajutages, it is obvious that there is not error
but fraud'. He was determined not to stand for either. *De
Aquis* is a work of applied science only and has less claim to
appear in a history of science than the *De Architectura* which,
though strictly a work of applied science, is rich in reflections
on the theory on which the practice is based. Yet the sense of
public service is becoming part of the modern conception of
science, and it is difficult to find a better example of science
in the service of the public than is supplied by Frontinus.
His sense of the benefits it can confer upon mankind is
beautifully expressed in the direct and simple statement with
which we conclude our account of his book. 'The effect of
this care displayed by the Emperor Nerva, most public-
spirited of rulers, is felt from day to day increasingly and
will be still more felt in the health of the City ... Not even the
waste water is lost. The appearance of the City is clean and
altered. The air is purer, and the causes of the unwholesome
atmosphere which gave the City so bad a name with earlier
generations are now removed.'

CELSUS

Some historians of science have seen in Cornelius Celsus, who has left us the best general treatise on medicine of all the ancients, a supreme example of the Roman ability to digest and organize the science created by the Greeks. This is a mistake. The merits of Celsus have been fully acknowledged when we recognize in him an admirable stylist. The work *On Medicine* which has come down to us under his name is a translation, with adaptations consisting chiefly of omissions, of the work of a Sicilian called Titus Aufidius who wrote in Greek. Greek medicine had become fashionable in Rome in the first half of the first century B.C. after the arrival in the capital of the attractive and energetic Bithynian physician Asclepiades. He had a number of distinguished pupils and among these was Aufidius, the writer whose work Celsus selected for translation. The debt of Celsus to Aufidius was obscure until it was revealed by the patient analysis of his modern editor, F. Marx. Samuel Butler somewhere observes that an author is apt to omit acknowledgements to an authority to whom he is very heavily indebted. This cynical remark, alas, applies to Celsus. He mentions Asclepiades and his disciple Themison. Aufidius he does not mention. Thus he managed to run away with the reputation of having himself arranged the excellent treatise which bears his name. It would have been better for his fame if he had been satisfied to be known as a translator and stylist. Here his achievement is unassailable. He is, as Sir Clifford Allbutt has called him, the creator of scientific Latin.

Roman writers who refer to Celsus describe him as a man of only moderate talent. Doubtless they knew that he was only a translator. Aufidius, however, had genius of a rare quality. He had a real intellectual style. His superiority shows itself in his grasp of the history of his subject, as well as of its present potentialities, in his adherence to the noblest traditions of practice, in the scrupulosity with which he gives credit to older physicians where credit is due, and in his readiness where necessary to criticize his contemporaries. His fairness and his fearlessness both spring from his conscious worth. He had a contribution to make to medical practice of great moment, greater than may appear at first sight. He was unwilling to regard any rule as of universal application. Recognizing the efficacy of bleedings, purgings, vomitings, and massage, he insisted that the time and degree of their employment must always be determined by the state of the patient's strength. This meant an immense emphasis on the importance of first-hand clinical observation. His patients were his books. He studied sick men, not diseases. He was in the line of the great healers. In his humanity, his intellectual integrity, and his respect for his art he points back towards Hippocrates and forward to the great clinicians of modern times. These qualities we shall illustrate by a quotation.

This is a fairly complete description of fevers. The methods of treatment vary according to the authorities. Asclepiades says it is the business of the doctor to effect a safe, speedy and pleasant cure. That is much to be desired, but too much haste and too much pleasure are both apt to be dangerous. We shall have to consider at each stage of the treatment how to secure the maximum of safety, speed and pleasure while restoring the patient to his original state of health.

The first point to be settled is the treatment of the patient during the first days. The old doctors strove to promote concoction by the giving of certain medicines, their particular dread being the opposite state of crudity. Next they tried by frequent evacuations to get rid of what seemed to be the noxious matter. Asclepiades did away with medicines. He did not employ evacuations so frequently, but still in every disease. His claim was that he used the fever itself as the chief cure for the fever. He thought the strength of the patient ought to be undermined by strong light, vigils and thirst. He would not even let the face be washed on the first day. The more mistaken they who supposed his regimen to have been pleasant throughout! The fact is that in the last days he pandered to the fancies of the patient, in the first he showed himself in the guise of a torturer. My own opinion is that medicinal draughts and evacuations should be employed only rarely, nor should their purpose be supposed to be to undermine the strength of the patient, since the chief danger is from weakness. Any superabundance of matter should therefore be reduced, but this is naturally digested if nothing new is added. There should thus be abstinence from food in the first days. The patient, unless he is weak, should be kept in the light by day. Thirst and sleep should be controlled in such a way as to secure wakefulness by day. At night, if possible, he should sleep. Even without drinking it is possible to avoid the torment of thirst. For, though the time is wrong for a drink, the lips and face can be bathed, if they are dry and offensive to the patient himself. It was a nice observation of Erasistratus that the mouth and throat often need liquid when the inner parts do not and that there is no point in making a patient suffer. Such should be the treatment at the beginning.

The best of all medicines is food given at the right time. It remains to determine the time. Many of the ancients fixed it late, on the fifth or even the sixth day. Possibly the climate in Asia or Egypt allows this. Asclepiades, after tiring the patient in every way for three days, proposed to feed him on the fourth. A very recent authority, Themison, took into consideration, not the beginning of the fever, but its cessation or lightening and gave food two days after that – immediately, if there had been no accession of fever; if there had been an accession, he waited till it stopped, or, if persistent, till it lessened. None of these rules is of absolutely universal application. Food may be given on the first day, or on the second, or on the third. It may be withheld till the fourth or fifth. It may be given after one accession, or after two, or after several. The determining factors always are the character of the disease, the state of the body, the climate, the age of the patient, the season of the year. In the great variety of these circumstances there can be no universal rule of time. In a sickness which exhausts the patient's strength food must be given sooner, and so also in a climate in which digestion is quicker. For this reason, it does not seem right for a patient in Africa to fast for a single day. Food should be given sooner to a child than to a young man, in summer than in winter. The one universal rule, good for every time and every place, is this, that the doctor should frequently take a seat beside the sick bed and examine the strength of the patient. So long as the patient has a reserve of strength, let him fight the disease with fasting. As soon as weakness is feared, let him come to the rescue with food. The duty of the doctor is neither to burden the patient with too much food nor weaken him with too little. Erasistratus, I find, knew this. He does not sufficiently make clear how one is to know when the stomach, or when the body itself, is growing weak. But when he says that these points should be observed before food is given, he makes it sufficiently clear that food should not be given while there is a reserve of strength, and that a watch should be kept lest the strength fail. From all this it is clear that one doctor cannot attend upon many patients. The ideal doctor, one who respects his art, is never far from his patient. But those who practise for profit, since there is greater profit in a numerous clientèle, gladly follow a school of teaching which does not demand such constant care. Fevers are a case in point. Even men who rarely see their patients have no difficulty in counting days and accessions. The man who is to see the only thing that really matters, namely when the patient is becoming too weak, must be constant at the bedside.

I have no space for further description of this book. Suffice it to say that what has been translated above is but two pages out of four hundred, and though they have been chosen for the special interest of their matter, they are a fair sample of the splendid quality of the whole. Furthermore the work is a balanced whole. Celsus dropped certain aspects of the subject as treated by Aufidius, notably the section or sections on the aetiology of disease. What remains, however, is the best and most comprehensive single work that has come down from antiquity on the maintenance and restoration of health. Aufidius probably flourished in the last half of the first century B.C. The translation was made under Tiberius between A.D. 20 and 40.

In fairness to Celsus it should be mentioned that not all historians accept Marx's view that the work *On Medicine* is an adaptation of a single source. The older opinion, expressed, for example, by Wellman in *Pauly-Wissowa* in 1901, was that the treatise was a compilation from several sources; and Sir Clifford Allbutt, in his *Greek Medicine in Rome* (1921), is still of this opinion and would interpret the word 'compilation' in a way that would allow a large share of originality, as a writer, though not, of course, as a practitioner, to Celsus. In any case it must be remembered that *On Medicine* is only the fourth part of an encyclopaedic work constructed according to a grand plan designed to cover the whole of life. The four parts were agriculture, medicine, rhetoric, and the art of war. The first two were concerned with the physical life of man, the second two with his life as a citizen. The art of agriculture provides the means of life, that of medicine the means of a healthy life. Medicine protects what agriculture creates. Similarly rhetoric, in the comprehensive sense it then bore, provided a complete training for the citizen in the arts of civil life, so that it might be said to create the civil life which the military art protects. To the work as a whole, then, we cannot deny the credit of being a new construction out of a variety of Greek materials exhibiting the characteristic Roman virtues of organization and design. In comparison with the design of Varro's earlier encyclopaedia we may detect perhaps a greater emphasis on the practical. Varro's extraordinary erudition produced a rounded circle of nine subjects the acquisition of which would certainly have produced an individual of rare academic attainments. Celsus seems to have cared less for culture and sought to provide his generation with a conspectus of the basic arts on which the life of the individual and society depend. Varro's is like a programme for the Arts Faculty of a University. Celsus has provided manuals for four professional schools.

PLINY

When we pass from Varro and Celsus to the third great Roman encyclopaedist, Pliny, it is not so easy to define the character of his work. It has been most variously estimated in modern times. The great French naturalist Buffon (1707–1788) overestimates his merits, but rightly judges the character of the *work* when he says that it deals with all the natural sciences and all the human arts, and the character of the *writer*, when he says that 'he has that facility for taking large views which multiplies science' and that 'he communicates to his readers a certain freedom of spirit, a boldness of thought which is the seed of philosophy'. A work which deals with all the sciences and all the arts and is the work of one man, is bound to be uneven in quality and dismaying to the reader by reason of its multifariousness. The younger Pliny, praising his uncle's book, said that it was 'not less various than Nature herself'. Nevertheless, although it is difficult to see the wood for the trees, there is order as well as grandeur in the plan.

By far the best book on Pliny is that by Littré, disciple of Comte, editor of Hippocrates, and famous lexicographer. He thus defines the plan of *The Natural History*. 'The author begins by setting forth ideas on the universe, the earth, the sun, the planets, and the remarkable properties of the elements. From this he passes to the geographical description of the parts of the earth known to the ancients. After the geography comes what we should call natural history, to wit, the history of terrestrial animals, fish, insects, and birds.

The botanical section which follows is extensive, the more so because Pliny introduces much information on the arts, such as the manufacture of wine and oil, the cultivation of cereals, and various industrial applications. The botanical section concluded, he returns to the animals in order to enumerate the remedies which they supply. Finally he passes to mineral substances and, in what is one of the most interesting parts of his book, he gives at once an account of the methods of extraction of these substances and of the painting and sculpture of the ancients.'

So much for the plan and the general nature of the contents. What of the work in detail? Pliny was a self-taught man who extracted the material for his encyclopaedia out of some two thousand books by some five hundred authors, mostly Greek. Admitting the likelihood that many of the Greek authorities he cites are quoted at second-hand from previous Latin compilations, it was still a work of enormous erudition and labour. With what degree of success was it performed? Nobody is now ever likely to contest the judgement of the judicious and sympathetic Littré, that 'scientific understanding, in the proper sense of the term, is nowhere to be found in him'. Yet the book remains of extraordinary value. Lynn Thorndike remarks of it in his *History of Magic and Experimental Science* that it 'is perhaps the most important single source extant for the history of ancient civilization'. This results not only from its comprehensiveness and variety but from its point of view.

This point of view, already indicated correctly by Buffon, is more fully defined by de Blainville (*Histoire des Sciences de l'organization,* I, p. 336), on the whole an unfavourable critic of Pliny, in this happy description of the book: 'It is a stock-taking, an inventory, an historical catalogue of what man had done up to that time with natural bodies.' It cannot be said (as Francis Bacon charged) that this point of view is totally absent from the natural histories of the Greeks.

Theophrastus, for instance, has many indications of the industrial uses of timber and of stones. But nowhere else does this constitute the informing spirit of an ancient natural history. Man for Pliny is in the centre of the picture and determines his choice of material. It is to this fact we owe it that, if he talks of metals, it leads to coinage, to finger-rings (including a disquisition on the middle-class, the Equites, at Rome), to seals and the administration of Italy by Maecenas in the absence of Octavius. It is to this fact we owe that, if he talks of animals, he passes on to describe the medical remedies derived from them. And so on throughout his book.

Another French writer (Egger: *Examen critique des historiens anciens de la vie et règne d'Auguste*, Sect. vii, p. 183) has well illustrated the novelty of the information we sometimes find in Pliny owing to the point of view from which he writes. 'Would Tacitus ever have told us that on the German frontier the captains of auxiliary bands in the service of the Romans used their native troops to hunt a kind of wild goose, the feathers of which were used to stuff pillows for the use of the Roman soldiers? Would Tacitus ever have condescended to tell us that the skins of hedgehogs were the object of an immense commercial activity in the Roman empire, that disorders resulting from monopoly in this commerce were at all times a cause of anxious concern to government and that more senatorial decrees exist on this subject than on any other!' But these details, unusual as they are, are not the most important of his contributions to social history. The opening of his eighteenth book is occupied with a brief but masterly sketch of the history of landed property in Italy and the provinces. Egger rightly remarks that, if Pliny is often mistaken in the history of the arts, the old savant, who had been consul, general, and admiral, is an authority of the first order on a sociological question of this kind. The more remarkable then is his famous verdict : 'If we admit the truth, it was the system of large estates which ruined Italy and is now also ruining the provinces.'

The frankness of mind and incisiveness of style revealed in this passage mark many a page of this strange encyclopaedia. Indeed in a very true sense Pliny's *Natural History* should be regarded as the prototype of Voltaire's *Dictionnaire Philosophique*. It gives him a chance to air his opinions on everything. Hence that freedom and elevation of which Buffon spoke. There is even humour, in the English sense. Thus, after a pregnant and epigrammatic dissertation on the varieties of religious belief, he concludes in this vein : 'For the imperfections of nature as revealed in man a peculiar consolation is this, that not even God can do everything. He could not, for instance, if he wanted to, commit suicide, which, in the trials of our mortal life, is his best gift to men. He cannot make mortals immortal, recall the dead, bring it about that one who has lived has not lived, or that one who has borne office has not borne office. He has no power over the past but oblivion, and, if I may be excused for illustrating our fellowship with God by trivial examples, he cannot make it that twice ten should not be twenty, and so on. By all this is unmistakably revealed the power of nature and the fact that it is this power we call God. I hope I may be pardoned this digression into what I fear have become commonplaces owing to the never-ending debate about God.' (Bk. II, 27.)

And here, in conclusion, is another passage, which owes some of its arguments to Lucretius, but is completely personal and characteristic. 'Beyond the grave lie the empty speculations about the spirits of the dead. For every man it will be the same after his last day as it was before his first. After death neither body nor spirit will have sensation any more than they did before he was born. This vanity of staking a claim on the future and imagining for oneself a life in the season of death takes various forms: the immortality of the soul, the transmigration of souls, the life of the shades in the underworld, the worship of the spirits of the dead, even the deification of one who has already ceased to be a man. As if, forsooth, we drew our breath in any way that could distinguish us from the other animals; as if there were not many creatures who live longer than we do, for whom nobody has imagined a similar immortality. These are the inventions of a childish folly, of a mortality greedy of never ceasing to be. Plague take it, what madness is this of repeating life in death? How shall those born ever rest, if sense is to remain with the soul on high or with the ghost below? Nay, this fond fancy destroys nature's chief blessing, death, and doubles the smart of him that is to die by the calculation of what is still to come. If life is to be so sweet, who can find it sweet to have ceased to live? But how much happier, how much more sure, that every man should come to trust himself and take from his proven insensibility of what was before he was born his warrant of the peace that is to be.' The author of these words lived an active, cheerful life in the service of his fellow-men and died an adventurous death while making too close an observation of Vesuvius in eruption.

GEMINUS

We pass now to the consideration of scientific works of this period written in Greek and come at once to a masterpiece of exposition in the *Introduction to Astronomy* of Geminus. This man (whose name is probably to be pronounced with the middle syllable long, and not like the Latin for twin) seems to have been a native of Rhodes and to have flourished about 70 B.C. He was a pupil of the great Stoic philosopher Posidonius and wrote a voluminous commentary to a work of his on astronomy. Later he himself made an epitome of his own commentary. This work remained in use for cen-

turies but has not reached us in the form in which Geminus
left it. In the fourth or fifth century, probably in Constantinople, portions of it were excerpted and trimmed with a little
additional material. So came into being the astronomical
manual we now possess under the title of *Geminus's Introduction to Astronomy*. It is a valuable source for our knowledge of Greek positional astronomy, mathematical geography, and calendar-making. Manitius, its most recent
editor (Teubner, 1898), detects errors as well as omissions in
it, which, however, he lays mainly at the door of the Con-
stantinopolitan excerpter. Wellman finds it free from prejudices and superstition and based throughout on scientific
research. The French scholar, Paul Tannéry, is enthusiastic,
regarding it as one of the best extant works of antiquity.
Heath is lukewarm, describing it as 'a tolerable elementary
treatise suitable for teaching purposes and containing
the most important doctrines of Greek astronomy represented from the standpoint of Hipparchus'. Being myself
one who needs a Hipparchus-made-easy, and finding it
in this book, I persist in calling it, as a text-book, a masterpiece.

Readers will already have met in our first part an excellent example of the simple expository style of Geminus,
namely, the passage in which he explains that astronomers
have always constructed their science on the supposition
insisted upon by the Pythagorean philosophers: that the
motion of the heavenly bodies must be assumed to be circular
and uniform. It is important to notice that Geminus has no
quarrel with this. In a fragment of his original *Epitome*,
which survives independently of the text-book made in Constantinople, he deals with this point. He approves of a significant division of labour between the philosopher and the
astronomer, according to which it is for the philosopher to
lay down principles within the limits of which the astronomer must work out coherent explanations of the celestial

phenomena. But the clarity with which he expounds this division of labour is all of a piece with the clarity which reigns everywhere in his book. We can best exhibit the quality of the exposition within the limits at our disposal by first giving the chapter headings of the whole and then quoting at length the context of the now familiar passage about the Pythagoreans.

The eighteen chapters in the edition of Manitius have the following titles: *The circle of the zodiac. The order and position of the twelve signs. The shapes of the signs. The axis and the poles. The celestial circles. Day and night. The times of rising of the twelve signs. The months. The phases of the moon. The eclipse of the sun. The eclipse of the moon. That the planets have a motion opposite to that of the cosmos. Risings and settings. The circles of the fixed stars. The terrestrial zones. The habitable portions of the globe. The use of the stars as weather signs. Synodic and other months.* To this is appended a calendar, or table of the time taken by the sun to traverse each of the twelve signs, and the accompanying weather signs.

Now for our quotation :

The times between the tropics and the equinoxes are divided in the following way. From the spring equinox to the summer tropic 94½ days. That is the number of days in which the sun passes through the Ram, the Bull, and the Twins and arriving in the first degree of the Crab makes the summer tropic. From the summer tropic to the autumn equinox 92½ days. That is the number of days in which the sun passes through the Crab, the Lion and the Maid and arriving in the first degree of the Scales makes the autumn equinox. From the autumn equinox to the winter tropic 88⅛ days. That is the number of days in which the sun passes through the Scales, the Scorpion, and the Archer and arriving in the first degree of Capricorn makes the winter tropic. From the winter tropic to the spring equinox 90⅛ days. For that is the number of days in which the sun passes through the remaining three signs of the zodiac, Capricorn, Aquarius, and the Fishes. The total of all the days in these four periods is 365, and that is the number of days we found in the year.

Here the question arises, how it is that, the four quarters of the zodiacal circle being equal and the sun moving always at a uniform speed, he yet traverses unequal arcs in equal times. For there underlies the whole science of astronomy the assumption that the sun and the moon and the five planets move at even speeds in perfect circles in an opposite direction to the cosmos. It was the Pythagoreans, the first to approach these questions, who laid down the hypothesis of a circular and uniform motion for the sun, moon, and planets. Their view was that, in regard of divine and eternal beings, a supposition of such disorder as that these bodies should move now more quickly and now more slowly, or should even stop, as in what are called the stations of the planets, is inadmissible. Even in the human sphere such irregularity is incompatible with the orderly procedure of a gentleman. And even if the crude necessities of life often impose upon men occasions of haste or loitering, it is not to be supposed that such occasions inhere in the incorruptible nature of the stars. For this reason they defined their problem as the explanation of the phenomena on the hypothesis of circular and uniform motion.

About the other stars we shall give the explanation in another place. Here we shall explain how it is that the sun, though moving at a uniform speed, traverses equal arcs in unequal times.

What is called the sphere of the fixed stars, which contains all the imagery of the signs of the zodiac, is the highest of all. It must not be supposed that all the stars lie on a single surface, but that some are higher and some lower. However, to the limitations of our vision the difference in height is not apparent. Below the sphere of the fixed stars lies Saturn, which traverses the zodiac in about 30 years, one sign in 2 years and 6 months. Below Saturn is Jupiter, which traverses the zodiac in 12 years, a sign a year. Next lowest is Mars, which traverses the zodiac in 2½ years, a sign every 2½ months. The sun holds the next place, traversing the circle of the zodiac in a year, and each sign in about a month. Below it is Venus, which moves at about the same speed as the sun. Next comes Mercury, which also moves at the same speed as the sun. Lowest of all is the moon, which traverses the zodiac in $27\frac{1}{3}$ days, and a sign in about $2\frac{1}{4}$ days.

Now if the sun moved at the same distance as the stars which form the signs of the zodiac, then certainly we would have found the times between the tropics and equinoxes equal to one another. Moving at uniform speed the sun must cover equal arcs in equal times. Similarly, supposing that the sun is lower than the circle of the zodiac but moves about the same centre as the circle of the zodiac, then also the times between tropics and equinoxes would have been equal. All circles described about the same centre are similarly divided by their diameters. Since the circle of the zodiac is divided into four equal parts by the diameters which lie between the tropic and equinoctial points, necessarily the circle of the sun would be divided into four equal parts by the same diameters. Moving thus at uniform speed in his own sphere the sun would have made the times of the four quarters equal. But in fact the sun moves not only on a lower but on an eccentric circle, as the accompanying figure shows (see p. 281). The centre of the circle is not the same as that of the zodiacal circle, but is thrust to one side. On account of this position the course of the sun is divided into four unequal parts. The greatest part of its circumference lies beneath the quarter of the zodiacal circle extending from the first degree of the Ram to the 30th degree of the Twins. The smallest part of its circumference lies beneath the quarter of the zodiacal circle extending from the first degree of the Scales to the 30th degree of the Archer.

Naturally therefore the sun moving uniformly in its own circle traverses unequal arcs in unequal times, the longest arc in the longest time, the shortest in the shortest. When it traverses the longest arc on its own circle, then it passes the quarter of the zodiac from the spring equinox to the summer tropic. When it moves over the shortest arc on its own circle, then it passes the quarter of the zodiac from the autumn equinox to the winter tropic. Since unequal arcs of the sun's circle lie beneath equal arcs of the zodiacal circle, inevitably the times between the tropics and the equinoxes are unequal, and the greatest time is that from the spring equinox to the summer tropic, the shortest from the autumn equinox to the winter tropic. The sun therefore moves always at uniform speed, but owing to the eccentricity of its circle it traverses the four quarters of the zodiac in unequal times.

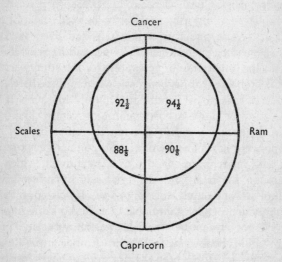

This long passage has been translated literally. Its style is repetitive and full, which makes the reading a little tedious. But we were anxious at all costs to preserve the text-book quality of the original, in which the writer leaves nothing to chance.

STRABO

Geminus's *Elements of Astronomy* is a compact manual, a schoolbook, at least in the form in which we now have it. The next book to which we shall turn, the *Geography* of

Strabo, is a large-scale work which for once has survived all but entire in its original form. Strabo was a native of Amasia in Pontus. He was born in 64 or 63 B.C., and his geography is thought to have been composed in the last decade of the pagan era. Its purpose was no less than to give a reliable and readable account of all the different countries of the habitable world which should be fully abreast of contemporary geographical science in all its branches. Readable and reliable it is, but it had to wait to be read. That Strabo aimed at a wide public is certain. He had lived at Alexandria, he had frequently visited Rome, and he is careful to insist on the importance of geography for the administrator. But it is probable that his book was written immediately for Pythodoris, Queen of Pontus, and published there. If so, Pontus did not prove a good publishing centre. His book remained unknown at Rome. Even the omnivorous Pliny had not heard of it. The Romans satisfied their geographical thirst with the relevant chapters of Pliny himself, which are not among his best, and the brief and superficial compendium of Pomponius Mela (*c.* 45 A.D.). It was not till after the foundation of Constantinople that Strabo came into his own. For the Byzantine world he was an authority. From Byzantium his book came to Western Europe at the Renaissance. It has sometimes been disparaged, but never forgotten since. Its centuries of neglect, which could be paralleled in the history of many other great books, remind us that when we know the contents of such books we are still far from knowing the history of the effective spread of science in the world. Strabo represents the level of achievement of his science in the Augustan Age, but probably very few Augustans had read him.

The unification of the world under Roman rule gave opportunities for the development of geographical knowledge and Strabo has a refreshing sense of the need to bring his subject up to date. His early chapters are filled with criticism of his predecessors, summoned for cross-examination in order, as he says, to justify his attempt by showing how greatly the subject stood in need of correction and addition (Bk. II, 4, 8). A glance at the history of geography will clarify his position.

Geography was an ancient science, but it owed little to any people other than the Greeks. It might have been expected that the Phoenicians, who preceded the Greeks as explorers and masters of the Mediterranean, would have laid the foundation of the science. In a limited sense, they did. Strabo recalls, for instance, that the Bear was not recognized as a constellation until the Phoenicians began to steer by it, and that it was from them an understanding of its use reached the Greeks. But in general the Phoenicians kept their knowledge to themselves, filling the world not with science but with fabulous stories of the difficulties attendant on the approach to the distant sources of their precious articles of commerce. Their contribution to science was as unintentional as that of monopolistic trusts at the present day. It was left for the Ionian Greeks to take the first steps. They, as we have seen (Part I, p. 35), were great colonizers. Strabo tells us that many Ionian and other colonizing expeditions had in early days come to grief for lack of geographical knowledge. The map of Anaximander, and the pioneer geographical treatise of Hecataeus, also of Miletus, written about 520 B.C., were the response to this situation. But, as was characteristic of these Ionian Greeks, out of the knowledge won to meet a practical need sprang a science which has remained to enrich the world.

The complex science of geography has been conveniently divided into four subdivisions: mathematical, physical, descriptive and political, and historical. All these branches were implicit in the work of the earliest Greek pioneers. Anaximander, who introduced the use of the gnomon to Greece, as well as made the first map, may be given the credit for founding mathematical geography. Physical geography found exponents in the poet-philosopher Xenophanes, who detected the phenomenon of raised beaches in the presence of shells and marine fossils inland, and in Herodotus, who accepts the opinion that the whole of the Nile Delta has been formed by alluvial deposits and speculates on how many thousand years it would take it to fill the Arabian Gulf if the Nile reversed its course. The beginnings of political and of historical geography are to be found in Herodotus, in Thucydides, in the Hippocratic tract *Airs Waters Places*, where descriptions of peoples and their institutions begin to be related to their habitat. Nor did this impulse to grasp the nature of the habitable world soon expire. Xenophon in his *March of the Ten Thousand* (401 B.C.) opened up the geography of Armenia. That doughty mariner, Pytheas of Marseilles (about 310 B.C.), a pioneer of scientific and commercial exploration, did the same for Britain and neighbouring seas and lands.

A second great period in the history of Greek geography came with the foundation of Alexandria and the conquests of Alexander in the East. At Alexandria geography could not fail to share in the mathematical advances of the time. With Eratosthenes the determination of latitudes by the sun-dial became the rule, although the number of determinations remained small. He estimated the dimensions of the globe and the shape and extent of the habitable portion of it, and, in carrying out his ambition to reform the map of the world, he drew across the parallelogram which represented the *oikoumene* (or inhabited world) eight parallels of latitude and seven meridians of longitude. The meridians were fixed by dead reckoning. Though later Hipparchus suggested the use of observations of lunar eclipses for determinations of longitude, this remained no more than a suggestion. Astronomical determinations of longitude were not effected in antiquity. The organization of science remained below its theory. Turning to the other branches of the science, we find that both physical and political geography were strikingly advanced by Posidonius, the Stoic philosopher of Rhodes, already referred to as the teacher of Geminus. He is criticized by Strabo for 'being too interested in causes in the manner of Aristotle'. Like Aristotle, however, he was very willing to use his eyes. His accounts of Spain and Gaul, both the countries and their inhabitants, were filled with observation and thought. Tozer has called him 'the most intelligent traveller in antiquity'. Other great exponents of political geography were Megasthenes and Agatharcides. The former (c. 290 B.C.) was the agent of the Seleucids at Palibothra on the Ganges. His account of Northern India, surviving in the borrowings of later writers, was remarkable for its fulness and accuracy. The latter, Agatharcides (c. 170–100 B.C.), penned an account of the Ethiopian gold mines and gold miners, which, preserved for us in the pages of Diodorus, is perhaps the most famous piece of descriptive sociology of antiquity. With the historians Ephorus and Polybius historical geography became a systematic study. Such had been the achievements of geography in its various branches when Strabo set out to renew the subject under the favourable conditions of the Augustan age.

It will be readily understood that no one man is likely to be equally competent in all branches of such a large and complex science. Where Strabo was weak was in mathematics. Here he was perhaps hardly abreast of the Alexandrians of the age of Eratosthenes. Everywhere else he contributed something of importance. In physical geography he has had the good fortune to earn the praise of Lyell for two anticipations of modern science. (1) He stresses the importance of inferring great past terrestrial changes from the smaller changes which take place before our eyes. (2) In discussing certain somewhat superficial views of Strato on the flow from the Euxine into the Aegean, and the supposed flow from the Mediterranean into the Atlantic, he shows an arresting boldness of thought in advancing the hypothesis of alternate elevations and depressions of ocean beds. But his real greatness is in descriptive and historical geography. Only extensive reading in his seventeen books can give a true impression of his powers as a descriptive or political geographer. Within the limits of our space it will be best to concentrate on his remarkable grasp of principle in the remaining field, that of historical geography.

Geographical determinism is a common error, not confined to modern science. The ancients too had sinned in this respect. Strabo is free of the fault. In many passages he shows an understanding, remarkable for his age, of the truth that the influence of geography and climate on a people is a very complex and difficult enquiry, not to be interpreted as a direct effect of nature on man, but as varying according to the level of industrial and political technique. 'The various arts, professions, and institutions of mankind,' he writes, 'once they have been introduced, flourish in almost any latitude and even in spite of the latitude. If some local characteristics come by nature, others come by habit and practice. It is not by nature that the Athenians are fond of letters, while the Spartans, and even the Thebans who live still nearer to them, are not. It is rather by habit. Similarly training and habit account for the various proficiencies of the Babylonian and Egyptian peoples' (Bk. II, 3, 7). His grasp of this principle makes Strabo a scientific observer of the advance of Classical civilization among backward peoples.

The favourable prospects for the advance of this civilization in Europe are analysed in a famous description of the continent, of which we quote a part. 'Of the habitable part of Europe the cold mountainous regions furnish by nature only a wretched existence to their inhabitants, yet even the haunts of poverty and piracy become civilized when they get good administrators. The Greeks are an example. They lived among rocky mountains, but lived well, because they took thought for the art of politics, for the arts of production, and for the art of living. The Romans again have taken over many people that were by nature savage because the places they inhabited were rocky, harbourless, cold or in some other way unsuited to a numerous population, and by bringing the isolated communities into touch with one another have brought them from savagery to civilization. Where Europe is level and temperate, nature co-operates to these ends. In a country blessed by nature everything tends towards peace, as in a country cursed by nature men are brave and warlike. Each kind of country can receive benefits from the other, the latter helping with arms, the former with agricultural and industrial produce and the training of character. But if they fail to help one another, the mutual harm they inflict is obvious. The violence of the warriors might indeed carry the day, if not counterbalanced by the greater numbers of the peaceable. But against this danger Europe is armed by nature. Throughout its whole extent it is diversified by plains and mountains so that everywhere the agricultural and civilized population dwells side by side with the warlike, but the peace-loving population is the more numerous and maintains control over the whole. The Greeks, the Macedonians, and the Romans have presided successively over the accomplishment of this civilizing process. For the reasons given Europe is markedly self-sufficient both for peace and war. The warlike population is abundant, and so is that which tills her soil and maintains her cities. She has the further advantage that she produces the best and most necessary fruits and all the useful metals, importing from abroad such inessential luxuries as spices and precious stones. Furthermore flocks and herds are numerous and wild animals rare. Such is a general description of this continent.' (Bk. 2, 5, 26).

This is a classical page of geographical science, and there are many such pages in Strabo. His account, for instance, of the river system of France – how it opens up the whole country to internal intercourse of its peoples as well as throwing them open to external influences by connecting the Ocean with the Inner Sea – has earned the enthusiastic praise of the brilliant modern geographers of that land (Bk. IV, 1, 4). Almost equally admirable is the account of Italy (Bk. VI, 4, 1). Here the character and situation of the peninsula are considered from the point of view of its suitability for world domination, and in his next paragraph he proceeds to 'add to his account of the country a summary account also of the Roman people who took possession of it and equipped it as a base of operations for the universal hegemony'. Geopolitics is hardly a new science.

His brief summary of Roman history has two leading ideas – that the Roman conquest was reluctant, and that it has meant the happiness of the conquered through good government. He has here, of course, a splendid theme. 'Replacing villages and cantons with cities on the shores of the Mediterranean', writes Vidal de la Blache, 'was the master-stroke of Greece and Rome. Contemporary observers of this phenomenon – Thucydides, Polybius, and Strabo – were not mistaken. They describe the *polis*, or ancient city, as the symbol and outward evidence of a superior civilization.' Strabo's justifiable enthusiasm for this process was such that he describes the conquest of his own country of Pontus without a pang. But the spread of the city civilization at the expense of the villages and cantons took its terrible toll of human life and happiness, and of this side of the process Strabo was an inadequate reporter. It is true he was not blind to the virtues of the simple tribesmen who were compulsorily civilized. He has forcible observations on the moral corruption of simple peoples by the spread of civilization, and on the connection between the growth of property and the growth of crime (Bk. VII, 3, 4 and 7). But he had at the same time acquired the convenient habit of discounting the sufferings of the victims of civilization on the score of their presumed insensibility. He offers proofs of the brutishness of simple peoples which are at least as eloquent of the brutality of their masters. 'When the Roman generals raid the mountain strongholds of these Corsicans and carry them off in great numbers for slaves, you then have at Rome the opportunity to discover their astonishing brutishness. Either they are as savage as wild animals or as tame as sheep. Some of them die in captivity. The rest are so apathetic and slow-witted that their angry purchasers, though they have bought them for a song, repent of their bargain' (Bk. V, 2, 7). Even more striking is his proof of the brutishness of the rebellious Cantabrian natives. 'On being crucified after capture they still kept on shouting their victory slogans from the cross' (Bk. III, 4, 18).

But this is by the way, a mere indication of the familiar fact that the progress of civilization has been a brutal thing. It is one of the chief lessons of history, but it has no particular bearing on Strabo who merely reflected the temper of the dominant peoples in his day. Our concern now is with his place in the history of science, and here his mastery is incontestable. His seventeen books are the greatest work of its kind produced in antiquity. We have taken our illustrations from the earlier books. It must not be inferred that the rest are inferior. Books twelve, thirteen, and fourteen, where he describes Asia Minor of which he was a native and where he relies most on personal observation, are among the best. But he also knew how to select his authorities, and his account of countries which he had not seen – India, for example, where he had Megasthenes to guide him – is a storehouse of reliable information. Vast as his design is, his work is not a compilation. The material so industriously collected is firmly controlled and deployed to illustrate great principles, and everywhere we are in the presence not only of a scientist with a point of view but of a writer with a sense

K

of style. He has deserved his great fame and was unfortunate not to win it immediately.

PTOLEMY

The mathematical side of geography in which Strabo was weak found its definitive expression in antiquity at the hands of Ptolemy, who flourished about A.D. 150. Mathematician, astronomer, geographer, physicist, he is one of the outstanding figures in the history of science. As a mathematician and astronomer he carried on and systematized the work of Hipparchus. His greatest mathematical achievement is the exposition of the spherical trigonometry created by Hipparchus. Since trigonometry was invented by Hipparchus for use in astronomy, spherical trigonometry naturally came first. In the first book of the *Almagest,* as we call it after an Arabic corruption of the Greek (Ptolemy himself called it *The Mathematical Collection in Thirteen Books*), after giving the mathematical proofs on which his determinations rested, he constructed a Table of Chords for arcs subtending angles increasing from ½ degree to 180 degrees by steps of ½ degree. This is the equivalent of a Table of sines for angles from ¼ degree to 90 degrees by steps of ¼ degree. It has been observed that this is the most permanent part of his work. For, while the lapse of time has superseded his astronomical system and his map of the world, the basis of trigonometry laid down by Hipparchus and Ptolemy remains unshaken.

The foundation of his system of astronomy is, of course, the geocentric principle of Hipparchus, with a leaning to the method of epicycles rather than eccentrics to explain the varied motions of the heavenly bodies. It is not easy briefly to describe the contents of the thirteen books. Books I and II lay down the mathematical foundation and give general explanations of the motions of the heavenly bodies in relation to the earth as centre. Book III is on the sun and the length of the year. It tells how Hipparchus was led to his discovery of the precession of the equinoxes. It also lays down a principle which has had a long and useful rôle in science, namely that in explaining phenomena the simplest hypothesis that is not contradicted by the facts is to be preferred. Books IV and V are on the motions of the moon. In his first book Ptolemy had described the instruments he employed for a fundamental measurement, that of the obliquity of the ecliptic. The beginning of the fifth book is taken up with a description of the astrolabe of Hipparchus, which Ptolemy himself also used in confirming the observations of his predecessor. Book VI is on solar and lunar eclipses. VII and VIII are on the fixed stars, and it takes the remaining five to deal with the specially vexed subject of the planets.

It is with this immense astronomical equipment that Ptolemy proceeds to renew the science of mathematical geography. An older contemporary of his, Marinus of Tyre, had again taken up the challenge of Hipparchus, to make a map of the world in which all the principal features should be correctly placed in respect of mathematically determined parallels of latitude and meridians of longitude. It is as the corrector and completer of Marinus that Ptolemy puts himself forward. The arrangement of his book was original and convenient for reference, and this increased its authority. Of its eight books the first and the last are concerned with mathematical and astronomical principles and discussions, but the central six books are made up of tables, giving the names of the places which figured on the maps of the different countries at that time, together with their latitudes and longitudes. The boundaries of the various countries are also defined and there are explanatory remarks of various kinds. But the essential of the treatise is the catalogue of names of places together with the authoritative-looking determinations of position.

This appearance of authority is, in fact, delusive. Some half-dozen latitudes only had been astronomically determined – Marseilles, Rome, Rhodes, Alexandria, Syene, perhaps a few more. No longitudes were astronomically determined. Within a frame of insecurely fixed parallels and meridians positions were obtained by reducing roughly measured distances to degrees. Some distances on land had been paced. Others were estimated in still rougher ways. At sea – for the use of the log was unknown – distances were guessed by times. By a singular misfortune the method of reducing distances to degrees was vitiated by a false figure. Hipparchus had arrived at a very correct determination of the circumference of the globe. Posidonius had 'corrected' this, reducing it to five-sixths of the first figure. Accordingly only 500 stadia (50 geographical miles) went to the degree instead of 600 stadia (60 geographical miles). Ptolemy adopted the erroneous figure of Posidonius. This meant that all his distances, invariably exaggerated in any case by the travellers who made them, were exaggerated a further 20 per cent in the hands of the expert. From the time of Dicaearchus (c. 310 B.C.) the most important line on the globe for Greek geographers had been the parallel of 36 degrees of latitude which runs through the Straits of Gibraltar at one end of the Mediterranean and the Island of Rhodes at the other. But what lay on or near this parallel? Ptolemy made it pass through Caralis in Sardinia and Lilybaeum in Sicily, errors respectively of over 3 and just under 2 degrees. Worse still, he put Carthage, which really lies nearly a degree north of it, more than a degree south of it. This wonderfully evened out the coastline of North Africa. His prime meridian was also unfortunate. He followed Marinus in placing this in the Canaries, but he supposed these islands to lie about 7 degrees east of their true position. All his calculations of distance were in fact based on Alexandria, but since for the purposes of his map-making they had all to be referred to his prime meridian he imported an error of 7 degrees into every position. Such were the general errors pervading his calculations. There were also particular ones due to various contingencies. He accidentally rotated his map of Scotland through an angle of 90 degrees so that it juts out to the east of England instead of extending north. In the Far East he was out of his range and makes Ceylon fourteen times its real size!

These errors are, of course, important. Nevertheless there is nothing easier than to exaggerate their significance. To convince oneself of this it is only necessary to look at the map of the world as known to Homer, with the River Ocean encircling the flat disk of the world, and set beside it the map which can be reconstructed from the data of Ptolemy, with its curved parallels and curved meridians, its fulness and comparative accuracy in regions about the Inner Sea, and its immense reach from Ireland in the north-west corner to vague indications of China and Malaya in the east. Still more convincing is it of the genuine worth of his science to look at the 'wheel maps' of the Middle Ages, in which the River Ocean again encircles a flat disk with Jerusalem at the centre and Paradise at the top, maps out of which all the laboriously acquired mathematics and astronomy of the Greek scientists have been drained. In such a setting we judge the achievement of Ptolemy and the other Greek geographers aright.

It only remains to add a word on another aspect of his work. He was not only a great observer, as his description of astronomical instruments, and the use he made of them, prove. He was also an experimentalist. The fifth book of his treatise on *Optics* contains observations on the refraction of light. This was bound to be of interest to astronomers who had knowledge, among other such refractive phenomena, of an eclipsed moon rising over against a setting sun. Ptolemy gives tables of refraction for various angles of incidence in experiments with air, water, and glass, and tries to work out a law. We observe here, as elsewhere, a combination of insight and system characteristic of the man.

GALEN

Passing from the great world of nature to the little world of man, we find in Galen (A.D. 129–199) one who holds the same place in the history of medicine as Ptolemy does in the history of astronomy and geography. As the astronomy and geography of the Renaissance resume and correct the work of Ptolemy, so do its anatomy and physiology resume and correct the work of Galen. We must attempt briefly to characterize his work, but it is a task of exceptional difficulty. Of his voluminous writings on a wide variety of subjects about a hundred genuine works under separate titles are extant. Kühn's edition (1821–1833), the only complete modern one, fills, together with the translation in Latin, twenty large volumes. Among this mass of material the experts with difficulty find their way, and the layman is confused by contradictory verdicts. But it is perhaps fair to say that the practising physicians who have written of him in modern times rank him higher than the academic critics. At all events we must recognize that this extraordinarily fluent writer, who from an early age poured out controversial books, not only on the various medical sects, but on the various philosophical schools, and in a general way on cultural and educational subjects, was also a most diligent observer and researcher. His therapeutical, physiological, and anatomical works were based on a first-hand acquaintance with nature which would have done credit to one who had not also found time to interest himself in so many other questions.

Some assistance in finding one's way through Galen's works is provided by a little tract on his own writings which special circumstances induced him to write. From this we draw the following interesting particulars. Once upon a time, in Shoemakers' Street in Rome, where most of the book-shops were, Galen witnessed a scene that must have delighted his author's heart. A book was displayed bearing the name Doctor Galen. A discussion began as to whether it was a genuine work of Galen's. An educated man, attracted by the title, bought it and began to read it at once to find out what it was about. He had not read two lines before he flung it aside exclaiming: 'The style isn't Galen's. The title is false.' He, Galen comments approvingly, had had a good old-fashioned Greek education at the hands of the grammarians and rhetoricians. But times have changed. Aspirants to medicine and philosophy, without having learned to read properly, attend lectures on these subjects vainly hoping to understand teachings which are the noblest known to men. Accordingly to avoid false ascriptions to him of inferior writings Galen proposes to list and describe his genuine works. He has the additional ground for fear that he knows that manifold defacements of his works are occurring on every hand. In different countries different teachers are reading out, as their own, works of Galen that have suffered additions, subtractions, and alterations. Friends have advised him of the necessity of his coming to the rescue of his own reputation, and he has had proof of the soundness of their advice.

The third chapter of the little tract *On His Own Books*, from which we have derived the above particulars, describes his anatomical researches and writings. A portion of this we shall translate in full, for his anatomical works are his most important contribution to science. 'First comes a book *On the Bones* for beginners. After this come other books for beginners, one concerning dissection of the veins and arteries, another that of the nerves. There is also one briefly recapitulating all the instruction on the muscles which is to be found in my *Anatomical Exercises*. If anybody, after reading the primer *On the Bones*, wants to pass straight to the *Anatomical Exercises*, he can skip the primers on the veins and arteries and on the muscles. He will find everything in the *Exercises*. In them the first book is about the muscles and sinews of the hand, the second about the muscles and sinews of the legs, the third about the nerves and vessels in the limbs. The fourth is about the muscles that move the jaws and the lips, the chin, the head, the neck and the shoulders. The fifth is about the muscles controlling the chest, belly, loins, and back. The sixth is about the nutritive organs, namely the stomach, gut, liver, spleen, kidneys, bladder, and the rest. The seventh and eighth contain the anatomy of the parts concerned with breathing. The seventh describes the dissection and the vivisection of heart, lung, and arteries. The eighth deals with the contents of the whole thorax. The ninth gives the dissection of the brain and the spine. The tenth that of the eyes, tongue, throat, and neighbouring parts. The eleventh that of the larynx and of what is called the hyoid bone, of the parts connected thereto and the incoming nerves. The twelfth deals with the arteries and the veins. The thirteenth with the nerves springing from the brain. The fourteenth with those from the spine. The fifteenth with the organs of generation. These are the essentials of anatomy, but there is much besides that is useful. For this I have provided by reducing the twenty books of Marinus *On Anatomy* to four, and all the works of Lycus to two. A table of contents of these works follows.'

The extraordinary importance of this anatomical research is obvious. True, the dissections were performed on monkeys, not on men; but this was a source of error unavoidable in the circumstances of the time. It was the resumption of this programme of dissection at the Renaissance, particularly by Vesalius, that laid the foundation of modern anatomy. Harvey, whose discovery of the circulation of the blood was destined to destroy the Galenic physiology, had been trained in the Galenic programme of dissections in the Vesalian school of Padua.

A word must now be said about the physiology of Galen. Like the astronomy of the time it rested partly on observation and partly on a body of philosophical principles which at the time seemed certainly true but which modern physiology has had to modify or discard. The various types of living things had long been classed in three great divisions – plants, animals, and men. Plants embodied the principle of growth, animals the principles of growth and locomotion, men the principles of growth, locomotion, and reason. It was the opinion of the Stoics, an opinion derived from various sources, that *pneuma* (or air), drawn in from the cosmos whose breath it was, was the vital principle of these three grades of living things. The physiological function of the complex human organism was to adapt this external pneuma to the three grades of life manifested in man, growth, locomotion, and thought. In its first adaptation the pneuma became *natural spirit* and caused growth. In its second adaptation it became *vital spirit* and caused locomotion. In its third adaptation it became *animal spirit* (from *anima*, the soul) and caused thought. Galen with elaborate ingenuity fitted what he knew of the digestive, respiratory, and nervous systems of man to the explanation of this threefold function of the human organism. The liver and the veins were the principal organs of the vegetable life of man. The heart, with the lungs and arteries, maintained the animal life. The brain and the nervous system were the seat of the intellectual life, the distinctive part of man, the rational animal.

We may briefly describe the functioning of his system. In the liver the ingested food was converted into blood which was distributed by the veins for the growth of the body. The motion of the blood in the veins was conceived of as a sort of sluggish oscillation to and from the liver. From the liver it came by the portal vein to the right ventricle of the

heart. Here it parted with its impurities, which were carried
off by the pulmonary artery to the lung and thence exhaled.
A portion of this purified blood was reserved for the second
adaptation. It passed through the septum into the left ventricle, where it met again with pneuma from the outer world
conveyed from the lung to the left ventricle by the pulmonary
vein, and there, in the left ventricle, it was elaborated into
vital spirit and distributed through the body by the arteries.
Of the arteries some lead to the brain. The arterial blood
which is sent to the brain passed through a network of vessels
known as the *rete mirabile*. Here took place the third adaptation. This portion of the blood became endowed with animal spirit and was distributed throughout the body by the
nerves. The system is complete and neat. It took account of
an enormous number of observed facts and interpreted them
in the light of a philosophy which the wisdom of generations
seemed to have confirmed. Galen must have found it impossible to imagine that it could be false. We, who know
that it is false, may profitably ask how it could ever come to
be shaken.

The explanation, of course, is that essential parts of the
theory rest on faulty observation. The account of the transformation of venous into arterial blood cannot be correct, for
it assumes that blood passes through the septum which is, in
fact, a solid wall of muscle. Equally incorrect is the account
of the transformation of the arterial blood into blood endowed with animal spirits. The organ (the *rete mirabile*) in
which it is supposed to take place, though prominent in
ruminants, where Galen had seen it, does not exist in man.
With the revival of anatomical research in modern times
these fatal obstacles to the Galenic physiology became clear.
For long, however, they merely constituted knotty problems
but did not destroy the theory. The Galenic physiology had
features which blinded enquirers to the essential truth await-
ing discovery. It was difficult to get a correct idea of the

circulation of the blood when one had learned from Galen that there were three different kinds of blood each with its own mode of distribution. Nor, even for those who knew that the septum is solid, was the heart's action easy to understand. For Galen the real work of the heart was done in the *diastole*, or expansion, which was supposed to suck air from the lungs. How was one to be sure that the real work was done in the *systole*, or contraction, which propels the blood through the arteries? Harvey sat many hours a day for many years looking at beating hearts, or holding a beating heart in one hand and a pulsing artery in the other, instructing his brain through his fingers, feeling his way to the truth, before he succeeded in reversing Galen's view, first in his own mind, then slowly in the world at large. Even then it was Galen who had triumphed over Galen, Galen the observer who had triumphed over Galen the philosopher, for it was Galen's technique Harvey had learned at Padua.

It remains to add a few particulars about Galen's life. Like nearly all the great scientists of Greek and Roman times he came from the east. He was born in Pergamum, where his father was an architect and mathematician. He studied medicine first at Pergamum, then at Smyrna, Corinth, and Alexandria. On completing his training he was surgeon to the gladiators in his native town for four years. I wish we had a precise account of his duties in this post, a picture of his working day. Subsequently he was attracted to Rome, where provincials then went to seek their fortunes. We know that he there enjoyed immense repute and that his services were required by the Emperor, Marcus Aurelius, who wanted him as his physician on an expedition against the German tribes. Somewhere in the intervals of a busy life he found the time to prescribe, dissect, and write.

BIBLIOGRAPHICAL NOTE

For the Latin grammarians see Keil, *Grammatici Latini*, Leipzig, 1855–70. There are translations of Lucretius in English prose by H. A. J. Munro and Cyril Bailey, of which the first is famous for the austere grandeur of its style, while the latter (Oxford 1910), by the best living English scholar in this field, takes note of later advances in scholarship. There is a more recent version by R. E. Latham (Penguin Classics). Vitruvius can be read in English in Morgan's *Vitruvius: Ten Books on Architecture*, Harvard Univ. Press, 1926, and in English and Latin in the Loeb edition by Granger, 1931–4. For Frontinus the Loeb edition by Bennett is good. There is also a Loeb Celsus; the fundamental edition is by F. Marx, Leipzig, 1915, with Prolegomena in Latin. The best book on Pliny the Elder is *Histoire Naturelle de Pline, avec Traduction en Français*, par M. E. Littré, Paris, 1877. For Geminus see C. Manitius, *Gemini Elementa Astronomiae*, Leipzig, 1898. For Strabo there is a Loeb edition in eight vols., and an excellent account of Strabo's position in the history of his subject in Tozer, *History of Ancient Geography*, Cambridge, 1897. The articles on Ptolemy as astronomer and geographer by Allman and Bunbury in the Encycl. Br., 9th ed., are excellent. The mathematical works of Ptolemy can mostly be found in the Teubner ed., the geography in the Tauchnitz. For an admirable account of Galen see Singer's *Evolution of Anatomy*, Kegan Paul, 1925. The little work *On His Own Writings* quoted in our text can be found in Marquardt, Müller and Helmreich, *Galeni Scripta Minora*, Leipzig, 1884. Clifford Allbutt's *Greek Medicine in Rome* is rich in information and ideas. Brock, *Greek Medicine*, is a useful conspectus of the subject with many passages quoted in translation. A translation, with commentary, of Galen's fundamental work, *De Anatomicis Administrationibus*, is expected soon from the pen of Dr Charles Singer.

CHAPTER FOUR

Résumé and Conclusion — Achievement and limitations of ancient science — The debt of modern to ancient science

★

RÉSUMÉ AND CONCLUSION

In the foregoing pages we have given a representative selection from the scientific writings of the Alexandrian and Graeco-Roman periods. But our treatment has not been exhaustive. A fuller treatment would demand a higher degree of specialization in various branches of science than the present writer can claim to possess. But, while much more might be said, enough has perhaps been said to indicate the range and brilliance of the science of classical antiquity. With astonishment we find ourselves on the threshold of modern science. Nor should it be supposed that by some trick of translation the extracts have been given a delusive air of modernity. Far from it. The vocabulary of these writings and their style are the source from which our own vocabulary and style have been derived. There is no illusion here. With the science of Alexandria and of Rome we are in very truth on the threshold of the modern world. When modern science began in the sixteenth century it took up where the Greeks left off. Copernicus, Vesalius, and Galileo are the continuators of Ptolemy, Galen, and Archimedes.

But, if our first impression is favourable, it is quickly succeeded by a strange doubt. The Greeks and Romans stood on the threshold of the modern world. Why did they not push open the door? The situation is paradoxical in the extreme. We have here surveyed a period of some five hundred years, from the death of Aristotle in 322 B.C. to the death of Galen in A.D. 199. But long before the end of this period the essential work had been done. Before the end of the third century B.C. Theophrastus, Strato, Herophilus and Erasistratus, Ctesibius and Archimedes had done their work. In the Lyceum and the Museum the prosecution of research had reached a high degree of efficiency. The capacity to organize knowledge logically was great. The range of positive information was impressive, the rate of its acquisition more impressive still. The theory of experiment had been grasped. Applications of science to various ingenious mechanisms were not lacking. It was not, then, only with Ptolemy and Galen that the ancients stood on the threshold of the modern world. By that late date they had already been loitering on the threshold for four hundred years. They had indeed demonstrated conclusively their inability to cross it.

Here, then, we have evidence of a real paralysis of science. During four hundred years there had been, as we have seen, many extensions of knowledge, much reorganization of the body of knowledge, fresh acquisitions of skill in exposition. But there was no great forward drive, no general application of science to life. Science had ceased to be, or had failed to become, a real force in the life of society. Instead there had arisen a conception of science as a cycle of liberal studies for a privileged minority. Science had become a relaxation, an adornment, a subject of contemplation. It had ceased to be a means of transforming the conditions of life. Even such established arts as were adapted to keeping society in repair – professions like those of the architect and the medical doctor – were on the edge of respectability. They approached it only to the extent to which the practitioner could be regarded as the possessor of purely theoretical knowledge by which he directed the labour of others.

When we look for the causes of this paralysis it is obvious that it is not due to any failure of the individual. The endeavour to explain great social movements by the psychology of individuals is one of the crippling errors of our time. No, while science as a whole became a prey to creeping paralysis, there was no lack of individual talent, no lack of individual genius, as these pages abundantly show. The failure was a social one and the remedy lay in public policies that were beyond the grasp of the age. The ancients rigorously organized the logical aspects of science, lifted them out of the body of technical activity in which they had grown or in which they should have found their application, and set them apart from the world of practice and above it. This mischievous separation of the logic from the practice of science was the result of the universal cleavage of society into freeman and slave. This was not good either for practice or for theory. As Francis Bacon put it, surveying according to the knowledge of his day the same facts that we have here surveyed, if you make a vestal virgin of science you must not expect her to bear fruit. The fruits of a general improvement in the material conditions of life and of a general emancipation of society from superstition were not such as could be produced by such a reverend maid as ancient science became in its decline.

With us to-day the concept of science carries with it the idea of a transforming power over the conditions of life. While we properly defend the ideal of science as involving a disinterested devotion to truth – indeed this ideal is itself a product of social history and has never shone more brightly than among those of our contemporaries who recognize and acknowledge the social responsibilities of scientific power – we recognize at the same time that from the well-head of pure science flow fertilizing streams which serve industry. We are nearly all Baconian enough to regard science as not only knowledge of nature but as power over nature. The complementary truth, that industry promotes science as much as science promotes industry, is also part of our usual view. The mutual action of science upon life and life upon science is a basic element in our consciousness. It was not so when antiquity was in its decline. Science was for the study and the few. Power over nature was increased, so long as this proved possible, by increasing the number of slaves.

ACHIEVEMENT AND LIMITATIONS OF
ANCIENT SCIENCE

The failure of ancient science was in the use that was made of it. It failed in its social function. Even when the acquisition of slaves became more and more difficult the ancients still did not turn to a systematic application of science to production. It is not claimed that such applications never occurred. Bromehead, for instance, adduces evidence which serves to modify Neuburger's conclusion that 'the art of mining appears to have made almost no technical progress during the whole of antiquity, that is, from the date of the earliest traces recorded to the fall of the Roman Empire'.[1] But the general truth remains that ancient society had set in a mould which precluded the possibility of an effective search for power other than the muscles of slaves. The dependence of society on the slave is everywhere reflected in the consciousness of the age. For Plato and Aristotle in the fourth century B.C. it was axiomatic that civilization could not exist without slaves. Three hundred years later, although slaves had become much more difficult to catch, the Alexandrian philosopher Philo is still of the same opinion. Life without slaves being unthinkable, he draws the conclusion (he was an earnest moralist) that the moral law permits the acquisition of slaves. His rules for their treatment, intended like those of Plato to be just and humanitarian, sufficiently reveal the

1. *The Evidence for Ancient Mining* by C. E. N. Bromehead. The *Geographical Journal*, Vol. XCVI, no. 2, August, 1940. The reference is to Neuburger's *Technical Arts and Sciences of the Ancients*, London, 1930, p. 7.

repressed bad conscience and the horrible social reality. He provides that a master who kills a slave should be killed, but adds that 'if the slave lives two days after being flogged' the master should be acquitted.

Philo was born in 25 B.C., but even after some centuries of Christianity society was still set in the same mould. St Augustine (A.D. 354–430) accepted slavery as the judgement of God on a world guilty of original sin. These opinions, pagan and Christian, are not an index to the character of individuals but to the character of the times. The slow operation of historical forces had brought about the slave system. Only powerful historical forces could sweep it away. The nature of these forces, and the slow change they effected in the mind of society, have been well described by Engels. 'Slavery', he writes in *The Origin of the Family*, 'no longer paid; it was for that reason it died out. But in dying it left behind its poisoned sting – the stigma attached to the productive labour of freemen. This was the blind alley from which the Roman world had no way out: slavery was economically impossible, the labour of freemen was morally ostracized. The one could be the basic form of social production no longer; the other, not yet. Nothing could help here except a complete revolution.' That revolution, the work of the northern barbarians, took place between A.D. 400 and 800. 'Though at the end', continues Engels, 'we find almost the same classes as at the beginning, the human beings who formed these classes were different. Ancient slavery had gone, and so had the pauper freeman who despised work as only fit for slaves. Between the Roman *colonus* and the new bondsman had stood the free Frankish peasant. The "useless memories and aimless strife" of decadent Roman culture were dead and buried. The social classes of the ninth century had been formed, not in the rottenness of a decaying civilization, but in the birth-pangs of a new civilization.'

This new civilization, arising out of the grave of slave

society, soon flowered in a series of new inventions which transformed the economic basis of life. In an article in *Le Mercure de France* (May, 1932) Des Noëttes offered a brief inventory of the chief inventions of the Middle Ages. He includes the watermill, which was known to antiquity but apparently little used.[1] This is his list:

IX century – The modern harness of the saddle-horse, with saddle, stirrups, bit, and nailed iron shoes.

X century – The modern harness of the draft-animal, with shoulder-collar, shafts, disposition in file and nailed shoes.

XII century – Watermill, windmill, mechanical saw, forge with tilt-hammer, bellows with stiff boards and valve, window-glass and glazed windows, the domestic chimney, candle and taper, paved roads,[2] the wheel-barrow.

XIII century – Spectacles, wheeled-plough with mould-board, rudder.[3]

XIV century – Lock-gates on canals, gunpowder, grandfather-clock, plane.

XV century – Printing.

In another of his writings, a masterpiece of research and of historical analysis,[4] Des Noëttes discusses the social consequences of this series of inventions. He is not wrong when he insists that 'by fundamentally transforming the means of production they fundamentally transformed the social organ-

1. His inclusion of the plane is also open to question. Museums show Roman examples.

2. As distinct from the Roman practice of constructing a massive wall of masonry in a trench three or four feet deep and using the top as a road. See Des Noëttes, *L'Attelage, le cheval de salle, à travers les âges. Contribution à l'histoire de l'esclavage*, Paris, 1931; also R. J. Forbes, *Notes on the History of Ancient Roads and their Construction*, Amsterdam, 1934.

3. As distinct from the ancient steering-oar.

4. Op. cit., note 2 above.

ism'. Nor is his conclusion lessened in importance when we understand that one of the transformations of the social organism involved was the disappearance of the last vestiges of slavery and the possibility of undertaking immense constructional works with free labour – works of a kind which had normally been performed in antiquity by the forced labour of slaves. This implied an immense improvement in the consciousness of the modern world over the ancient. For, as Des Noëttes remarks, 'the ancients in reality knew nothing of the rights of man; those of the citizen were all that existed for them'.

The same point has been taken up more recently by an American enquirer, whose conclusions are worth quoting here.[1] 'The cumulative effect of the newly available animal, water and wind power upon the culture of Europe has not been carefully studied. But from the twelfth and even from the eleventh century there was a rapid replacement of human by non-human energy wherever great quantities of power were needed or where the required motion was so simple and monotonous that a man could be replaced by a mechanism. The chief glory of the later Middle Ages was not its cathedrals or its epics or its scholasticism: it was the building for the first time in history of a complex civilization which rested not on the backs of sweating slaves or coolies but primarily on non-human power.'

It has been naïvely taught, and is still sometimes naïvely believed, that the science of the Renaissance arose because Greek books from Constantinople arrived in western Europe. If this were the whole truth of the matter, we might well ask why the modern world was not born in Alexandria, or in Rome, or in Constantinople, where the old books survived. There is another aspect of the truth to be considered. Graeco-Roman science was

1. Lynn White, Jr., *Technology and Invention in the Middle Ages,* Speculum, XV, 1940, pp. 141ff.

good seed, but it could not grow on the stony ground of ancient slave society. The technical revolution of the Middle Ages was necessary to prepare the soil of western Europe to receive the seed, and the technical device of printing was necessary to multiply and broadcast the seed before the ancient wisdom could raise a wholesome crop.[1]

The point has been admirably made by Professor Fawcett.[1] 'The peoples of western Europe had the advantage of living in a region where three of the important natural resources for the simpler forms of power were more abundant than in the lands of the older civilizations. The climate gave them more continuous vegetation, and thus allowed them to have more work-animals; it also gave them wind enough at all seasons to drive the ships on their seas and simple windmills on land; and the abundance of rain, combined with the absence of a dry season, enabled them to have widespread small-scale water-power on their streams. Thus, when they had learned how to make use of these resources, they built up a society in which humans were freed from a large part of the necessary drudgery. These technical advances led to social changes; for the chattel slave and the galley slave were no longer needed, and those crude forms of compulsory labour slowly disappeared. They were replaced partly by serfdom and partly by the organizations of craftsmen; both of which merged later into the wage system of modern capitalistic democracy.'

THE DEBT OF MODERN TO ANCIENT SCIENCE

The creators of modern science in the sixteenth century, working again in an age of technical advance in which ancient social abuses were being swept away, recapture the humanitarian as well as the scientific zeal of old Ionia. Reading their pages we seem to breathe a purer and freer air.

1. *The Basis of a World Commonwealth*, Watts, 1941, p. 3.

When Plato wrote his Utopias he was haunted by the necessity of repressing a servile labour force. In St Thomas More's *Utopia* the workers are free men and society is organized in their interest. 'The chief end of the constitution is to regulate labour by the needs of the commonweal, and to allow the people as much time as is necessary for the improvement of their minds, in which they think the happiness of life consists.' It should not be overlooked what a novel conception this is of a labour force with mental needs and joys. In Plato's analogy between man and society the rulers had been equated with the head, the police with the chest, and the workers with the belly and the loins.

In the literature of this age the new temper finds frequent expression. Whereas Archimedes had expressed his contempt for the useful applications of science, Simon Stevin (1548–1620), who is known as the Archimedes of the Low Countries, is anxious above all to be useful. Introducing his decimal system of notation to the public he says humbly : 'It is not a great invention, but it is eminently useful to everyone.'

Where in antiquity shall we find a learned treatise on mining? In the middle of the sixteenth century appeared the *De Re Metallica* of Agricola, in which the whole process of the extraction of minerals is expounded. It is an education to read in his opening pages the list of the basic sciences he considers necessary for this industry. The connection between an actively developing theory and its practical applications is disclosed in a manner characteristic of the modern world but foreign to ancient science in its decline. Not less admirable than his descriptions of machines and processes is his defence of the social utility of the industry.

Soon chemistry too, which in antiquity had lived an underground existence because its practitioners – the fullers, the dyers, the glass-makers, the potters, the compounders of drugs – were outlawed from society, began to assert its claims to be an honoured science with many protestations on the part of its pioneers that it was no occupation for those who were too proud to dirty their hands. Chemistry is a subject we have neglected in this volume, its origins being unusually obscure. But that the difficulties this science experienced in trying to get born were social rather than inherent in the nature of the matter to be investigated is suggested as much by the writings of Bolos Democritus (*c.* 200 B.C.) in antiquity as by those of John Rudolph Glauber (1604–70) in modern times.

Glauber, like Agricola, had a lively sense of the contribution science could make to life.[1] When this aspect of science came again to the fore, it was not long before the effect of the industrial applications of science on the health of the workers forced itself upon the attention. This effect had been observed but neglected in antiquity, when slaves and condemned criminals were sent to the quarries and the mines, and dangerous trades in general were not the serious concern of governments. The Hippocratic doctors had written of the effect of the *environment* on health, but they considered only the *natural* environment. It remained for the modern world to discover that the most important aspect of the environment for the worker is the job. Paracelsus (1490–1541) is the first to draw attention to this gap in the medical theory of antiquity. Discussing the dreadful effects of their trades on miners and metal-workers, the asthmas, consumptions, and vomitings, he comments: 'There is absolutely nothing about these diseases to be found in the ancient medical tradition, whence, up to the present day, no remedy is known.' These conclusions were later extended to almost all known occupations by the great Ramazzini (1633–1714), whose classic work *De Morbis Artificum* rivals the merits and exceeds the humanity of the greatest works of antiquity.

Perhaps the most decisive defeat of the scientific spirit in

1. He assessed the technical possibilities of Germany in an acute and comprehensive way.

antiquity had been the loss of the sense of history. History is the most fundamental science, for there is no human knowledge which cannot lose its scientific character when men forget the conditions under which it originated, the questions which it answered, and the function it was created to serve. A great part of the mysticism and superstition of educated men consists of knowledge which has broken loose from its historical moorings. It is for this reason that we have stressed the sketches of civilization given by Democritus and Lucretius and characterized them as the most important achievement of ancient science.

The process by which the knowledge of one generation can be transformed into the superstition of the next can conveniently be studied by passing from the *De Rerum Natura* of Lucretius to the *Aeneid* of Virgil, though Virgil's motive in stringing oracles, omens, portents, and miracles so thick on his epic thread is no doubt a complicated one worthy of patient analysis. It can also be studied in what the learning of Alexandria made of the Hebrew scriptures when they were translated into Greek. It might have been expected that the addition to Greek literature of the historical record of a strange people would deepen their historical sense. In fact the historical interpretation of the Hebrew scriptures is a product of recent times. The classical world had turned its own history into myth before it acquired a knowledge of the Old Testament and it treated it unhistorically from the first. It would hardly be possible to be more learned than Origen (A.D. 186–254), who applied all the resources of Alexandrian scholarship to the work of biblical criticism. But in the absence of any historical sense it is admitted that his interpretations are entirely arbitrary. What history lost theology gained, and human history dwindled to the proportions of a small act in a cosmic drama. The real events were the Revolt of the Angels, the Creation, the Fall, the Redemption, the Millennium, and the Last

Judgement. Lost in these mysteries time shrank to the limits of six thousand years and human history had significance only in relation to the transcendental framework within which it was contained.

The greatest achievement of modern science has been the rebirth of the historical sense. This is a subject on which we cannot enter here, but a brief allusion to it will form the appropriate conclusion to our book. We have mentioned the names of some of the great founders of modern science – Copernicus, Vesalius, Galileo, Stevin, and others. The man who gave supreme expression to the spirit of this age was the Englishman, Francis Bacon (1561–1626). He turned on the whole question of the revival of science an acute historical sense, remarkable for his day and little understood by his successors. The body of the Baconian writings constitutes one great comment on human history, the sense of which is that the real history of humanity can only be written in terms of man's conquest over his environment. His subject was, in his own words, The Interpretation of Nature and Man's Dominion over it. He penetrated behind the veil of politics to the economic reality and judged man's past achievement and future prospects in terms of his mastery over nature, not denying other aspects of his culture but relating them to this basic fact.

The sense of the reality of time, the reality of historical change, and the influence exercised by man over his own destiny, were contributions to the profound philosophy of Vico (1668–1744), who, in the light of his intuition that Man makes his own History, was justified in his claim to have made of history The New Science. Bacon glimpsed the truth that man makes his mental history in the process of conquering his world. Vico saw more clearly than Bacon that this is not an achievement of individual man but of society. In the fundamental institutions of human society he saw the instruments whereby man, who began as a brute, has transformed himself into a civilized being. Later philosophers, notably Hegel and Marx, have deepened and developed these ideas until they have become precious tools for man by which he can consciously labour at the amelioration of his own society. In the light of these conceptions the history of science assumes a new importance. It becomes, not the history of one among several branches of human knowledge, but the essential clue to the process by which man achieves his self-transformation from the animal to the human kingdom. It is in the conviction that the better understanding of any stage in this long journey must contribute to the attainment of the final goal that this study has been written.

BIBLIOGRAPHICAL NOTE

For a general account of ancient technique especially in the Alexandrian Age see Diels, *Antike Technik*, 3rd ed., Leipzig, 1924. The essential studies on Bolos Democritus are by Wellman in *Abhandlungen der Preussischen Akademie, Philosophisch-Historische Klasse*, 1921, No. 4, and 1928, No. 7. For the revival of historical studies in modern times, see R. G. Collingwood, *Autobiography* (Pelican) and *Vico: His Autobiography*, by Fisch and Bergin, 1945.

INDEX